# Land and Water Use

A symposium presented at the Denver meeting
of the American Association for the Advancement of Science,
27–29 December 1961

*Edited by*
**WYNNE THORNE**

*Publication No. 73 of the*
AMERICAN ASSOCIATION FOR THE ADVANCEMENT OF SCIENCE
WASHINGTON, D.C.                    1963

Printed in the United States of America
The Horn-Shafer Company
Baltimore, Maryland

# Preface

The primary concern of this symposium is with the concept of land and water as related resources. Since the presentation took place at the 1961 meetings of the American Association for the Advancement of Science in Denver, Colorado, it seemed appropriate to emphasize the mountain and plains region—but we have more intrinsic reasons for giving special attention to this region. In this arid land with its wide expanses of open country are concentrated many of the nation's most critical problems of land and water.

More than half of the intermountain area and a small part of the plains region are owned by the federal government. This land reserve has become a symbol to many people. It represents security, freedom, opportunity, anticipated pleasures, and a heritage for the future. The image that has been created in the public mind concerning these lands may be vague and frequently is false, but it is powerful and demands increasing attention.

Competition for the region's resources results in pressures on both private interests and government to adopt diverse and often conflicting courses of action. This symposium is properly concerned, therefore, with meanings, with present and future needs for land and water, with the impact of science and technology, with alternative public policies, and with the long-time consequences of the application of these policies.

Participants in the symposium were drawn from a variety of disciplines and organizations to emphasize the range of viewpoints and of information that is available concerning these basic natural resources. Each writer was carefully selected as one who had something significant to say about land and water and could say it effectively. The published papers have been chosen from those presented at the Denver meetings under the auspices of Section O (Agriculture); from those in the general Society program on "Water and Climate," which was arranged jointly by Section O and the Southwestern and Rocky Mountain Division of the AAAS Committee on Desert and Arid Zones Research; and from papers presented in the symposium on "Civilizations in Desert Lands" conducted by Section H (Anthropology). An additional paper by L. A. Stoddart and J. W. Floyd was prepared by special invitation to round out the subject matter.

The first paper "Land and Water Use: A Perspective," was prepared to introduce the symposium and to trace the relationships between some of the thoughts that appear in the subsequent papers. No attempt was made to give a complete or even a representative summary of the content of individual papers. It is hoped, however, that the introductory paper may set the stage for what follows. In the writing of the paper, material was drawn freely from the various presentations and often without cross-referencing. The names of authors are parenthetically inserted where the statements involved were taken almost directly from the paper so designated.

The symposium on "Land and Water Use," arranged by Section O (Agriculture), was jointly sponsored by the following professional societies: American Dairy Science Association, American Farm Economic Association, American Geophysical Union, American Society for Horticultural Science, American Society of Agricultural Engineers, American Society of Agronomy, American Society of Animal Production, American Society of Range Management, Ecological Society of America, Gamma Sigma Delta, Society of American Foresters, Soil Conservation Society of America, Wilderness Society, Wildlife Management Institute, Wildlife Society.

The symposium was strengthened by the chairmen who presided and led the discussions at the annual meetings: President Roland Renne, Montana State College; Dean F. E. Frolik, College of Agriculture, University of Nebraska; President W. E. Morgan, Colorado State University; and Dr. R. E. Hodgson, Director, Animal Husbandry Division, Agricultural Research Service. Dr. Howard B. Sprague, of Pennsylvania State University and Secretary of Section O, assisted with organization of the program and with arrangements for the Denver meetings. The directors of Section O assisted in selecting the symposium subject and in choosing the participants. Dr. Terah L. Smiley, of the University of Arizona and Chairman of the Committee on Desert and Arid Zones Research, arranged the program for the symposium on "Water and Climate" and presided at the session. The symposium on "Civilizations in Desert Lands" was arranged and chairmaned by Dr. Richard B. Woodbury, of the University of Arizona. Special gratitude is expressed to Miss Lois Cox, who assisted with preliminary editing of the papers and made numerous suggestions that greatly improved the entire presentation.

WYNNE THORNE

1961 Chairman of Section O

# Contributors

HOMER ASCHMANN, Department of Geography, University of California, Riverside, California

EMERY N. CASTLE, Department of Agricultural Economics, Oregon State University, Corvallis, Oregon

MARION CLAWSON, Resources for the Future, Inc., Washington, D.C.

J. WHITNEY FLOYD, College of Forest, Range, and Wildlife Management, Utah State University, Logan, Utah

WILLIAM E. FOLZ, Department of Agricultural Economics, University of Idaho, Moscow, Idaho

B. DELWORTH GARDNER, Economics Department, Brigham Young University, Provo, Utah. Now Associate Professor of Agricultural Economics, Utah State University, Logan, Utah.

C. R. GUTERMUTH, Wildlife Management Institute, Washington, D.C.

JOHN W. HARSHBARGER, Department of Geology, University of Arizona, Tucson, Arizona

ROY D. HOCKENSMITH, Soil Conservation Service, U.S. Department of Agriculture, Washington, D.C.

R. E. HODGSON, Animal Husbandry Research Division, Agricultural Research Service, U.S. Department of Agriculture, Beltsville, Maryland

JOHN A. HOPKIN, Bank of America, San Francisco, California

PAUL R. JULIAN, High Altitude Observatory, Boulder, Colorado

MAURICE M. KELSO, Department of Agricultural Economics, University of Arizona, Tucson, Arizona

FRED H. KENNEDY, Forest Service, U.S. Department of Agriculture, Albuquerque, New Mexico

LUNA B. LEOPOLD, U.S. Geological Survey, Washington, D.C.

A. L. McCOMB, Department of Watershed Management, University of Arizona, Tucson, Arizona

RAYMOND L. NACE, U.S. Geological Survey, Washington, D.C.

WILLIAM I. PALMER, U.S. Bureau of Reclamation, Washington, D.C.

N. KEITH ROBERTS, Department of Agricultural Economics, Utah State University, Logan, Utah

STEPHEN C. SMITH, Department of Agricultural Economics, University of California, Berkeley, California. Now Professor of Economics, Colorado State University, Fort Collins, Colorado

L. A. STODDART, College of Forest, Range, and Wildlife Management, Utah State University, Logan, Utah

WYNNE THORNE, Agricultural Experiment Station, Utah State University, Logan, Utah

MORRIS K. UDALL, Congress of the United States, House of Representatives, Washington, D.C.

M. L. UPCHURCH, Farm Economics Division, Economic Research Service, U.S. Department of Agriculture, Washington, D.C. Now Staff Economist, Agricultural Economics, U.S. Department of Agriculture, Washington, D.C.

NATHANIEL WOLLMAN, Department of Economics, University of New Mexico, Albuquerque, New Mexico

# Contents

## III  CRITERIA AND POLICIES

## IV  ROLE OF GOVERNMENT

# 1  INTRODUCTION

# Land and Water Use: A Perspective

Wynne Thorne

*Agricultural Experiment Station, Utah State University, Logan*

The mountain and plains region can be broadly defined to include most of the area of the 17 western states, excluding the three along the Pacific Coast. This is the country that is often referred to as the *western hinterland*. Within it, the problems of land and water resources are sharply focused, and conflicts over whether the government or private interests should develop, control, and manage these resources are nowhere else more sharply defined. A brief résumé of the region's history may help to provide the necessary background for our understanding.

## HISTORICAL BACKGROUND

With the general settlement of the Middle Border and the admission of the Central States to the Union in the first half of the nineteenth century, the rest of the country developed an intense interest in the West. Southern planters and adventurers who moved into the Texas Territory eventually brought about a revolt from Mexico in 1836 and the territory's admission to the Union as a state in 1844. This was followed almost immediately by the Mexican War, and in 1848 Mexico was further forced to yield land comprising California, Arizona, Utah, Nevada, and parts of New Mexico, Colorado, and Wyoming. The Gadsden Purchase, which resulted from the aforementioned chain of events, rounded out our present southwestern boundaries.

Meanwhile, Yankee trappers, missionaries, and adventurers had been exploring the Northwest Territory; settlements had been carved from the wilderness; and conflict with England had developed. In 1846 the border between British and Oregon territories was fixed at the 49th parallel.

Discovery of gold at Sutter's Fort in 1848 brought more than 100,000 people West within 2 years. The western migration was swelled by the Mormons, who first settled the Great Salt Lake Basin in 1847 and then continued to bring a steady stream of immigrants from Europe and the eastern United States.

Miners moved from California into Nevada and other territories, and during the next 20 years such famous centers as Virginia City, Nevada; Helena, Diamond City, and Butte, Montana; and Silver Reef, Utah, reached their zeniths. Stories of quick and easy wealth created excitement about the West and stimulated the influx of more settlers and new industries.

The Homestead Act of 1862, which provided free land, and the completion of the first transcontinental railroad span near Ogden, Utah, in 1869, also made notable contributions to the development of the West. The railroads were given large areas of land in checkerboard square-mile patterns along both sides of their routes. Some railroads, such as the Great Northern, used these lands and the provisions of the Homestead Act in great advertising and promotion schemes to bring people West.

Prerailroad settlers had passed over the Great Plains warily and with considerable trepidation regarding Indians, water, and weather. With easy transportation to the East provided by railroads, however, cattle empires spread rapidly over the plains, and they no longer constituted a major hazard.

It is estimated that in 1884 a million head of cattle were moved to the north from their Texas breeding grounds by 4000 cowboys supplied with 30,000 horses and ponies. These cattle drives commonly terminated in loading stations and points of rendezvous such as Dodge City, Wichita, and Abilene, Kansas. The free ranging of cattle over the plains country lasted from about 1870 to 1890. During the latter part of this period declining prices, severe drought, inroads by settlers under the Homestead Act, and barbed-wire fences brought a rapid and often difficult transition from the nomadic cowboy to a less transient type of agriculture. Wheat became king, and the large cattle herds moved farther West onto the High Plains and into the mountain areas.

Grazing territories had been adjusted between ranchers before the government set up policies and procedures for public lands.

The Forest Reserve was established in 1891, and grazing territories previously claimed by individual ranchers soon were formalized by the government into areas covered by grazing permits. The U.S. Forest Service was authorized in 1905, and the Taylor Grazing Act was passed in 1934. The latter resulted in the Grazing Service, which was replaced by the Bureau of Land Management and given somewhat broader functions. The Forest Service and the Bureau of Land Management adopted similar grazing-permit policies.

The evolution of practical irrigation methods was another influential force in the pattern of western development. In the Southwest, irrigation was practiced by the Indians long before the land was invaded by white men. Spanish missions adopted the practice and irrigated small areas. The Mormon settlers in Utah began to use irrigation on an extensive basis in 1847, and they established many of the principles and practices that are widely used today. Irrigation agriculture made it possible for people to establish permanent farms, live comparatively close together, and develop a degree of community life in an arid environment. It stabilized crop production and permitted the provision of supplemental forage for the livestock that harvested varying proportions of their feed from both private and publicly owned ranges. The nation's growing population reaped the benefits of these developments.

The Great Plains became the heartland of the nation's mechanized wheat ranches. Although this is still the great wheat region, crop failures on poorly adapted soils, combined with unpredictable extremes in weather, have resulted in gradual downward adjustments from peak wheat acreages and an appreciable return to grass and cattle.

Many factors, then, have been interwoven with its natural characteristics to evolve the region as it exists today.

## LAND, WATER, AND PEOPLE

The mountain and plains region, when it is defined to include all of the 17 western states except the three on the Pacific Coast, experienced a population increase of 43 percent from 1930 to

1960. The present population of 23.7 million will probably reach about 33.5 million by 1980 and more than 45 million by 2000 (Smith). The needs and wants of people living within the region, plus increasing pressures from without, are placing progressively more stress on its land and water resources.

Demands for land and water are numerous and varied and are increasing. Because governmental channels are important avenues for expressing these demands, it is imperative that we clarify the issues and the relative roles and responsibilities of public and private agencies in resources development and management (Smith).

Public interest in, and demands for, definite patterns of land use are especially relevant in the West because of its large area of undeveloped "public" lands. The federal government owns an average of 54 percent of the land area in the 11 western mountain and coastal states; this ranges from 36 percent in Washington to 84 percent in Nevada. Perhaps another 6 percent of the region consists of state-owned lands managed by state agencies. Much of the public land is interspersed with private holdings.

### Adequacy of resources

The resources of the West must be considered in relation to the needs of the entire United States for food, fiber, forests, and recreation, and for urban and industrial developments.

The United States has never been in a more favorable position regarding its ability to provide food and fiber for its people. During the past 10 years, crop yields have increased on an average of 2.5 percent per year, while the population gain has averaged 1.7 percent (Hockensmith). When these trends are projected into the future (which seems justified in the light of known and anticipated technology), they indicate that by 1975 the country will need 43 million fewer acres of total cropland than are now in production. Twenty-five million acres of the land now being cropped are unsuitable for this purpose. Anticipated shifts out of cropland would involve transferring an appreciable part of this unsuitable cropland to pasture and trees.

In the United States 637 million acres are suitable for cropping.

The best of this land should be cropped to meet the nation's needs, and the remainder should be used for pastures or trees. The 633 million acres now classed as pasture and grazing land probably will be increased by future shifts from crop and forest land. Acreages removed from forest are expected to equal approximately those newly planted to trees. Improved management practices applied to present total acreages can easily provide for

Areas such as this face increasing demands for use for water supplies, recreation, grazing, and wood products. (Courtesy U.S. Department of Agriculture, Soil Conservation Service)

the lumber needs that are expected to materialize during the next 15 years.

Highways, airports, and urban developments are removing about 1 million acres of land from other uses every year. Recreation-related developments may require large additional acreages in the future. These are estimated at slightly more than 1 million acres annually. Land-use patterns throughout the nation are in flux (Hockensmith).

Demands for water differ from, but are no less intense than, the demands for land; and, although water is an especially limiting resource in the West, local water-deficiency problems occur in many parts of the country (Palmer). The U.S. Senate Select Committee report of 1960 anticipates that, unless bold water-development projects are carried out, serious shortages will occur in 8 of 22 major water basins by 1980. The paralyzing effects of water limitations can be offset only by full development of resources and by regional planning of uses, augmented by increased research and broader application of its findings to prevent waste of available supplies, and, where possible, to increase these supplies.

## Land and livestock

The proportionately large areas of land that are unsuitable for cropping and the natural limitations imposed by shortages of water have fostered the development of livestock ranching operations in much of the West. The dependence of ranch livestock on forage from public, as well as private, lands is the source of increasing conflicts between ranchers and public land-administration agencies. Livestock and wild game are the primary harvesters of forage from the grazing land in the West; this situation fosters additional conflicts between livestock interests and recreationists.

The public benefits from having domestic livestock graze federal and state lands, primarily because the practice assures an adequate supply of meat and wool. By 1980 the meat requirements of the nation are expected to increase to one-third more beef, one-sixth more lamb, two-fifths more pork, and one-fourth more milk. Today more than half of the nation's beef cattle, 61 percent of the breeding cows, and three-fourths of the sheep are in the 17 western states (Hodgson). The area, therefore, is a major meat-production center for the nation's growing population.

The 240 million acres of federally owned grazing lands in the West supply only about 1.2 percent of the livestock feed consumed annually in the United States. In recent years government programs have removed from crop production 5 times as much feed-producing capacity and have shipped abroad 2 times as much feed as is harvested from public lands. Such figures suggest that grazing of public land is of little concern (Upchurch).

Reduced to the base of the 11 western mountain and coastal states, about one-eighth of the livestock feed comes from grazing public lands. Of even more significance, however, is the way that western ranches have developed a balanced system of operation, one in which each part depends on the other for over-all success. By producing feed on irrigated land to supplement grazing on public and private lands, the ranchers have evolved a workable economic equilibrium.

The responsibility of the Forest Service and the Bureau of Land Management to maintain public lands in a permanently productive state has resulted over time in large-scale adjustments in livestock grazing permits. Animal-grazing unit-months on the national forests have been reduced to one-third of the 1918 peak, and reductions have been one-half since 1933 (Gardner).

The reduction of livestock grazing on public lands has been accompanied by a 21-percent increase in cattle in the West. Both trends have placed more of a burden on private lands. Evidence does not indicate, however, that the condition of private ranges has deteriorated in the process (Gardner).

Reductions in grazing permits on public lands represent a net loss in agricultural wealth for the ranchers concerned. Since charges for grazing public lands have been nominal, grazing permits have been prized and have been given an unofficial market price. In Utah permits for grazing BLM lands have sold for $8 to $12 per animal-unit-month, and Forest Service permits have sold for $18 to $24 (Roberts). The ranchers who originally were awarded grazing permits had a windfall, but as the ranches were sold the value of the grazing permits was added to the selling price. Today's ranchers have paid, therefore, for a privilege over which they have no control. The obligation of the government to compensate ranchers for reductions in grazing permits is an area of disagreement and controversy.

Many ranchers who presently depend on grazing permits on public lands to allow economic operations have potential opportunities to adjust if permits are reduced and shifts are made to other land uses. Reseeding of good range sites to improved forages with control of brush and poor feed-producing plants can absorb much of the shock. Several million acres have profitably undergone such reseeding, and appreciably more land should be so treated. Pasture and feed production on irrigated and wet lands can be intensified. Many ranch operators are attaining only a fraction of possible production levels on their own lands.

In many instances ranchers can incorporate entirely different types of enterprises into their ranch operations. They can sell hunting and fishing rights to restricted groups and then can also supply cabins, guide service, horses, camping equipment, and other facilities to people who are interested in this and other forms of recreation.

Obviously, not all ranchers have an equal opportunity to make these alternative adjustments, and it would seem that the government does have some responsibility to assist with the transition. This may consist of technical advice in planning and some financial aid in reseeding or otherwise improving land. In the process, however, ranchers also will have to assume a cooperative attitude toward necessary changes.

## Man and land

Arid land environments have had pronounced effects on the development of man. They often have served as a place for the evolution of complex civilizations. This role may be attributed in part to the restricted number of water sources in such areas, which necessarily leads to geographically extensive, fairly involved social contacts, and in part to the open terrain, which demands social cooperation for mutual protection and survival, rather than permitting isolated seclusion. Once agricultural practices are established in such an environment, the advantages of water control become apparent and require cooperation among large numbers of people. Distinctive patterns of civilization then come as a matter of course (Aschmann).

In ancient times the limited acreages that could be irrigated by primitive methods and the lack of marginal land in the desert where innovations could be developed often caused the cultural systems to become rigid and even static. In modern times cultural patterns within arid zones are modified by technology and a close association with people in other climatic zones.

Urbanization is one such modern trend that has initiated a dramatic change in attitudes toward open country. It is now looked upon not only as a possible place to live but as an area that offers recreational opportunities and a chance to escape from the confinements of city life. In our present adulation of wide-open spaces, however, we are likely to overlook the fact that from an economic point of view, at least, the ratio of people to land may be out of balance.

The economic problems of space in the mountain and plains region arise, not because the space exists, but because of its relative balance with human wants (Kelso). The mountain area has 8 people per square mile and the plains area 30, compared with 50 for the rest of the United States. This is the case in spite of the fact that there are several metropolitan areas in the West; if these were deleted, much sparser population-land ratios would exist. Compared with other parts of the United States, the per-capita income per square mile in the mountain and plains region is very low, road mileage per person is high, and costs of medical service, government, and education are high. Here the average family spends more for basic living costs but attains a lower level of services than families in more populated areas.

These extra costs of living in the spacious West have to be balanced against other values if a true picture is to be realized. Part of the costs of space are also borne by people outside of the area, and this proportion may become larger as more people look to public lands for recreation.

**Recreation demands for resources**

Outdoor recreation has increased at the rate of about 10 percent per year since World War II. Much of this has been water-oriented, but pressures on land areas also have undergone a major upswing. In 1960 total expenditures for visits to national forests, national parks, federal wildlife refuges, U.S. Army Corps of Engineers reservoirs, Tennessee Valley Authority reservoirs, and state parks exceeded $11 billion. About one-half of this was spent in the home community, one-fourth in or near the recreation area, and one-fourth en route (Clawson).

The increased participation in outdoor recreation and the important place that recreation-oriented enterprises are assuming in the economy are fostering more widespread interest in the potential use and value of public lands for recreation. This type of value is difficult to assess. An economic measure of the value that people place on specific recreation sites could be made, however, by setting incremental increases in charges for site use and determining what effects different rates of charge had on the number of visitors (Clawson).

### Impact of science and technology on water supplies

To the extent that science and technology can conserve or increase water supplies they have a major impact on use practices and public policies. The potentials for such developments have been poorly exploited to date, but the future looks promising.

Available water supplies in the West can be traced in origin to large areas of land that act as watersheds and collect the precipitation not used by evapotranspiration processes into streams or underground basins. Watersheds that are effective in stream development generally occur as humid islands in the higher mountains surrounded by subhumid to desert expanses. Several acres of watershed are needed to support 1 acre of irrigated land.

As much as 90 percent of the precipitation in the arid Southwest is lost near the point of impact through evaporation and transpiration. In areas of higher precipitation, these losses may be reduced. Along streambeds and in areas that have wet soils, rapid and serious water losses may be attributed to water-loving plants. These losses can aggregate as much as 20 million acre feet per year in the West. Substantial reductions in the amounts of water lost can be attained by controlling vegetation types, stabilizing stream channels, and draining waterlogged land.

Preliminary findings from studies underway in Arizona, California, Colorado, and North Carolina by the U.S. Forest Service indicate that under many conditions, water yields from watersheds can be increased by such vegetation modification practices as thinning the tree stand or replacing the trees or brush with grass (Kennedy). Further research on such practices is needed before extensive adoption can be recommended, and the public's attitude toward such changes also will have to be considered. The esthetic value of trees compared with grass may have to be evaluated against benefits from enhanced water supplies.

Irrigation practices frequently waste water. On an average, less than half of the water diverted for irrigation is stored in the soil in a position useful for crop plants. Improved distribution systems and better irrigation practices can save up to half of the water now being lost. Such water savings are encouraged by government programs that participate in paying the costs of leveling land, lining ditches, and installing water-control structures. General adoption of water-conserving practices does not seem likely, however, unless the cost of water is increased until it becomes an important item in farm operating costs, or unless the supply becomes a substantially limiting factor in crop yields.

In the West evaporation losses from water surfaces aggregate 25 million acre feet per year (Palmer). Science is making progress toward partial control of these losses through the use of chemical films on reservoir and lake surfaces.

By 1980 canal lining, treating of reservoir surfaces, and control of phreatophytes are expected to save 4.5 million acre feet of water per year that is now being lost.

Some of the latest findings in meteorology-hydroclimatology indicate that broadened knowledge of the physical laws that control climate will facilitate more accurate long-time forecasting and permit more effective planning for water use (Julian). Air-borne moisture for precipitation has its major source region over oceans and moves poleward from subtropical regions. The North American continent acts as a moisture sink in winter and as a weak moisture source to the atmosphere in summer. Additional information about sources of moisture and storm patterns will permit more efficient use of water resources and may lead to increased supplies by facilitating weather modification. Currently, statistical treatment of meteorological data is providing a better basis for design and management of water-storage and control systems.

Water supplies can be conserved and handled more effectively by more imaginative use of underground storage reservoirs (Harshbarger). Shoestring-type underground reservoirs in alluvial valleys have unique possibilities for economical storage and distribution of water. Procedures for recharging such underground reservoirs are still fraught with technical difficulties. Many fine-grained rocks contain large quantities of water that could be released by fracturing, if research can find an economical way to do it.

Scientific advances in efficient desalinization of ocean water are not likely to be helpful to inland areas, such as Arizona, because the cost of lifting and transporting may exceed by 3 or 4 times the rather high initial costs of desalinization. These inland areas have related problems, however, since much underground water is brackish. Considerable quantities of such water occur in a heated state and can be tapped by deep wells. Possibilities for economically desalinizing these heated waters appear to be promising (Harshbarger).

Pollution of water by industrial and urban developments is increasing in scope and must be faced realistically. Government aid to community pollution-control facilities and to state and federal pollution-control regulation agencies indicates that a decisive attack is to be made on this problem. Pollution control and treatment of polluted waters can return large quantities into useful channels.

Science and technology have already provided man with many ways to conserve and make more efficient use of available waters. New discoveries that may have far-reaching impacts appear to be in the offing.

## CRITERIA AND POLICIES FOR RESOURCE USE

Apparently little is to be gained by examining past civilizations in the hope of finding a basis for our present-day adaptations to the use of land and water in an arid environment. It is often stated that when irrigation is the economic basis for the development of a civilization, a strong centralized government results. Under some circumstances this may be the only viable solution to the problems of an arid environment, but this pattern has not been true in our West.

Irrigation constitutes a significant factor in the history of the arid West, but the complexity of our modern civilization quickly relegated it to the position of being one among many competing uses for water. Actually, a prime problem in resource allocation today is how to ascertain and measure the values associated with each potential use. For instance, if water were the dominant value, a tin roof or pavement might be put over watersheds to maximize surface supplies (McComb). A related judgment involves determination of the value of different increments of water for different purposes. How do we measure the value of trees, shrubs, and flowers on our watersheds compared with more acres of irrigated land or a new industry? Difficulties in assessing the place of esthetics and recreation in the necessarily complex use of land and water stem from deficiencies in our knowledge about the psychological, social, and economic values associated with the out-of-doors and how these are related to landscape qualities. We also suffer from lack of knowledge on how future developments are likely to affect the shifting demands of our increasing population for various types of recreation and other leisure-time activities.

According to Aschmann, institutional structures are a secondary development and come after man is able to extract more than his individual sustenance from the land. The common assumption that a strong and somewhat paternal government is essential to develop the facilities needed to support a population through irrigated agriculture would seem to require further analysis before it is accepted unequivocally.

**Bases for allocation**

Because land and water are becoming increasingly scarce resources, and since they are in vociferous demand by different groups for widely varying uses, we are confronted with the problem of which criteria and procedures should be applied to allocate them among the demands. Lands may be used for such diverse purposes as watersheds, grazing, wildlife, recreation, timber production, cropping, or some combination of these. The concept of multiple use has been popularized as a basis for maximizing possibilities for meeting these demands. Water resources are subject to similar conflicting pressures. Here the idea of sequential use is being accepted, because it can indicate a series of priorities of uses arranged in some practical sequence on the basis of factors such as decreasing quality requirements.

Since limited water has been a vital consideration in the West from the time of the first settlement, a complex system of laws and institutions was evolved to circumscribe its use. Through the years, however, the trend has been toward the allocation of the water to the use that brings the higher economic return, and legal interpretations have supported this trend.

The economic consequences of use of water in the Upper Missouri Basin by agriculture, by urban groups, and by industry (with consideration given to swamp- and wetland habitats for ducks and geese) have been analyzed (Wollman). Under the conditions of the analysis, the allocation of all water to agriculture would produce about $500 million in value added. If all water were directed to water-related manufacturing, it would produce $31.2 billion in value added. The costs of water would not significantly affect its distribution. In this situation economic advantages clearly result from the allocation of water to industry. Even complete industry development in the region, however, would leave an appreciable quantity of water available for wetlands and agriculture.

Not all contributors to the symposium agree that the values people attribute to resources can be reduced to an economic base or that government policies and practices should be strictly controlled by such criteria. Enjoyment of scenic beauty can rarely be equated with a given sum of money and is seldom related to ability to pay. The value judgments that underlie economic analyses have not been objectively analyzed. Government policy recognizes this in part by permitting certain portions of the costs of reclamation projects to be charged to wildlife, scenic beauty, and recreation, and by accepting the fact that these costs are not reimbursable by the water or land users (Castle). It may be worth while to consider whether equality in consumption may tend to become a dominant goal in an affluent society that professes the democratic creed.

## Multiple-use and optimum-use concepts

Specialists in the field of resource management (McComb, and Floyd and Stoddart) argue that the concept of multiple use provides the most practical approach in seeking maximum benefits from land resources. Management for multiple products is based on human value systems and fulfills human needs by increasing total useful production, or by changing yield ratios among products (McComb). Regardless of their theoretical basis, however, management systems should be avoided that seriously reduce long-run productivity. A flexible policy that involves at least a moderate level of multiple use seems to be the management program that is most likely to serve the future welfare of the nation. Even in our national parks, sight-seers and vacationists make intensive use of only a small part of the total area. A program that attempts to substitute sweeping national policies on resource use for the judgment and supervisory skill of a management specialist is not likely to provide full or best use of our wildlands (Floyd and Stoddart).

The concept of multiple use has limited value as a basis for setting policies for public agency planning or management, because it provides no criteria for choosing among competing alternatives (Hopkin). The concept of multiple use might well be replaced by the concept of optimum use. Such a transition will require, however, extensive research on resources and better criteria for estimating optimum use.

Land inventories by the Forest Service, Bureau of Land Management, and Soil Conservation Service have attempted to describe the qualities of specific parcels of land, but many of these inventories lack detail. A complete inventory of all land resources would be a major step in facilitating satisfactory decision-making on the optimum use for specific land areas.

A truly optimum pattern of resource use should be consistent with a people's culture, but in the United States we have been reluctant to choose among our historically evolved cultural values (Castle). An analysis of "best" use is complicated, because it depends on value judgments that involve such areas as economic gain, mass recreation, and wilderness preservation. Since people agree more readily on what they oppose than on what they support, it may be vain optimism to hope for any general agreement on any set of values. Consequently, the social optimum in resource use can be stated only partially and incompletely. In order to clarify policies, resource-use planners should develop alternative plans that bring conflicts into sharp focus, rather than bury them. Planners should search for a range of possible solutions, rather than for a social optimum, thus permitting a more intelligent choice by the decision-maker.

Current decisions on resources should be based on the logic of optimum use and the theoretical postulates of the "science" of resource management. These considerations should be modified further by better communication between all resource users and resource managers in relation to the users' needs and preferences. When decisions are made about the nation's resources, the desires of the public, expressed through its elected representatives, are often shunted aside by a bureaucracy that not only interprets and administers legislation but frequently writes the laws (Hopkin). Public agency policies are being guided by advisory boards, pressure groups, and national elections. These should be supplemented by surveys of public preference.

A commonly voiced criterion often involved in deciding the best way to use a publicly owned or controlled resource is the slogan "the greatest good for the greatest number." This is a deplorably inadequate guide to resource decisions, since both key words, *good* and *number,* defy specific definition for most situations. *Good* is easily translated into a personal or agency preference, and adequate programs have not been established to determine preferences or interests of the general public regarding resource use (Gardner).

## ROLE OF GOVERNMENT

As in the past, so also in our time, the place of government in relation to man and his resources seems subject to a variety of interpretations. In particular, the functions of government in developing resources for use have not been clearly defined. As their patterns of living change, so do the interests and demands of the people governed, thus creating a need for adjustments in the uses made of land and water.

## Some legal aspects

One role of government in resource use has been implemented through its legal statutes. The impact of laws on resource development is most clearly exemplified in the case of water.

Water development and use are governed principally by state laws. These laws have evolved from different concepts. Title to most surface waters in the West has been established under the prior appropriation law as modified by the doctrine of beneficial use. Underground waters are regulated on the basis of riparian rights in California and Arizona and appropriative rights in most of the other states. Riparian law as applied to underground water permits competitive pumping from these sources, frequently to the extent of depletion. Prior appropriation laws protect initial users of underground supplies from having them depleted by those who develop uses at later dates.

## Responsibilities of agencies

Government should give more comprehensive attention and support to its resource-managing agencies (Gutermuth). A centralized review of all agency programs and objectives is needed. Recreation sites on lands of the Forest Service and Bureau of Land Management can be better administered by those agencies than by the National Park Service. The national parks were created to preserve unique natural areas for all time; recreation has never been an assigned responsibility of the Park Service.

Outmoded word connotations applied to public and private investment in resource development may be hindering effective action, regardless of the specific agency involved. The popular concept is that the government only spends money on resources, whereas when individuals or private agencies put money into similar developments it is an investment.

At one time private capital could not cope with large reclamation or power projects. Evolution of the modern corporation with its extensive financial resources, however, made economic justification for the role of government in resource development more difficult to sustain (Folz). Analysis by the usual economic model theory, which is concerned primarily with direct benefits, must be supplemented in these cases by consideration of how government land- and water-development programs affect the general economic growth of a region.

Government agencies concerned with land and water have grown up with competing and often conflicting interests. The Department of Agriculture clears and drains land, while the Department of the Interior saves wetland; the Reclamation Service stores water, while the Army Corps of Engineers releases it for navigation (Udall). Innumerable attempts to bring consistency to these varying programs and agencies through consolidation or reorganization have failed because of the many friends of each agency.

Criteria and codes should be established to regulate the activities of all government agencies that are involved with resource development and management. A proposed bill in the Congress would establish a Cabinet-level "Water Resources Council" and would provide for comprehensive river-basin planning with the cooperation of all agencies. This top-level coordination is proposed to provide greater uniformity in planning procedures and in criteria for evaluating resources and their best use.

Legislation is needed: to force recognition of the esthetic and recreational value of water; and to provide for allocation of water supplies, increased efficiency of water use, and new methods of distributing the costs for water projects between direct beneficiaries and the public (Udall).

**Policy needs**

The federal government originally entered the resource picture of the West in the dual role of guardian and developer (Leopold and Nace). The developer role has been played far less by the government than by private enterprise, but pressures are increasing in many quarters for more such government participation. The functions of guardian and of developer frequently overlap and often may conflict. Such conflicts commonly are hidden behind the cloak of conservation, which has been all things to all men where land and water are involved.

Guarding the national interest is a primary burden of the federal government. In some cases this interest is clear, but it is becoming increasingly difficult to define rigidly. Flood control, irrigation, navigation, provision for waterfowl, pollution, watershed erosion, and power generation, all occur in one river basin, and each has a claim to national interest.

The overriding responsibility of government is to assure the maximum benefit to the country from resources in the long-term future, with specific attention to a thorough reevaluation of "the public good" (Leopold and Nace). Financial gain cannot serve as the whole measure of social good. If a park is evaluated in terms of hotdogs, fishing tackle, and gasoline sales, its true worth is overlooked. Only a full understanding of all the benefits that can come from the use of a resource and a prevision of the consequences of alternative actions will be an adequate basis for government policy in the resource field.

It is proposed that the government give greater emphasis to securing a more adequate scientific base for resource management and that it reassert the need to protect resources whose principal value is noneconomic. Americans will not be satisfied with a financially lucrative economy in an environmental desert (Leopold and Nace).

The increasing concern of the American people for their land and water resources and the rapid expansion in often conflicting demands for the use of these resources emphasize the critical need for a more detailed evaluation and a possible revision of our natural resources policy and management programs.

## SUMMARY

Among the major points emphasized in these symposium papers as needing attention are the following: (i) A detailed inventory of our water and land resources should evaluate specific characteristics and best use. (ii) A better assessment of public needs in resource development and use should place values such as esthetic enjoyment and leisure-time use in balance with economic demands. (iii) Responsibilities and functions of all levels of government and their agencies in relation to the nation's water and land resources should be more clearly defined. (iv) Policy criteria should be established to guide future government actions and place comparable services, when they are implemented by different agencies, on a uniform basis.

# II  THE RESOURCE SETTING

# Population Demands for Land and Water Resources of the Hinterland

STEPHEN C. SMITH

*Department of Agricultural Economics, University of California, Berkeley**

The recent and continuing growth of population in this country and throughout the world is plainly evident. For those who ponder the relationships of man to natural resources and work with these problems on a day-to-day basis, the seriousness of the grinding momentum of the current population tide is appalling when it is judged by the standards of today's Western culture and by the rate at which known technology is being adopted in many regions of the world.

Although we live in a wonderfully dynamic age, man is man and moves forward step by step while holding onto that which is familiar and serves to link him with his past. In this process of moving forward while looking backward, a difficult problem is posed in relating population "demands" to "supplies" of land and water. Today's interrelationships between man and his resources involve the old confrontation of those who seek to maintain the status quo and those who respond to the dynamism of new institutional eruptions.

Within the plains and mountain regions of the United States, population has increased by 43 percent since 1930—from 16,555,- 200 to 23,666,922. One estimate that projects into the future has the hinterland containing 33,449,300 people in 1980 and 45,344,- 600 by 2000 (Table I). But to translate population growth into demands for resources, account must be taken not only of the de-

---

* Present address: Department of Economics and Sociology, Colorado State University, Fort Collins.

Table I. Population projections of the hinterland, 1970, 1980, and 2000[a]

| Year | Low | Middle | High |
|------|-----|--------|------|
| | Migration assumption No. 1 | | |
| 1970 | 27,456,600 | 28,276,200 | 30,297,900 |
| 1980 | 30,856,300 | 33,449,300 | 38,086,600 |
| 2000 | 36,724,800 | 45,344,600 | 59,321,300 |
| | Migration assumption No. 2 | | |
| 1970 | 27,155,100 | 27,965,700 | 29,918,700 |
| 1980 | 30,788,700 | 33,376,200 | 38,003,000 |
| 2000 | 36,858,000 | 45,509,400 | 59,536,500 |

[a] Migration assumption No. 1: "The average annual migration of the period 1950–58 is assumed to prevail to 1970 and then the average annual amount of migration of the 1940–58 period is assumed to prevail for the period 1970–80." Assumption No. 2: "Average annual amount of migration during the period 1958 to 1980 is assumed to equal one-half that of the 1940–58 period." After 1980, for both, "it was assumed that the change in the proportion of population in each state between 1980 and 2000 will be the same as the change in the proportion that occurred between 1970 and 1980, as implied by the projections for these dates." (U.S. Congress, Senate Select Committee on National Water Resources, *Population Projections and Economic Assumptions*, 86th Congr., 2d sess., 1960, Comm. Print 5, pursuant to S. Res. 48, p. 5.)

cisions of future parents to bear children but also of the character of internal migration, the level of economic activity, the distribution of wealth and income—which is an important factor that conditions desires—and the rate and direction of technological change.

Forces originating outside, as well as within, the region call for new ways of accommodation, regardless of whether the rates and directions of change cause stress. Although the hinterland is not an economy unto itself, it does have distinctive characteristics. The elements that set a consideration of demand for natural resources in the hinterland apart from similar considerations in other locales are depicted in the first section of this paper.*

The term *demand* has many shades of meaning. The economist sees many subtle points necessary for logical rigor in the analysis

---

* The author acknowledges that discussions with John McGuire, Forest and Range Experiment Station, Forest Service, Berkeley; M. F. Brewer, S. V. Ciriacy-Wantrup, and William Bentley, University of California, Berkeley, have been helpful in the preparation of this paper.

of a market-exchange economy; others equate the concept only with population numbers and with desire. At times the functional price-quantity relationship is too fuzzy and places too much emphasis on a presumed "physical" requirement concept. Although elasticities are becoming more commonly understood, particularly where agricultural products are concerned, they still have a quality that frequently proves illusive to those concerned with policy.

In considering demands for natural resources, a basic concern must be with returns to man. Demands for land and water are related to their ability to produce a product or render a service. Demand in this context necessarily operates in an economic complex of many factors, and the familiar market structure may not be present to give demand its conventional meaning relevant to land and water. A demand concept is still pertinent, however, somewhat broader than usual in its connotation perhaps, but no less precise for its assigned task.

The continually changing demands for the hinterland's water and land are partially evidenced in the shifting markets for the hinterland's products. Changes in demand also may cause modification of the public policies that affect the supply characteristics. The way these changes affect the process of public planning are examined in the second section of this paper.

Space limits a detailed application. However, portions of the Forest Service's activities and the structure proposed in the Water Resources Planning Act of 1961 will receive attention in the third section.

## WHAT IS THE HINTERLAND?

The hinterland's position in our political economy—with all its magnificence of decentralization and plurality—is unique when it is compared with other regions of the 48 contiguous states. This uniqueness affects judgments concerning its return to man—affects the channels through which demand and supply consummate their union.

The region is vast—containing 956,929,000 acres (Table II) between the "100th meridian" and the Sierra Nevada and Cascade Mountain ranges. The major river systems of the West rise in

Table II. Total land area and federally owned land area in the hinterland

| | Total acres (1000's of acres) | Owned by federal government | |
| | | Acres (1000's of acres) | Percentage |
| State | | | |
|---|---|---|---|
| Plains states | | | |
| Kansas | 52,549 | 367 | 0.7 |
| Nebraska | 49,064 | 706 | 1.4 |
| North Dakota | 44,836 | 1,965 | 4.4 |
| Oklahoma | 44,180 | 1,153 | 2.6 |
| South Dakota | 48,983 | 3,349 | 6.8 |
| Texas | 168,648 | 2,686 | 1.6 |
| Subtotal | 408,260 | 10,226 | 2.5 |
| Mountain states | | | |
| Arizona | 72,688 | 32,500 | 44.7 |
| Colorado | 66,510 | 23,972 | 36.0 |
| Idaho | 52,972 | 34,328 | 64.8 |
| Montana | 93,362 | 27,719 | 29.7 |
| Nevada | 70,265 | 61,025 | 86.9 |
| New Mexico | 77,767 | 27,135 | 34.9 |
| Utah | 52,701 | 36,410 | 69.1 |
| Wyoming | 62,404 | 30,196 | 48.4 |
| Subtotal | 548,669 | 273,285 | 49.8 |
| Total | 956,929 | 283,511 | 29.6 |

Source: U.S. Dept. of Commerce, Bureau of the Census, *Statistical Abstract of the United States* (1961), p. 183.

the snow-covered highlands and flow through a land that defies easy characterization. It is a land of extreme contrasts in the distribution of resources—from humid forested areas, snow-capped peaks, and grassy meadows to plains, irrigated land, and desert—with an occasional clump of metropolitan growth. Much of the area is under the public stewardship of the Bureau of Land Management, the Forest Service, the Park Service, the military departments, states, and local governments. Almost 30 percent is owned by the federal government.

Historically, the region was a land to be crossed—a land to be endured until the trail ended on the Pacific slope. But some demanded more from the region and started cattle and sheep to graze the range, the ax and saw to cut the timber, the pick and other mine tools to extract the minerals, the plow to break the prairie sod, the diversion structure and pump to irrigate the dry-land and to quench the thirst of the people and their industry, the dynamo from the run of the river or a high power drop to generate electric energy, and their minds to cherish the many natural phenomena of beauty. The western frontier taxed the individual's ingenuity to plan collective action that would aid him but not limit his freedom.

Public organizations—districts, the Bureau of Reclamation, and the Army Corps of Engineers—have been used in developing water facilities: irrigation, hydroelectric, and flood-control structures. The settlers of the area evolved a workable system of water law, a system that has been continually adapted in a struggle of economic interests.

Over the years the Department of Agriculture and the land-grant colleges of the hinterland have studied and taught ways of farming adapted to the region's uncertain climate. Changing times have led the Department of Agriculture, with the region's farmers, to develop programs designed to adjust agricultural production and its marketing. Prices of some materials are set, and research in the utilization of oil shale is a governmental project. Tariffs, import restrictions, and stockpiling play important roles in the hinterland's economy.

The final chapter has not been written in these dynamic adjustments. On a region-wide basis, population has been increasing, but such an aggregate view is deceptive when it is used to analyze the pushes and pulls of the underlying economic forces. In many areas, settlement is becoming more sparse, rather than filling in. Of the 930 counties in the hinterland, 556, or 59.8 percent, lost population between 1950 and 1960. The tax assessor or the school superintendent in many a rural county can tell the story of a three-decade population exodus (see Fig. 1). Maintenance of community organization in the older tradition is increasingly strained. The demand for land is shifting.

Urban growth has been active, increasing from 37 percent of the population in 1930 to 63 percent in 1960 (Table III). Many towns and cities have expanded, and the surrounding countryside

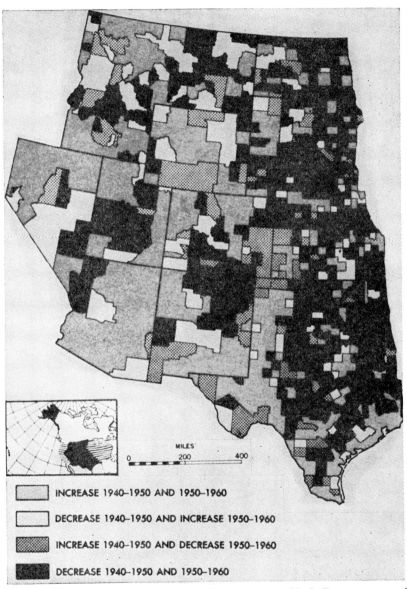

INCREASE 1940–1950 AND 1950–1960

DECREASE 1940–1950 AND INCREASE 1950–1960

INCREASE 1940–1950 AND DECREASE 1950–1960

DECREASE 1940–1950 AND 1950–1960

Fig. 1. Population trends, 1940–1960. (Source: U. S. Department of Commerce, Bureau of the Census)

Table III. Urban and rural population in the hinterland

| Year | Urban population | Per-centage | Rural population | Per-centage | Total |
|---|---|---|---|---|---|
| | *Current urban definition* | | | | |
| 1950 | 10,760,081 | 55 | 8,762,647 | 45 | 19,522,728 |
| 1960 | 15,837,790 | 67 | 7,829,132 | 33 | 23,666,922 |
| | *Old urban definition* | | | | |
| 1930 | 6,129,105 | 37 | 10,426,095 | 63 | 16,555,200 |
| 1940 | 7,120,893 | 41 | 10,182,126 | 59 | 17,303,019 |
| 1950 | 10,107,993 | 52 | 9,414,735 | 48 | 19,522,728 |
| 1960 | 14,977,495 | 63 | 8,689,427 | 37 | 23,666,922 |

Source: U.S. Dept. of Commerce, Bureau of the Census.

has felt the push of the subdivision bulldozer. Twenty-three areas were classified urban in 1950 and 40 in 1960, containing 852 and 2060 square miles, respectively. Of the 40 standard metropolitan areas, however, three states have none; ten have between one and three; and Texas has 20, mostly in the southeastern half. Between 1950 and 1960 the area classified as fringe increased from 310 square miles to 1048, according to the census.

Some rural areas have intensified their economic activity via the catalyst of water development and irrigation (Table IV). Land and water originally developed for agriculture have been shifted to urban uses. The forces of intensification and urbanization have sometimes generated a land-market boom, an urban sprawl, and, on the part of some individuals, a desire to utilize the public devices at their disposal to plan the "great" community. These urban growths directly affect the character of the demand for land and water, and they often act as relay stations for economic and political forces that originate from beyond the region.

The hinterland is all of these things and many more. Highways crisscross in every direction, carrying a stream of motorists to the major points of interest and economic activity, as well as to the once remote and secluded retreat. Airlines, trucks, modern railroads, radio, telephone, and television have completed the task that was started by the pony express, the telegraph, and the early railway. The hinterland is no longer remote; the New York

Table IV. Irrigated land on farms in the hinterland, 1930–1959 (preliminary)

| State | Irrigated land (acres) | | | 1959 (preliminary) |
|---|---|---|---|---|
| | 1930 | 1940 | 1950 | |
| Plains states | | | | |
| Kansas | 56,939 | 82,872 | 138,686 | 762,231 |
| Nebraska | 404,481 | 473,775 | 876,259 | 2,077,926 |
| North Dakota | 10,651 | 19,975 | 35,294 | 47,656 |
| Oklahoma | 2,109 | 4,437 | 34,071 | 197,632 |
| South Dakota | 59,361 | 54,073 | 78,069 | 115,629 |
| Texas | 594,287 | 894,638 | 3,131,534 | 5,653,382 |
| Subtotal | 1,127,828 | 1,529,770 | 4,293,913 | 8,854,456 |
| Mountain states | | | | |
| Arizona | 448,806 | 575,464 | 963,560 | 1,124,913 |
| Colorado | 2,291,927 | 2,467,548 | 2,872,348 | 2,684,757 |
| Idaho | 1,634,321 | 1,895,048 | 2,137,237 | 2,576,580 |
| Montana | 1,343,035 | 1,578,602 | 1,716,792 | 1,874,520 |
| Nevada | 390,192 | 755,636 | 727,498 | 542,776 |
| New Mexico | 371,269 | 436,402 | 655,287 | 731,835 |
| Utah | 917,139 | 911,135 | 1,137,995 | 1,061,683 |
| Wyoming | 1,431,767 | 1,284,027 | 978,106 | 1,469,911 |
| Subtotal | 8,828,456 | 9,903,862 | 11,188,823 | 12,066,975 |
| Total | 9,956,284 | 11,433,632 | 15,482,736 | 20,921,431 |

Sources: Columns 1-3: U.S. Dept. of Commerce, Bureau of the Census, *Census of Agriculture: 1950*. Column 4: U.S. Dept. of Commerce, Bureau of the Census, *Census of Irrigation: 1959* (preliminary).

Stock Exchange ticker flashes in Denver, Salt Lake City, and Reno, as well as in towns to the north and the south. The center of the livestock and grain markets still remains just east of the region —but the trend is toward the west. And the demand for the un-excelled open space of the hinterland is so great at points that the nature of the product itself has changed. With 8,928,000 visits to the region's national parks in 1960, the recreational experience of just a decade ago differed from that of today. Hunters from San Francisco, Chicago, or New York seek out the deer herds on the Nevada-Idaho border or the pheasants of the Dakotas. Fish-ing, skiing, and sight-seeing also affect the growing demand for the region's land and water and have their impact on the ecological environment.

The picture of the hinterland that I have been attempting to paint is intentionally somewhat impressionistic, rather than one constructed entirely of numerical cubes. Many such cubes are readily available in other reports—some are cited. The contributions of these important efforts, however, are but one facet of the over-all situation. Another facet is concerned with the intricacies of the demand-supply interrelationships—of how the changing pattern of demand is reflected in present and prospective rates and directions of land and water use.

## DEMAND AND SUPPLY IN THE AREA

The uniqueness of the hinterland is one reason why demand and supply converge there in a somewhat different fashion from that in other regions. Here, governments are the largest proprietors of land. They also are the developers of the biggest land and water projects. Private property relationships predominate in the economy, but public policy plays an important role by functioning in such vital areas as water-rights determinations, land-use planning procedures, and the regulation of economic activity, and by contracting for services in defense, construction, and other fields.

Within this context, Harold Lasswell's point—that we move from a central focus on transactions to a concern with decisions (6) *—may add insight for interpreting the hinterland's situation. Without belaboring the semantics of the point, the idea of a transaction has been used in a market sense as a bargaining procedure, or in a hierarchical sense as a managerial relationship, or in a governmental sense as a rationing activity (4). The concept of a transaction as a rationing activity and Lasswell's "decisions" indicate an area of economic action where the market in its conventional sense is not the form of organization through which demand is expressed and supply fulfilled. This lack of a conventional market in the institutional structure of part of the hinter-

---

* Italic numerals in parentheses refer to references.

land's economy may provide an opportunity for action on the basis of the expected consequences to man of a land-water adjustment.

Competition for land and water centers in and around the governmental machinery, and pressures continue to mount on those who can render a specific decision or change the machinery itself. This issue of competition is often neglected when demand-supply relationships are considered. Our understanding of how the demand-supply forces function in nonmarket, as well as market, contexts must be improved. The existing national systems for decision-making are those of a political economy in which "programs and prognoses" are intertwined in a fashion similar to that suggested by Streeten (10). The valuations of demand for natural resources currently come from within the governmental system and are not foreign and exogenous to it.

When population demands were fewer and less complex, special-purpose agencies were created to dispose of the public domain, manage forests for timber production, develop land and water to promote the growth of the West, and so forth. Differences of opinion with respect to conflicting interests were resolved within the structure. Those who are familiar with the history of the West's land and water development are well aware that differences existed and competition was vigorous within agencies. As the volume and diversity of demands increased, the agencies themselves came into conflict and contended against one another.

The Congress traditionally has been a forum and a decision-making organization in which the competing within-agency and interagency forces came together. Over the years, the Congress has become increasingly concerned with problems of investing authorized money so that benefits would accrue to the nation as a whole, as well as to particular classes or regions. The congressional structure is not inherently conducive toward generating this point of view (7), but the increasing magnitude of the public sector in our economy has precipitated its more intensive examination of over-all effects. The point to be made here is that progressively greater care necessarily has been taken within agencies to select and propose projects that would meet congressional criteria. A step-by-step, and at times a halting, forward movement toward improved planning thus has evolved within the agencies. These planning activities gradually have become more detailed and now include improved data-collection systems and more refined methods of analysis. Yet, for the most part, these planning systems —systems for improving the process of decision-making—have made less progress toward becoming comprehensive.

Increased comprehensiveness has not been entirely neglected, however. Recreation is being accepted as an objective of natural resource planning and programming, and water-quality control is beginning to have status as an integral part of multipurpose water management. But in a sense these are small steps, albeit important, and a tremendous demand buildup had to precede them.

Demand and supply in relation to natural resources have met and can formally come together in this nonmarket framework during the process of planning for land and water use. At times, their point of juncture has come before, or in anticipation of, pressure and at other times only after pressure. Of course, the total coming together of supply and demand involves more than just this one point; for example, in the federal decision-making complex it involves a whole series of points arrayed on the executive side, as well as on the congressional side. In other systems or organizations, several points of contact also are established before a choice is made. Planning and decision-making processes must have both detail and breadth built into their structure if they are to maximize their effectiveness.

In planning natural resource use, emphasis should be given to future potentials, rather than to the past developments. Great weight is given in the West to public planning, because of the large area of public concern within the region. Planning in the modern corporation, cooperative, or farm business is also becoming increasingly accepted and insisted upon by top management. Greater communication between public and private planning may be expected to materialize in the future. Interest even has been evidenced in learning more about planning above the operating levels; for example, the Water Resources Planning Act of 1961 proposes planning by state governments in addition to national and regional planning. Planning above operating levels would include both the investment function and the broader frame of reference within which private action takes place.

Pressure for comprehensive planning has been generated to some extent by population demands on land and water resources. The philosophical basis for planning is not now, and should not be, anchored into the function of "the state" as sovereign in the sense that "the state" is something apart from the people, although the state's sovereignty may be utilized to implement the wishes of the people. Without going into the debates of political theory, planning is "for freedom." To use Eugene Rostow's phrase, "The issue is not whether to plan, but what to plan and how to plan" (8). The current question is how are these population demands being reflected in the total decision-making process relevant to the hinterland; and, more particularly, how do they function in the planning procedures, which will become increasingly important in the future?

Again, when land and water use is being planned, the neat bargaining transaction of demand and supply is not the focal point. This does not mean that the concepts of demand and supply are not useful constructs. In fact, they must be specifically identified if their interaction is to be spelled out in a clear, meaningful fashion. With such identification, confusion in analysis can be reduced, as is pointed out in several articles that deal with the meaning and use of water requirements and projections of demand (1, 2). Separating supply and demand without concern for their interactions can be misleading in dealing with policy issues. For this reason, it is important to understand the ways in which they interact.

Decisions to permit use of federal land are related to the supply side—the rate of cut for timber, the recreational carrying capacity, the number of animal-unit-months allotted to grazing, and other such factors. A major factor behind the support of public investments in forests, parks, ranges, or water is the effect on supply. Investment analyses, which have been common in the process of gaining approval of public investment for water facilities, are at an earlier stage of systematization and development in other areas. But even here, they are beginning to be utilized. Also, other types of public actions function to provide a framework for private actions and thus impinge directly on supply—zoning, acreage limitations, marketing quotas, and other such measures. In making these decisions, the function of demand should be taken into account.

Improved and more comprehensive planning procedures would permit exploration of a range of action prior to formal commitment. Such procedures could effectively weight the pressures from special interests and, at the same time, recognize the wide variety of demands. Explicit identification of the variety of demands for resources would do much to improve the quality of planning activities. This implies the need for a strong relationship between research and planning.

## PLANNING: ITS PROBLEMS AND PROCEDURES

The many points of contact between the forces of demand and the hinterland's supply of water and land resources cannot be detailed in the allotted space. Two illustrations, however, can highlight the type of analysis that is requisite to understanding and accounting for these relationships. The first illustration comes from the planning procedures of the U.S. Forest Service. This agency is responsible for a large portion of the hinterland's resources, and professionalism has been established in the Forest Service for a longer period of time than in most civilian governmental activities. The second illustration consists of a brief look at a proposed planning structure that was to receive congressional attention in 1962, namely, the Water Resources Planning Act of 1961 (11).

Planning in the Forest Service is of long standing, particularly as it is exemplified by the timber-management plan. Within the last 15 years the Forest Service has completed several nationwide functional plans of a long-range nature, and others are currently in preparation. Planning in this context is not performed exclusively by a separate unit but is carried out by both staff and line personnel in the central and field offices. One purpose of these plans is to consider demand and supply in terms of anticipated action. The crucial importance of the process can be seen in the use of national plans of this type as the basis for bargaining when

budgetary ceilings are being established. Used in this way, they
are fundamental to the control of the supply factor for a given
interval or year. If a penetrating look is to be taken at the relationships of the demand for, and the supply of, the hinterland's
land and water, careful attention must be given to the way in
which planning processes and budget allocations interact. Budgeting is not exclusively an administrative task; it is a fundamental
part of the demand-supply area to be taken into account in research, as well as in program planning.

Demand also functions at many other points in the planning activities of the Forest Service. Only two are mentioned to illustrate
how these points should be identified in various situations. One
of the planning procedures used in recent years utilized the management directive to implement the framework within which
planning takes place. Management directives eventually work
their way from the regional forester to the ranger district. The
framework, which permits more detailed planning and action,
consists of a system that divides the forest lands into zones, with
management priorities established within each zone. For the
Westside Sierra subregion, California region, seven zones are
utilized: crest, westside intermediate, valley front, waterfront,
streamside, roadside, and special areas of unusual public interest.
Within each zone, primary and secondary management priorities
are established for the adjustment of competing uses. For example, in the westside intermediate zone, water is primary in
heavy snowpack areas, and timber is primary elsewhere; wildlife
and grazing are secondary. In the roadside zone, recreational activities are primary and recreational occupancy is secondary.
These zones are established "on the basis of their location, their
existing or probable uses" (12).

Although the physical basis for this zoning is evident, questions
should be raised regarding how and to what extent criteria of demand were reflected in the number of zones established, the priority rating for land use within the zone, the decisions made concerning intensity of use within the planning area, and the recommendations for public investments or the allocations of budgets
to carry out the plan. The phrase "existing or probable uses"
is very important. Equality in weighting all waterfront, stream-

side, or roadside zones is not appropriate. In fact, the whole system implies a demand relationship that needs more explicit recognition, since it performs an important economic function. Simply stated, the system singles out and identifies, in an area or geographic context, the resource base that yields the forest's multiple products. Demand and supply meet at this point of product definition. Such definition is no easy task in many situations, because the interaction between the area's extent and the use priorities must consider complementarity and competitive resource-use relationships.

The forces of demand also impinge on land and water resources through Forest Service procedures in the determination of "allowable cut" within zones that have a merchantable timber product. Allowable cuts are established within working circles "through the application of technical forestry conditions" (13). These technological criteria, applied within a working circle, may not be appropriate as a safe minimum standard (3) of forest regeneration when the concern is with whole forests, regions, and the national demand for wood. Again, the forces of demand come into play in this decision. In fact, differing aspects of demand, such as local fluctuations and national trends, must be considered.

A general problem in taking demand into account is how to handle cross-functional relationships. Even within an agency such as the Forest Service, this creates major problems. When several major agencies are involved, such problems are even more troublesome. Interagency coordination has been given special attention in the water resources field and remains a major area for organizational invention. Interested professionals, presidential commissions, congressional commissions, and interagency commissions are among those that have delved into these problems. Rather than review this large literature or examine additional situations, let us look at the latest proposal that is before the Congress and has Administration backing, namely, the water Resources Planning Act of 1961.

This legislation would establish a Water Resources Council composed of the Secretaries of the Interior, Agriculture, Army, and Health, Education, and Welfare. The council would study the adequacy of water supplies in terms of quantity and quality;

appraise policies and programs and make recommendations; establish principles, standards, and procedures for the preparation of comprehensive regional or river-basin plans; and formulate and evaluate federal water resources projects. Title II of the bill calls for the appointment of river-basin commissions at the request of one governor in the region. A commission would have a non-agency chairman, one member from each federal department or agency with a "substantial interest," one or more members from each state, and, when appropriate, one member from interstate and international commissions. These river-basin commissions would make studies; formulate "comprehensive, integrated, and joint plans"; and report to the council and to the Congress through the President. Title III of the bill authorizes the appropriation of $5 million annually, to be distributed as grants-in-aid to the states for water planning.

Some have vigorously supported this bill in the Congress on the assumption that it is a step toward more comprehensive planning in the water resources field. Others have cautioned that a final version should insure a broader base for interest representation, particularly of states in the commissions. Presumably, the council structure would force agency heads to reach agreement before proposals could be sent to the President and the Congress. Competitive demands would have to be faced within the executive branch, and complementarities of demand would have to be capitalized upon to a degree acceptable to all agencies. Failures in these respects would presumably be questioned in the President's Office or in the Congress. However, the basic obligations of the agencies to reflect the demands of their constituencies are not changed. If the agencies could establish a mutuality of interest, the pressures for acceptance of development and management proposals would be many times greater than they are at present. This would assume that problems of functional orientation could be overcome. Current experience with interagency river-basin commissions might be helpfully assessed in this light (5).

Is the council structure strong enough to prevent dissociation and fragmentation on the one hand and friendly logrolling (thus creating a bigger public investment bill with little reference to returns) on the other hand? Of course, the character of the individuals on the council and their staff would play a fundamental role in over-all results. A staff truly independent of the departments, yet sensitive to the demands for "water and related land resources," could perform a valuable public service.

The word *could* is used advisedly, for the pressures on the integrity of this central group would be great. It would be in a position different from other federal agencies at the presidential level. To be most effective, freedom to study the whole spectrum of water policy problems should be granted as a matter of both policy and budgetary allocation. Such a procedure would permit the group to examine comprehensively the demand for water, both through facilities of the existing agencies and independently. *Independently,* in this context, does not mean duplication of efforts but implies a broadening of the base of interest representation in public decision-making (9). The opportunity to improve water resources decision-making exists, but the hazards must be thoroughly understood if success is to be achieved.

If such a framework were created, the public's demands for the hinterland's water would suggest several types of activities for these planning groups. Both the regional (larger than river basin) and river-basin approaches would be necessary and would have to include interstate and international commission participation. The demands of basins could not remain separated from those of regions, because of the major transbasin diversions of water currently in operation, planned, or proposed. Power distribution is rapidly jumping the basin boundary, and the demand for recreational water usage crosses the same boundary. In fact, one problem would be to designate areas large enough to encompass the forces that influence use. If the river basin or region were narrowly defined, the fragmenting tendencies already in operation would be enhanced.

The composition, character, and purview of these commissions should be such that they could grasp the broad spectrum of water policy problems and not just questions of federal investment. State, local, and private actions will continue to play very significant roles throughout western water development. The demands for water that are voiced through these channels are not unrelated to basin and regional activities. For example, state water-rights systems, ground-water development and management, and water-quality controls have been of paramount state, local, and private interest. Commission representation and work groups would have to be organized to investigate problem areas such as these. The particular function of the commission staff would be to focus on the interrelationships for integrating development and management programs across functional lines, as well as across state lines and between state and federal levels. These commission problems may take a longer time to surmount than those of the proposed council.

Careful personnel selection and organization would be essential to assure adequate weighing of the multitude of demands. Differing interests have used a variety of organizational structures to represent their demands for western water. If the council and commissions are created, they have a potential for providing constructive catalytic action, but the danger of just piling report upon report and of starting arguments without an effective forum for reaching common agreement is ever present. On the other hand, competently prepared reports and studies that would range broadly in terms of interest representation and geographic concern and be based on a depth of technical knowledge could be an important factor in coping with the growing and complex demands for the hinterland's water resources.

## SUMMARY

The hinterland encompasses vast expanses of "open" land and has unevenly distributed water. The population demand for this land and water generally will continue to grow. The impact or force of this growth is complex, and overgeneralization can be misleading. In major respects the area has unique qualities that must be taken into account. Markets for the region's products have been analyzed and are under constant scrutiny. Governmental channels are particularly important as avenues for expressing demands for the hinterland's land and water. Widespread awareness and understanding of resource-use problems are lacking. In addition, much basic knowledge has to be acquired before the present situation can be improved.

Detailed and comprehensive planning is gaining in practice and public acceptance. In fact, judging from congressional hearings, its acceptance as a necessary preliminary activity that can improve public decision-making in our economy is widespread. Many states now have departments of natural resources, of resource planning, or counterparts. Local governments—rural and metropolitan—are struggling to integrate effectively the planning activity into their economies. What has not achieved such widespread acceptance is the fact that this process should be brought under the scrutiny of social science research. Important beginnings certainly have been made, but if—as demands for the hinterland's water and land increase in both volume and complexity—the process of reflecting demands is not improved, the problems we now face will seem small in retrospect.

## REFERENCES

1. Brandt, K., "Problems in planning for future demand of water," in *Economics of California's Water Development,* S. V. Ciriacy-Wantrup and S. C. Smith, Eds. (Univ. of California, Comm. on Research in Water Resources, Berkeley, 1958), pp. 7-19.
2. Ciriacy-Wantrup, S. V., "Projections of water requirements in the economics of water policy," *J. Farm Economics* 43, 197-214 (1961) (Univ. of California, Giannini Found. Paper 193).
3. ———, *Resource Conservation, Economics and Policies* (Univ. of California Press, Berkeley, 1952).
4. Commons, J. R., *The Economics of Collective Action,* K. Parsons, Ed. (Macmillan, New York, 1950).
5. Fox, I. K., and I. Picken, *The Upstream-Downstream Controversy in the Arkansas-White-Red Basins Survey* (Univ. of Alabama Press, University, 1960) (Inter-University Case Program 55).
6. Lasswell, H., "Strategies of inquiry: the rational use of observation," in *The Human Meaning of the Social Sciences,* D. Lerner, Ed. (Meridian, New York, 1959), p. 98.
7. Marshall, H., "Rational choice in water resources planning," in *Water Resources and Economic Development of the West,* Rept. 8 (Comm. on the Economics of Water Resources Development, Western Agricultural Economics Research Council, San Francisco, 28-29 Jan. 1960), pp. 1-18.
8. Rostow, E. V., *Planning for Freedom, the Public Law of American Capitalism* (Yale Univ. Press, New Haven, Conn., 1959), p. 24.
9. Schubert, G., *The Public Interest, a Critique of the Theory of a Political Concept* (Free Press, Glencoe, Ill., 1960).

10. Streeten, P., "Programs and prognoses," *Quart. J. Economics* **68**, 355-376 (1954).
11. U.S. Congress, 87th Congr., 1st sess., H.R. 8197, *Water Resources Planning Act of 1961.*
12. U.S. Forest Service, California Region, *Management Direction for the Westside Subregion, Region 5* (U.S. Dept. Agr., Forest Serv., San Francisco, 1956).
13. Zivnuska, J. A., "Coordinating resource development in a competitive economy," paper for the Natural Resource Sect., California State Chamber of Commerce, Los Angeles, 30 Nov. 1961 (School of Forestry, Univ. of California, Berkeley, mimeographed), p. 3.

# Land Resources and Potential Uses

Roy D. Hockensmith

*Soil Conservation Service, U.S. Department of Agriculture, Washington, D.C.*

This paper deals with the present land-resources situation in the United States and the land-use pattern and adjustments that are expected by 1975. The productive potential and the principles of maintenance necessary to meet national requirements, avoid "surpluses," and reward the farmers adequately for their time, skill, and investments are stressed.

Soil resources of the United States are adequate to keep pace with the growing population for many years if they are given proper care. The use of new methods, equipment, and materials has led to fewer but larger farms with higher production levels per acre and per man-hour. This trend is expected to continue.

Private lands, including Indian lands, comprised 72 percent of the entire land area (1902 million acres) of the 48 contiguous mainland states in 1959 (*11*). Federal land equaled 22 percent of the land area in the same year. Nearly all of the federal land is in grass or trees. It is important for its timber, minerals, grazing use, recreational purposes, watersheds, and wildlife (*2*).

State and local government lands in 1959 totaled about 6 percent of the land area. This included state parks, wildlife refuges, recreational areas, school-grant lands under lease or permit for farming and grazing, institutional lands, watersheds, highway rights-of-way, and other public facilities.

## PRESENT AGRICULTURAL USE OF LAND

Nearly one-fourth of the total mainland area is in cropland; about one-third is grassland pasture and range; and one-third is forest. These proportions have remained about the same since 1920 but are not uniform throughout the nation. For example, the Great Plains section is nearly one-third cropland and two-thirds pasture and range with little forest. In the mountain and intermountain section west of the Great Plains not more than one-eighth is in cropland. In this paper the data for the Great Plains apply to the region that comprises the 422 counties recognized as eligible for inclusion in the Great Plains conservation program under Public Law 1021 enacted in 1956.

In addition, our two youngest states, Alaska and Hawaii, together contain only slightly more than ½ million acres of cropland, 3 million acres of grassland pasture and range, and 5 million acres of wildland range in use or available for use. Most of this cropland area and improved pasture is in Hawaii. Alaska has several million acres of additional potential range. Alaskan forests total 132 million acres and Hawaiian forests 2 million acres.

Cropland acreage reached a peak between 1920 and 1930, with 480 million acres. Since 1950, cropland acreage has dropped by 21 million acres and now is at its lowest point since 1910. On the basis of present farm efficiency levels and requirements for food and fiber, the needed cropland acreage may drop to about 415 million acres by 1975. The magnitudes of these changes differ among the various sections of the country. Generally, the expected changes indicate decreases in the East, increases in the West, and no great change in the Central States.

Grassland pasture and range acreage was 22 million acres lower in 1959 than it was in 1930. Much of this change could be traced to reversion to forest in the forest regions and absorption by non-agricultural uses. A considerable amount of interchange between cropland and pasture has occurred in the good land areas. When field crops are in great demand, cropland increases; when demand is lower, cropland tends to decrease, with part of the excess acreage going into grassland pasture.

Although total acreages of cropland, grassland pasture, and range have changed by only a few percentage points since 1920, significant changes have taken place within and among the major land uses. Foremost among these trends has been a gradual improvement of land for crops and grassland pastures by drainage, flood control, irrigation, and brush clearing. Substantial shifts also have been made among uses within some regions. For example, cropland has been concentrated more and more on fertile and level areas, and hilly and eroded land has been shifted to grass and trees. Shifting field crops to the better soil areas has increased average yields per acre.

## URBANIZATION

Significant changes have also taken place in some areas as farms were absorbed by urban, industrial, and other developments. Not only has land been shifted to nonfarm uses, but in fringe areas much farmland has been only partly used because of the availability of more attractive nonfarm employment and because of high taxes on agricultural land assessed at urban values.

Highways, airports, and urban expansion are expected to absorb about 1 million acres per year in the immediate future. An equal, or perhaps slightly greater, amount can be expected to go into recreational areas, including national, state, and local parks, fish and wildlife areas, wilderness, and related areas. Public installations and facilities, such as areas devoted to national defense and water-control reservoirs, may require an additional 4 million acres by 1975. In total these uses may be expected to increase from 147 million acres to 185 million by 1975—a net shift of 38 million acres from agricultural to nonagricultural uses.

Land shifts can be guided in many instances in a way to preserve valuable agricultural land for future food production. We recognize, of course, that urbanization and highways must necessarily take some good agricultural land but, where a choice exists between good land and inferior land for agriculture, we should make this information available to the responsible planning groups. This is especially important where soils inferior for agriculture are just as desirable for building sites, highways, and parks as are good agricultural soils.

We recognize that some soils are potentially suitable for many different uses, and some are limited to a single use or only a few uses. For example, deep, moderately permeable, well-drained soils on nearly level topography offer many choices in use. They can be used for cultivated crops, grass, trees, building sites for industry, subdivisions for homes in suburban areas, or recreational areas, including parks. Other soils are unsuited for cultivated crops or for building sites or subdivisions. We are generally aware of which soils are unsuited for cultivated crops. But only recently has there been an increasing awareness of the differential suitability of soils in suburban areas for subdivisions. The stability of soils as foundations for buildings, as well as their suitability for small gardens, lawns, and shrubbery, is attracting increasing attention. This is highlighted by examples of spectacular damage owing to severe cracking in walls of newly built houses and by disappointments of owners of new homes with lots composed of very slowly permeable soils in which sewage-disposal fields were inadequate and septic tanks failed to function.

As the need and demand for "open space," "greenbelts," and park areas near cities increase, local planning groups are designing layouts and land patterns that attempt to match soils with their desirable uses. Thus, more good soils are saved for cultivated crops, especially highly valued specialty crops, and residential subdivisions are established on soils desirable for this purpose. Soils not suited for these purposes are used to meet the increasing need for "open space" and recreation. As this nation grows, more people in cities should be able to find recreational facilities within 1 or 2 hours' drive from their homes.

## LAND RESOURCES IN THE UNITED STATES

A knowledge of our potential soil resources in relation to present uses should help in planning future uses. During the past 5 years the U.S. Department of Agriculture, working through county committees of technicians who were well acquainted with local conditions, has made a national inventory of soil- and water-conservation needs. Estimates of the acreage of nonfederal land suitable for various uses were obtained from soil surveys of sample areas (1). The Statistical Laboratory of Iowa State University and the Biometrics Unit of Cornell University developed the plan for statistical sampling. The Soil Conservation Service made soil surveys showing soil type, slope, erosion, and present land use of the sample areas representing nearly 1.5 billion acres of nonfederal land. These and other data were used in land-capability interpretations. Acreage data categorized by land capability and present land use (cropland, pasture and range, forest and woodland, and other), as well as by soil type, slope, and erosion, were recorded on punch cards. The data were identified by counties, watersheds, and land-resource areas. On the basis of this and other information, the county inventory committees estimated probable changes in land use by 1975 (9, 10).

The land-capability classification (5) used in this study places soils in classes that are numbered from I to VIII to indicate increasing hazards or limitations in use. Soils in classes I through IV are suited for cultivation, as well as for the production of grass, trees, wildlife, or recreation. Class I soils have few limitations that restrict their use; classes II and III may be used for regular cultivation with appropriate conservation treatment; class IV soils are suited for limited cultivation or a very narrow choice of crops and require very careful management. Soils in classes V through VII are generally not suited for cultivation but can be used for the production of grass, trees, wildlife, or recreation. Class VIII soils and landforms have limitations that preclude their use for commercial production, but they may have values for wildlife, recreation, water supply, or esthetic purposes (Table I).

These data show that, of the total nonfederal, nonurban land of the U.S. mainland (1450 million acres), more than two-fifths (or 637 million acres) is suitable for regular cultivation. About 36 million acres of this is first-class land with a minimum of problems. The remaining 601 million acres require moderate to intensive treatment for protection, improvement, and sustained production.

Soil erosion is a dominant conservation problem on about half (738 million acres) of the nonfederal land in the 48 contiguous states. Other problems, such as wetness in sloping soils with claypans or droughtiness in sandy soils, are often closely associated with the erosion problem on many of these acres. Excess water is the dominant problem on about 246 million acres (9, 10).

Nearly three-fifths, or 370 million acres, of the soils suitable for regular cultivation are being cultivated. About 240 million acres more are now being used for pasture and woodland. Much of this acreage would be available when needed for cultivated crops, although many operating farm units need a reasonable amount of pasture and woodlots, even on soils suitable for cultivation. Obviously the needs for wood products and for grass for livestock production will have to be balanced with cultivated crop production and with other uses such as wildlife habitat and recreation.

Table I. Relation of land capability to present land use

| Capability class | Total | Crop-land | Pasture and range | Forest and wood-land | Other land | Total | Crop-land | Pasture and range | Forest and wood-land | Other land |
|---|---|---|---|---|---|---|---|---|---|---|
| | *48 contiguous states* (Percentage of 1450 million acres of nonfederal, nonurban land) | | | | | *Mountain-intermountain region* (Percentage of 267 million acres of nonfederal, nonurban land) | | | | |
| I | 3 | 2 | 1 | tr[a] | tr | 2 | 2 | tr | tr | tr |
| II | 20 | 13 | 3 | 3 | 1 | 6 | 5 | 1 | tr | tr |
| III | 21 | 10 | 5 | 5 | 1 | 9 | 5 | 2 | 1 | 1 |
| IV | 12 | 3 | 4 | 4 | 1 | 8 | 3 | 3 | 2 | tr |
| V | 3 | tr | 1 | 2 | tr | tr | tr | tr | tr | tr |
| VI | 19 | 1 | 12 | 6 | tr | 33 | tr | 21 | 12 | tr |
| VII | 20 | 1 | 9 | 9 | 1 | 36 | tr | 22 | 13 | 1 |
| VIII | 2 | tr | tr | 1 | 1 | 6 | tr | 1 | 2 | 3 |
| Total | 100 | 30 | 35 | 30 | 5 | 100 | 15 | 50 | 30 | 5 |
| | *Great Plains* (Percentage of 341 million acres of nonfederal, nonurban land) | | | | | *East of Great Plains* (Percentage of 842 million acres of nonfederal, nonurban land) | | | | |
| I | 1 | 1 | tr | tr | tr | 4 | 3 | 1 | tr | tr |
| II | 14 | 10 | 4 | tr | tr | 27 | 17 | 4 | 5 | 1 |
| III | 21 | 14 | 7 | tr | tr | 25 | 10 | 4 | 9 | 2 |
| IV | 13 | 5 | 8 | tr | tr | 13 | 3 | 3 | 6 | 1 |
| V | 1 | tr | 1 | tr | tr | 4 | tr | 1 | 3 | tr |
| VI | 29 | 3 | 25 | 1 | tr | 10 | 1 | 3 | 6 | tr |
| VII | 20 | tr | 18 | 2 | tr | 16 | tr | 3 | 12 | 1 |
| VIII | 1 | 0 | 1 | tr | tr | 1 | tr | tr | tr | 1 |
| Total | 100 | 33 | 64 | 3 | tr | 100 | 34 | 19 | 41 | 6 |

[a] *tr* means less than 0.5 percent.

Many of the 240 million acres suitable for regular cultivation would require clearing, draining, or other improvement to fit the soils for cultivation. Moreover, many of these acres occur as small or irregular areas and cannot be used efficiently with modern machinery. Thus, it would not be economically feasible to bring all of these areas into cultivation.

About 169 million more acres are suitable for limited or occasional cultivation if they are subjected to very intensive treatment. About one-fourth of this land now is being cultivated.

About 25 million acres now serving as cropland are unsuited for cultivation. This cropland constitutes 1.7 percent of the total nonfederal, nonurban land. These acres should be shifted into other uses.

Although these studies provide reliable estimates of the amount of land in each category, the precise location of these acres would require a detailed soil survey. Thus, as a basis for intelligently guiding desirable shifts in land use, accurate soil surveys should be completed at an early date for the remaining two-thirds of land not now covered by such surveys.

Attention is being given to these land-use adjustments. For example, in Kansas, local county committees estimated that about 1 million acres of cropland in class VI, which is not recommended for cultivation, will be converted to grassland use by 1975. During the last 5 years for the entire United States, cultivated land has been converted to grass at the rate of 2 to 2.5 million acres per year. From $\frac{1}{3}$ to $\frac{1}{2}$ million acres of cultivated land has been converted annually to trees and shrubs. On the other hand, some land (about $\frac{1}{3}$ million acres per year) suitable for cultivation has been brought from grassland and forest land into use for cultivated crops in order to provide efficient family-sized operating units.

## SOIL RESOURCES AND LAND USE IN THE
## GREAT PLAINS AND MOUNTAIN REGIONS

In contrast to 1.7 percent of the nation as a whole, about 3.1 percent (about 11 million acres) of the Great Plains consists of cropland that should not be cultivated. In the area west of the Great Plains this undesirable land-use situation prevails on less than 1 percent, while east of the Great Plains the figure is 1.5 percent (1).

As one travels westward from Omaha to Denver and on to Grand Junction, Colorado, great contrasts in the type of land can be noted. For example, land suitable for regular cultivation

Table II. Distribution of land-capability class groups across Nebraska
and Colorado

| Capability class | Eastern Nebraska (%) | Nebraska Great Plains (%) | Colorado Great Plains (%) | Western Colorado (%) |
|---|---|---|---|---|
| I–III | 80 | 35 | 19 | 7 |
| IV | 10 | 10 | 20 | 14 |
| V–VII | 10 | 55 | 59 | 74 |
| VIII |  |  | 2 | 5 |

in the prairie land of eastern Nebraska amounts to 80 percent, in
contrast to 35 percent in the Great Plains area in western Nebraska, 19 percent in the Great Plains part of eastern Colorado,
and 7 percent in the mountain and intermountain areas in western
Colorado (1) (Table II).

In the entire area of the 10 Great Plains states, the land suitable
for regular cultivation is 61 percent in the prairie area, 37 percent
in the Great Plains, and 10 percent in the intermountain area.
Similar differences exist between regions with regard to the actual
use of the soils. In the entire area of the 48 mainland states, 5.6
percent of the present cropland acreage is on soils not really suited
for cultivation. However, for the section east of the Great Plains,
this figure is 4.4 percent; for the Great Plains, it is 9.6 percent;
and west of the Great Plains, it is 3.4 percent (1) (Table III).

Uneven regional shifts in land use are illustrated by comparison
of the estimates from the conservation-needs inventory for the 10

Table III. Cropland on land unsuited for cultivation

| Region | Total cropland (1000's of acres) | Cropland on classes V–VIII (1000's of acres) | All cropland on classes V–VIII (%) |
|---|---|---|---|
| Entire United States | 441,804 | 24,856 | 5.6 |
| Mountain | 40,478 | 1,392 | 3.4 |
| Great Plains | 110,648 | 10,625 | 9.6 |
| East of Great Plains | 290,678 | 12,840 | 4.4 |

Great Plains states with the estimates for the states to the east and to the west of this region. These estimates for land use in 1975 indicate an expected reduction of 2.5 percent in the acreage used for crop production in the Great Plains states. The expected reduction is 3.8 percent in the eastern states, but an increase of 5.4 percent (about 2 million acres ) is expected in the mountain-intermountain states to the west.

## PROBABLE REQUIREMENTS FOR CROPLAND

More recent estimates of national trends, based on higher per-acre yields, indicate a need for fewer acres of cropland. If present trends continue, the probable requirement for cropland may not be more than 415 million acres, in contrast to the 436 million estimated in the conservation-needs inventory. This projection is based on the assumptions that per-acre crop production will increase about 2.5 percent per year and population will increase 1.7 percent per year.

These estimates should not lull us into complacency about *preventing unnecessary waste and deterioration of our soils.* The expected increases in crop yields are contingent on the application of modern techniques of soil and water conservation, including the use of soils within their capabilities, and on the adoption of the right combinations of practices for each kind of soil.

Progress is being made in this direction. For example, in the Great Plains conservation program 6900 farmers and ranchers had entered into contracts covering conservation plans for 18 million acres as of 30 June 1961. About 30 percent (600,000 acres) of the cropland is scheduled for conversion to less intensive uses with the aid of technical assistance and cost sharing. Also, the reseeding of about 557,000 acres of rangeland is underway as part of the Great Plains program.

## NEED FOR SOIL CONSERVATION

Although fewer people will be on farms in the future, they will be expected to feed 25 percent more people in the United States within the next 15 years. This will require more precision in applying scientific knowledge to farming operations and in getting a more accurate fit of practices to each specific kind of soil. These fewer and more skillful farmers have a right to anticipate a satisfactory economic status in relation to other professions if they are expected to *maintain and improve the basic renewable natural resources on which the welfare of this nation depends.*

Contrary to the general public impression, the current agricultural abundance represents a great achievement of the United States farmers and a great benefit to the consumer. For example, United States consumers spend only 20 percent of their income for food, compared with a world-wide average of about 60 percent.

The temporary surpluses of some farm commodities that exist today should not distract us from our *responsibility to safeguard and improve the soil resources that will be needed to produce the food, fiber, clothing, and shelter for future generations.* To do this means following the concept of soil conservation that is exemplified in the soil conservation district program.

The amount of land in cultivation at any one period should be matched to the demand for farm commodities, so that family farms of an adequate size can be operated efficiently and assured of parity of income. Three main objectives of modern soil conservation are (i) to protect and hold in reserve potentially cultivable soils until there is a demand for farm commodities from these soils, or until they are needed for efficient farm units; (ii) to use immediately the better grades of cultivable soils on which needed commodities can be produced efficiently with a maximized net gain per acre (this should help the farmer to reach a level of income and standard of living more nearly equal to those of managers in industrial enterprises) ; and (iii) to convert the land least suitable for cultivation to grass, trees, recreation, or other uses.

These three objectives mean fewer acres in cultivation now but higher yields on the acres that are cultivated and greater net profits as a result of greater efficiency in agricultural production. The primary aim of soil conservation, therefore, is to use efficiently the soils needed for the nation's several purposes without wasting either physical or human resources (6).

## PLANNING FOR THE FUTURE

Technological advances, along with increasingly efficient skills of farmers, are resulting in larger yields per acre (7). Ample evidence indicates that production from soils may be increased even more rapidly in the future than in the past by improved agricultural technology and new scientific discoveries. We can expect further research breakthroughs in moisture conservation, including reduction of evaporation losses. In addition, improvements in tillage methods, along with better management of crop residues, should lower costs of production and reduce soil deterioration.

Improvements in a single practice, however, unless they are accompanied by comparable improvements in, and applications of, other related practices often fail to give sufficient increases in production to pay the added costs. But when a practice is used in the right combination with other practices, the resulting interactions give highly rewarding returns. For example, when adapted varieties, proper seeding, and the needed practices and treatments, such as contour tillage, terraces, fertilizers, and water conservation, are properly combined with disease and pest control and fitted to the local kind of soil, startling increases usually can be expected (3, 4).

As we plan for the future, we should, as nearly as practicable, try to match land use to kinds of soil. The soils should be used within their specific capability. The better soils should be cultivated more intensively as needed, and all soils should be used and managed in a way to produce efficiently and abundantly in keeping with existing demands for farm commodities and other products that come from the land and satisfy human needs.

## SUMMARY

Soil resources of the United States are adequate to keep pace with the growing population for many years if they are given proper care. This requires prudent soil use and diligent attention to conservation and management of soil resources. It includes careful selection of soils for specific crops, the application of inter-related technologies, and use of the right combination of practices fitted to the specific kinds of soil. In brief, this means that those who work and manage the land efficiently will have adequate rewards for their labor. Present surpluses of a few farm crops do not reduce the need to improve and maintain the potential productivity of our soil resources.

Nearly one-fourth of the land area (1902 million acres) in the 48 contiguous states is cropland; about one-third is grassland pasture and range; and one-third is forest. Of the total nonfederal, nonurban land (1450 million acres) about two-fifths, or 637 million acres, is suitable for regular cultivation. About 36 million acres of this acreage is high-quality first-class land with a minimum of problems. The remaining 601 million acres require moderate to intensive treatment for protection and improvement.

Nearly three-fifths, or 370 million acres, of the land suitable for regular cultivation is being cultivated. About 240 million acres more are now being used for pasture and woodland.

About 169 million more acres are suitable for limited or occasional cultivation with very intensive treatment. About one-fourth of this land is being cultivated. About 25 million acres now being used as cropland are unsuited for cultivation.

We can expect our soil resources to continue to produce ample food and fiber for our needs now and for future generations *only through efficient land use* coupled with protection and improvement practices.

## REFERENCES

1. Adams, H. R., unpublished soil survey data being assembled in 1961 and 1962 from statistically selected sample areas used in the soil and water conservation needs inventory of the U.S. Department of Agriculture, Soil Conservation Service.
2. Clawson, M., B. R. Held, and C. H. Stoddard, *Land for the Future* (Johns Hopkins Press, Baltimore, Md., 1960).
3. Kellogg, C. E., "Prospective land use and adjustments: opportunities and limitations," in *Problems and Policies of American Agriculture*, E. O. Heady, Ed. (Iowa State Univ. Press, Ames, 1959), pp. 388-405.
4. ————, "Productivity of the arable soils of the United States:

1927-1959," *Trans. Intern. Congr. Soil Sci., 7th (Madison, Wis.)* **1** (1960).

5. Soil Conservation Service, "Land-capability classification," *U.S. Dept. Agr., Agr. Handbook 210* (1961).

6. Timmons, J. F., "Principles of resource conservation policy," Comm. on Soil and Water Conservation, *Natl. Acad Sci.–Natl. Res. Council Publ. 885* (1961).

7. U.S. Agricultural Research Service, "Farm production," *U.S. Dept. Agr., Agr. Infor. Bull. 239* (1961).

8. U.S. Congress, Senate Select Committee on National Water Resources, Comm. Print 12 (Washington, D.C., 1960).

9. Williams, D. A., "Conservation needs in a changing agriculture," *J. Soil and Water Conserv. (U.S.)* **17**, 50-54 (1962).

10. ———, G. E. Young, and B. Osborn, "Conservation and change," *Yearbook Agr. (U.S. Dept. Agr.)* **1962** (1962).

11. Wooten, H. H., K. Gertel, and W. C. Pendleton, "Major uses of land and water in the United States: summary for 1959," *U.S. Dept. Agr., Agr. Econ. Rept. 13* (1962).

# Water Resources: Development and Uses

William I. Palmer

*U.S. Bureau of Reclamation, Washington, D.C.*

For two and a half centuries after the first Anglo-Saxon colony was established in America, the development and uses of water resources in the Colonies, and later in the federated states and the Union, presented no major problem. The early settlers of America, because of geographic proximity, first colonized the eastern, humid portion of the country, where natural streamflow is ample and rainfall is generally adequate to bring adapted agricultural crops to maturity. The scanty population, essentially rural economy, and generally small communities meant comparatively little competition for the then abundant supplies of fresh water.

By the middle of the nineteenth century, however, America's growing population was reaching across the Mississippi River and into the semiarid and arid parts of the country, where water was a scarce and vital resource. In this challenging frontier land, much of the limited moisture comes during the winter months as snow. In most places west of the 100th meridian, which roughly bisects the land area of the nation, the water that falls as rain during the growing season is seldom sufficient to bring field crops to maturity. Many streams are raging torrents during the spring snow melt but are reduced to a trickle during the summer and fall months. Other streams under arid conditions flow only intermittently.

In America, therefore, the problems of water-resource development and use during modern times really date from the western colonization movement of the mid-1800's.

Prior to that time, of course, there had been a long history of limited water-resource development and use in western America.

Ancient Indian tribes in the Southwest, some of which had disappeared before the coming of the white man, irrigated their lands and had small village settlements. An ancient canal system found in the Gila River Basin in Arizona has been estimated as capable of serving as many as 250,000 acres of land, although the area actually cultivated at any one time probably was comparatively small and was limited by primitive tools and methods (7).

Spanish missionaries in California, Arizona, and New Mexico also irrigated their streamside farms and vineyards for many years before the eastern seaboard was colonized. Marcus Whitman reportedly was using irrigation in Washington in the early 1840's, and there undoubtedly are other examples of isolated or sporadic use of stream diversion and irrigation in the development of the West.

Settlers of America who came from the very humid British Isles brought with them the legal doctrine of riparian rights as applied to water resources. For centuries under English common law, society had developed the principle, enforced by the courts, that no one has the right to interrupt a flowing stream. Under this legal principle, the owner of lands contiguous to a stream or lake has a valued property right in the water adjoining his lands. An upstream property owner cannot unreasonably impair the quantity or the quality of a stream to the detriment of riparian owners below.

It was against this centuries-old background of legal precedent and principle that pioneer American farmers and miners ventured into the West. Conflicts between necessity and established custom and common law property rights were not long in forthcoming.

Within a day after the arrival of the first founding party of Mormon pioneers in Salt Lake City on 24 July 1847, the waters of City Creek, which flow through the center of the area, had been diverted so that the sun-baked earth could be plowed and a bushel of potatoes planted. This marked the beginning of the first large-scale use of water for irrigation by English-speaking colonizers in the West (1). For all practical purposes the doctrine of riparian rights had been eclipsed in the semiarid West; out of necessity, these agricultural pioneers set a new precedent. It stated that a stream could be diverted and its waters appropriated for beneficial use wherever the water could be transported.

## WATER RECOGNIZED AS A PUBLIC RESOURCE

The Utah pioneers believed in, and put into practice, the principle that water in the desert is a public resource; that only the *use* of it could be appropriated by an individual, and then only for beneficial purposes. A widely quoted statement of the pioneer leader, Brigham Young, was, "No man has a right to waste one drop of water which another man can turn into bread." The principle was established early in the pioneer days of Utah that the precious water supply belonged to the people, and that no man could gain title to more than he could use in a beneficial quantity.

This dedication of water to the public subsequently found expression as a constitutional provision in the neighboring state of Colorado in 1876, when she was admitted to the Union. The Colorado constitution declared public ownership of all unappropriated water and recognized the doctrine of priority of appropriation for beneficial use. Most western states have made such a dedication in their constitutions, or have given similar expression in their state statutes (2). California, Texas, and other states recognize to varying degrees both appropriative and riparian rights. Utah's statutory provision, incidentally, not only applies to surface waters but specifies that all water "whether above or under the ground" is the property of the public.

## "FIRST IN TIME, FIRST IN RIGHT"

Another variety of water use developed in the gold fields of California. The prospectors and miners required water for the sluicing of gold in placer operations. They, like their agricultural counterparts in Utah, disregarded riparian rights and diverted streams whose normal channels were frequently many miles from mining operations.

The California miners are believed to have been primarily

responsible for a major contribution to the appropriative doctrine —a method of determining who had the right to use a given flow of water. The miners applied a standard of priority already in effect in their mining operations (6). Under customs of the mining field, enforced by community pressure until mining laws were enacted and courts established, the first discoverer had the prior right to the mining ground. This is expressed by the legal maxim, "First in time, first in right."

In adjudicating claims between rival users of water, therefore, the mining community recognized the first user who actually put water to beneficial use. As with mining claims, the miners limited the quantity of water a person could lay claim to and required a certain performance of use and diligence in constructing and maintaining facilities to preserve the claimed right of use.

These new principles of water law, now known as the *doctrine of prior appropriation,* saw early expression in court decisions in the West. In 1855, for example, the California supreme court handed down a decision upholding the appropriative principle in litigation between a canal owner who had diverted water from public land and a miner who had later located on public lands bordering the stream from which water had been diverted (3). In the ensuing century of litigation and lawmaking, state water codes and administrative procedures were evolved that could effectively control the development and use of water in semiarid and arid sections under the new appropriative legal concept.

## CONTRIBUTIONS OF THE APPROPRIATIVE DOCTRINE

In most cases, the water rights for the carry-over water supply that fills the storage reservoirs throughout the West were developed by appropriation under state law, utilizing legal provisions and administrative procedures developed in America since the mid-1800's. The availability of an equitable, tested legal procedure for allocating and adjudicating water rights made this tremendous, orderly development possible.

Informed legal authorities recognize that the doctrine of prior appropriation is perhaps the outstanding contribution western America has made to water law, but they also recognize its inherent limitations. For one thing, its operation can give advantage to the first area that develops beneficial uses and storage capacity on a given drainage system.

This problem occurred in the development of the Colorado River, which flows through one of the most arid regions of the country, a 242,000-square-mile area that constitutes one-twelfth of the land surface of the continental United States, excluding Alaska. Settlement of the problem created by early appropriations and large-scale agricultural development in the lower reaches of the river basin delayed for many years the construction of Hoover Dam, the country's first big multiple-purpose storage development.

Despite its recognized merits, the upstream states of Colorado, Utah, Wyoming, and New Mexico opposed the construction of Hoover Dam, because they felt that a reservoir impoundment of 30 million acre feet in the lower basin would endanger their future right to utilize the river. Under the doctrine of prior appropriation, they asserted, downstream users on a controlled river could put all of the available water to use and thus establish priorities that would preclude additional development in the upper-basin states, where, they argued, 90 percent of the flow of the river originated.

This controversy was settled by negotiation and ratification of the Colorado River compact of 1922, a historic interstate agreement apportioning the available water in the river between the respective upper and lower basins. This compact paved the way for a $465-million development on the lower Colorado River. The four upper-basin states ultimately—in 1948—negotiated another interstate agreement, apportioning the upper basin's share of Colorado River water. This agreement made possible the billion-dollar Colorado River storage project, approved in 1956. The lower-basin states were unable to agree on a similar compact, and two of the states, California and Arizona, are nearing the end of several years of litigation in the United States Supreme Court over their respective rights to Colorado River water.

Compacts, amicably arrived at, can apportion interests in water-resource development and facilitate tremendous savings in time, energy, and money if litigation is reduced or avoided. A number of interstate compacts were concluded subsequent to the precedent-setting Colorado River compact, the most recent one being on the Delaware River in the humid East (4).

All sections of the country can and will benefit from the experience and techniques that have been acquired during the past century of water-resource development in the West. This same experience is providing data that are usable throughout the world. Water problems have a common denominator everywhere and tend to differ only in details and degree.

## IRRIGATION DEVELOPMENT ACTIVITIES

For nearly six decades, the Bureau of Reclamation and its predecessor agency, the Reclamation Service, have been helping the western states to develop their limited water resources.

Extensive transmountain diversions have been made from western streams. In my native state of Utah, the Bureau of Reclamation on one of its first projects drilled a tunnel through the Wasatch Range to transport waters from the Colorado River Basin to the Bonneville Basin, thus helping to create an agricultural-industrial oasis in water-short central Utah. Later on, the bureau drilled one of America's longest tunnels (the 13.1-mile Alva B. Adams Tunnel) to bring water from the west slope of the Colorado Rockies, under the Continental Divide, and down the east slope of the Rockies for use along the South Platte River nearly to the Nebraska border. In California, water is transported in river-sized canals for nearly 500 miles in the great Central Valley project. In the state of Washington, the world's largest pumps at Grand Coulee Dam discharge a river-sized stream of water from the Columbia River for irrigation use on the Columbia River project—an intrabasin diversion of great magnitude. In Texas, a proposed river-sized canal about 450 miles long and with capacities up to 9000 cubic feet per second is being considered under the Texas basins project.

Considered over all, the total contributions have been tremendous, ranging from large, complex storage at transbasin developments to simple stream diversions. There are now in operation on reclamation projects more than 300 storage and diversion dams, with a total reservoir storage capacity of 87 million acre feet; 7180 miles of canals; 20,800 miles of laterals and sublaterals; 9450 miles of drains; 42 hydropower plants with a total capacity of 5,199,550 kilowatts; and various other facilities, including works essential to flood control, navigation, public recreation, fish and wildlife propagation, and other benefits.

The Bureau of Reclamation also is now engaged in a construction program that, when completed, will add approximately 44,962,000 acre feet of needed reservoir storage capacity to what has already been provided, more than 1.8 million kilowatts of hydroelectric capacity, a full water supply for irrigation of 1,463,000 acres, and a supplemental water supply for 836,000 acres of farmland.

This impressive federal water-resource development program, supplemented by works built by the U.S. Army Corps of Engineers and the U.S. Department of Agriculture, nevertheless, has been eclipsed many-fold by water-development projects carried out by private interests and by state and local government agencies. In developing water for irrigation, for example, federal projects in 1959 supplied water to 6.8 million acres; nonfederal interests delivered water to 26.2 million acres.

## NEW CHALLENGES FOR THE SECOND CENTURY OF WESTERN WATER DEVELOPMENT

It is said that what is past is prologue. This is certainly true of water-resource development. In spite of the accomplishments during the past century, challenges of comparable magnitude are still ahead of us in the water-resource field. Furthermore, instead of being a largely regional problem, the question of an adequate water supply has become a national problem of increasing urgency.

One fact in the continuing necessity for water-resource development is population pressure. Based on medium-scale projections of population experts, the population of this country is expected to increase 40 percent or more by 1980, and to double by the year 2000. The West itself will increase from its 1960 level of about 44 million to an estimated 108 million by the year 2000.

The U.S. Senate Select Committee on National Water Resources, in a 2-year study concluded in January 1961, reported that substantial areas of water shortage already exist in many of the river basins in the western half of the United States. The committee concluded further that, on the basis of water supply-demand studies, full development of all the available water resources in the south Pacific, Colorado River, Great Basin, upper Rio Grande-Pecos River, and upper Missouri River regions would be required by 1980 or earlier if the projected increases in population and economic activity are to be achieved. By the year

Many additional water-storage facilities are needed to assure the necessary water in most basin areas of the West. (Courtesy U.S. Department of Agriculture, Soil Conservation Service)

2000, three additional regions—one in the humid Midwest—will be added to this list: upper Arkansas-Red rivers, western Great Lakes, and western Gulf.

In other words, this Senate Select Committee found serious, impending water shortages in 8 out of 22 water-resource regions if bold projects in water-resource conservation and utilization are not conceived and carried out. This challenge still centers in the western states and is roughly comparable to that facing the colonizers of the West a century ago. Today, however, we are equipped with greater know-how and engineering and legal experience in meeting such problems.

## Storage requirements

Many hundreds of millions of dollars will have to be spent for water storage, carriage, and distribution facilities during the coming years. This expense will be in addition to the many other millions required for flood-control and navigation structures, pollution-control and public recreation facilities, and other multiple-purpose works. The committee estimated that the nation's minimum storage needs for water supply and pollution abatement would be an additional 315 million acre feet of reservoir capacity by 1980 and another 127 million acre feet by the year 2000. This combined total requirement of 442 million acre feet of reservoir storage in 40 years is roughly 5 times the total water-storage capacity built by the Bureau of Reclamation in 58 years.

## Underground water sources

Considerable effort and research are required to locate and utilize underground water supplies, which today supply about one-fifth of the fresh water withdrawn for use in the United States.

In past years, these apparently boundless sources of water have been overdrawn, literally "mined" by unrestricted use. This overuse has caused serious drops in underground water tables and, in some areas, has required artificial recharging of the underground basins with surface water. Recently, however, some states have come to realize the value of these underground water supplies and have taken steps to ascertain their usable storage capacities, inflow rates, and potential yields. The need for control of use and recharging when there is a significant decline in water levels has also been recognized.

The economic importance of this water source has been demonstrated in the state of Nebraska, which has advanced from tenth to fifth rank among the states in total irrigated acreage in the last

decade. Much of this increase resulted when the farmers discovered they could economically pump water from a well-defined
subterranean course of water flowing across the state from the
northwest to the southeast.

The governor of Arizona reported to the Senate Select Committee on the critical water supply situation in that state, where
6.6 million acre feet of water is used annually, but only 2.1 million
acre feet is available from surface sources (5). In spite of estimates that only 1.5 million acre feet can safely be pumped annually from the underground water pool, Arizonians have been
pumping 4.5 million acre feet per year. Furthermore, municipal
and industrial water needs in Arizona are expected to more than
double by 1980. Unless some other source of water is developed,
this entire increase will be met by taking water from agriculture,
with the resultant loss of fresh fruits and vegetables for which
the "Valley of the Sun" is so famous. This is one of many areas
in the country where the ground-water supply is becoming a
subject of serious concern.

### Reduction of water losses

In discussing problems of future water supply, attention generally is focused on the construction of additional storage structures or improved techniques for utilizing ground-water supplies.
However, a great potential for additional water for the future
is in reducing losses from water pollution, evaporation, and seepage, and through limiting transpiration by water-loving, but
generally worthless, plants that invade reservoirs and conveyance
channels.

It has been estimated that the western states annually lose
about 25 million acre feet of water through evaporation from
exposed fresh-water surfaces—principally ponds, lakes, and reservoirs. This tremendous annual loss represents almost enough
water to fill America's largest man-made storage vessel—Lake
Mead, which backs up behind Hoover Dam. At five persons
per 1 acre foot, it also represents enough water to provide for
municipal use by 125 million people.

The Bureau of Reclamation studied this problem for the Senate Select Committee in 1959 and reported that by 1980 improvements in irrigation-water-conveyance works could reduce seepage losses by about 1½ million acre feet; surface treatment of reservoirs could save about 2 million acre feet of water; and eradication of nonbeneficial plant growth could reduce consumptive water losses by another 1 million acre feet. This potential water-saving, if achieved, would constitute a large new supply, available without conflicts over water rights or competition with other water users.

Promising new vistas also are opening in the perennially challenging problem of converting saline or brackish water to fresh water. A major breakthrough in this area of water-resource research would be of inestimable benefit to the United States and to virtually all other semiarid and arid countries in the world.

### Saline-water conversion

Extensive field research in saline-water conversion has been underway in this country only since 1958, but three large demonstration plants already have been completed and two others are nearing the construction stage. These installations, which are being constructed under the demonstration-plant program of the Department of the Interior's Office of Saline Water, are designed to demonstrate the reliability, engineering, operating, and economic potentials of the most promising of the presently known processes for making sea or brackish water suitable for drinking or industrial use. Much has been learned in this field during the past decade, and the first session of the 87th Congress authorized an additional $75 million for research in this important natural resources program during the next 6 years. Development of an economically feasible conversion system would mean a major new water supply for the United States and the rest of the world, including many underdeveloped countries that have no other source of needed additional water.

It also should be realized, however, that any possible additions to the total water supply achieved through new storage facilities, reductions in water losses, or conversion of saline waters may be offset by new demands or by increases in competing water uses.

## COOPERATIVE DEVELOPMENT: A MAJOR CHALLENGE

Among the foremost recommendations for follow-up action to the studies of the Senate Select Committee was a proposal to organize a Cabinet-level Water Resources Council. The committee also recommended authorization for the formation of river-basin water-resource commissions for comprehensive planning of water- and related land-resources development on a river-basin basis. A third element of the proposal was for federal assistance to water- and related land-resources planning by the states. Legislation to accomplish this forward-looking program has been recommended by President Kennedy and was considered by committees of the 87th Congress under the title "Water Resources Planning Act."

Tremendous basin-wide programs are now well underway in the Missouri River Basin and in the Colorado River Basin. Lessons learned in the development of these river basins and in the smaller but more widely known Tennessee River Valley in the eastern United States can be applied to other river basins if federal, state, and local interests cooperate in the planning, construction, and operation phases of the projects, and if their goal is multiple-purpose development for the good of all concerned in the respective basins.

In an approach of this kind, local or particular special interests may have to give way to broader regional or basin objectives, and an occasional eruption of controversy or spinning of the wheels while conflicts are worked out are to be expected. Nevertheless, the future need for water is obvious enough to demand the cooperation of all concerned and to deny as outmoded most single-purpose resource developments on our streams and rivers.

The newly developing emphasis on a multiple-purpose approach underscores the interrelationship of water-resource functions and the necessity for comprehensive development of the resources. As the need for additional supplies increases, and as the costs mount for the large, complex works needed to provide additional water today, close cooperation and sound working relationships among all organizations engaged in water-resource conservation and utilization will be essential. This is perhaps the biggest challenge of the coming years.

The recent tendency fortunately has been to build multiple-purpose projects to serve all possible uses of water, including the rapidly expanding uses for public recreation and for fish and wildlife propagation. The first session of the 87th Congress was notable for the passage of legislation that authorized construction of storage facilities for use in water-pollution control during periods of low streamflow. This storage authorization, combined with an increasing volume of federal, state, and local funds being advanced for sewage-treatment works, will do much to make our streams more useful for all purposes.

Fortunately, however, we have more than 100 years of experience in the physical and human problems involved in large-scale water-resource development in America. The technological problems are largely conquerable or within sight of solution with modern tools. The human problems, however, remain almost as challenging as they were when the pioneer and the miner moved into the western frontier land.

Can we exhibit the understanding, patience, know-how, and determination to make our basic water law more flexible and adaptable to changing conditions? Can we improve our administrative organization and techniques in a way to assure wiser and more efficient control and use of our increasingly inadequate water supply? These are sobering challenges to westerners—to all Americans.

## SUMMARY

The legal doctrine of riparian rights as applied to water resources was brought to America from the humid British Isles and was adhered to by the settlers in the East, where abundant precipitation and a small population meant comparatively little competition for water. As people moved into the arid and semi-arid areas of the West, the necessity for making beneficial use of all available water sources brought about the development of the doctrine of prior appropriation, an outstanding contribution by western America to water law.

For nearly six decades, the Bureau of Reclamation and its predecessor agency, the Reclamation Service, have been helping the western states to develop their limited water resources. This has included the building of extensive transmountain diversions, the transportation of water long distances through canals, and the construction of unique engineering works.

Much remains to be done, and the question of an adequate water supply has become a national problem of increasing urgency, owing to the rapidly increasing population. Solution of the problem will require establishment of additional water-storage facilities, the finding and utilization of underground water sources, reduction of water losses by evaporation and phreatophytes, and development of efficient saline-water-conversion procedures. Future water developments will depend increasingly on cooperative effort by all concerned.

## REFERENCES

1. *Encyclopedia Americana* (1959), vol. 15, p. 397.
2. Hutchins, W. A., "Selected problems in the law of water rights in the West," *U.S. Dept. Agr. Misc. Publ. 418* (1942), pp. 78-80.
3. Irvin V. Phillips, 5 Cal. 140. Reported in *The American Decisions,* compiled and annotated by A. C. Freeman (Bancroft-Whitney, San Francisco, 1886), vol. 63, pp. 113-116.
4. U.S. Congress, 87th Congr., Act of 27 Sept. 1961 (75 Stat. 688), Public Law 87-328, Delaware River Basin Compact Act.
5. U.S. Congress, Senate Select Committee on National Water Resources, Comm. Print 6 (Washington, D.C., 1960), pp. 5-8.
6. U.S. Dept. of the Interior, *Central Valley Basin* (Washington, D.C., 1949). A comprehensive report on the development of water and related resources in this area.
7. U.S. Dept. of the Interior, *The Colorado River* (Washington, D.C., 1946), pp. 45-46. A comprehensive report on the development of the water resources of this river basin.

# Livestock Interests in Public and Private Lands of the West

R. E. HODGSON

*Agricultural Research Service, U.S. Department of Agriculture, Beltsville, Maryland*

The effective and efficient use of land and water resources in the mountains and plains of our great western country is a timely subject, and I have endeavored to indicate the importance of the livestock industry and the contribution that it makes to the utilization of land and water resources in the production of foods. Certainly, the livestock producers in this area have a great stake in its land and water resources, for they are largely dependent on them. At the same time, they are looked to in great measure for the proper use of the vegetation grown from these resources in their production of animal foods.

The history of the settlement and development of the West is a story of livestock, extending from the oxen that hauled the pioneer's covered wagons accompanied by the trailing family milk cow to the modern, efficient herds of cattle and flocks of sheep. In the process, open prairies gave way to modern-day farming and ranching. The buffalo was replaced by the Longhorn and then by improved breeds and strains of modern cattle. The conflicts over the fencing of land areas and the ultimate sorting out of cattle and sheep raising into their proper places took place. The deterioration and then the beginning of improvement of the range occurred, and the development of irrigation on choice fertile valleys was started. Throughout this transition a constant battle has been fought against a difficult climate, droughts, and many other hazards. The tenacious rancher with his animals figured prominently in this development of our West.

Table I. Livestock and poultry on farms and ranches in the 17
western states, 1 January 1960

| Class | Number (1000's) | Percentage of total in U.S. |
|---|---|---|
| All cattle | 44,915 | 46.2 |
| Beef cattle and calves | 38,305 | 57.0 |
| Beef cows, 2 years old and over | 16,611 | 61.2 |
| Dairy cattle and calves | 6,975 | 22.5 |
| Milk cows, 2 years old and over | 4,324 | 22.1 |
| Sheep and lambs | 24,377 | 74.0 |
| Pigs | 12,681 | 14.3 |
| Hens and pullets | 84,631 | 24.0 |
| Commercial broilers | 205,616 | 11.4 |
| Turkeys | 2,781 | 45.8 |

Source: *U.S. Dept. Agr. AMS* **DA-3-61** (Feb. 1961); **LMS-115** (Mar. 1961); **PES-213** (May 1961).

## LIVESTOCK IN THE WESTERN STATES

Livestock production is no less important today. It constitutes the largest use of land resources in this vast area. The products of the region's farms and ranches make important contributions to the food and fiber supply for our people. A few statistics will bear out these facts. Table I shows that more than half of the nation's beef cattle population and nearly three-fourths of the sheep population are kept in the 17 western states. These are the users of the rangelands. Nearly three-fourths of the breeding ewes are in the western states. Breeding beef cows make up a proportionately larger share of the herds than in the East, 61 percent compared with 39 percent.

Swine, although not heavy users of pasture and range but large users of feed grains, amount to one-seventh of the nation's total. Western dairy cattle make up one-fourth of the nation's total. For the most part, they are kept in the more humid areas and on the irrigated lands of the region. Of the nation's poultry, 24 percent of the chickens and pullets, 11 percent of the commercial broilers, and nearly 46 percent of all the turkeys are raised in the 17 western states.

Formerly, many of the West's range cattle were moved East to feedlots for finishing, but in recent years this practice has changed, and increasing numbers are being fattened for market in the West. Especially noteworthy has been the growth of large feedlot operations.

As is shown in Table II, the number of cattle and calves on feed more than doubled from 1950 to 1961. The proportion of all cattle and calves on feed that are fed in the 17 western states increased during that period from about 42 percent to more than 50 percent. A similar trend, though less pronounced, is apparent also for sheep and lambs on feed. In addition, the number of cattle slaughtered in the 17 western states has been going up, as is shown in Table III. The number of cattle slaughtered in this area increased by almost 40 percent between 1950 and 1959, but the percentage of cattle slaughtered for the whole country increased only 2 percent, from 38 to 40 percent in this time. By contrast, fewer calves were slaughtered in 1959 than in 1950. This suggests that more calves are being raised to older ages and fattened by feedlot operations before going to slaughter.

These trends all suggest that, as more adequate feed supplies are developed in the West, more of the region's cattle are being fitted for market and processed into meat close to home. In further support of these shifts, large centralized packing-plant operations are tending to move out of big cities to outlying areas that are closer to their sources of production. This dispersion has been largely toward the West.

The rapid growth in population and the greater per-capita use of animal foods will require large increases in livestock production.

Table II. Cattle and sheep on feed in the 17 western states

| Animal | Number in 17 western states | | Percentage of total in U.S. | |
|---|---|---|---|---|
| | 1950 | 1961 | 1950 | 1961 |
| Cattle and calves on feed | 1,835,000 | 3,822,000 | 41.8 | 50.4 |
| Sheep and lambs on feed | 300,100 | 360,800 | 82.4 | 84.5 |

Source: *U.S. Dept. Agr. AMS* **LMS-88** and **LMS-115** (Mar. 1961).

Table III. Cattle and calves slaughtered in the United States and in
the 17 western states

|  | Number slaughtered (thousands) | | | | Percentage of total in U.S. | |
| Animal | U.S. 1950 | West 1950 | U.S. 1959 | West 1959 | 1950 | 1959 |
| --- | --- | --- | --- | --- | --- | --- |
| Cattle | 17,900 | 6804 | 22,930 | 9215 | 38.0 | 40.2 |
| Calves | 7,683 | 1944 | 9,972 | 1459 | 19.6 | 19.0 |

Source: U.S. Dept. of Agriculture, *Agricultural Statistics* (U.S. Govt. Printing Office, Washington, D.C., 1951; 1960).

Much of this, particularly beef, lamb, and mutton, will come from livestock production in the rangeland areas. By 1980, to meet consumer demands will require one-third more beef, one-sixth more lamb, two-fifths more pork, one-fourth more milk, one-half more eggs, and one-third more poultry meat.

Animal production will have to be expanded, first by greater production per animal unit and per acre of land used, and second by more animal units. Mutual understanding and an effective cooperative relationship must be maintained among the interests that control land and water resources in order to provide for the needs of the livestock producer, the forester, the conservationist, and the public.

## WESTERN LIVESTOCK'S CONTRIBUTION TO THE NATION'S FOOD SUPPLY

Our people enjoy a liberal supply of high-quality animal products, as is indicated by the current high per-capita consumption of these foods, which is shown in Table IV. The demands for beef are increasing. Consumers are indicating a preference for meat cuts that, although well marbled, carry less fat. Producers, in attempting to supply this kind of meat, are beginning to breed and develop animals that are larger and more rangy, are fast gaining, and have a higher ratio of muscle to bone and fat in the carcass. Feeding practices are beginning to shift to the production of finished animals that possess these desirable characteristics. This kind of beef animal and the new type of feeding practices favor western beef production.

As is indicated in Table V, two-fifths of the beef, one-third of the veal, one-half of the lamb and mutton, one-third of the eggs, one-fifth of the pork, milk, and poultry meat supplies, and three-fourths of the domestic wool production come from this area.

In terms of cash receipts from farm marketing, Table VI shows that farmers in the 17 western states accounted for nearly 42 percent of the total for meat animals, 33.6 percent of the total for all livestock and livestock products, and 38.7 percent of the total for all farm-produced commodities. The poultry and pig industries, although not large users of land and range areas, are significant users of feed grains produced in the area.

## IMPORTANCE OF RANGE GRAZING

Good estimates are not available for calculating the percentage of total feed consumed by western livestock that comes from range grazing as compared with that from irrigated and dryland farms. It is generally considered that for beef cattle at least 60 percent of the feed consumed comes from range and pasture. For sheep the percentage is around 75 percent. Since these are over-all averages, the contribution of range and pasture to beef and sheep production probably would be somewhat larger in the West. It is typical of many operations that range and pasture and irrigated and dryland forage and grain production complement each other.

Table IV. Per-capita consumption of animal foods in the United States in 1960

| Class | Pounds |
| --- | --- |
| Beef | 85.2 |
| Veal | 6.2 |
| Lamb and mutton | 4.8 |
| Pork | 65.3 |
| Milk | 654.0 |
| Poultry meat | 34.6 |
| Eggs | 347.0[a] |
| Wool | 3.1 |

[a] Number of eggs.
Source: *U.S. Dept. Agr. AMS* **LMS-120** (Nov. 1961); **DS-286** (Nov. 1961).

Table V. Production of livestock and poultry products in the 17 western states

| Class | Pounds (1000's) | Percentage of total in U.S. |
|---|---|---|
| Beef | 2,505 | 40.5 |
| Veal | 356 | 35.6 |
| Milk | 27,318 | 22.3 |
| Lamb and mutton | 395 | 53.5 |
| Pork | 2,563 | 21.4 |
| Poultry meat | 1,560,200 | 17.9 |
| Eggs | 16,863[a] | 27.4 |
| Wool | 196 | 74.7 |

[a] Number of eggs.
Source: *U.S. Dept. Agr. AMS* **DA-3-61** (Feb. 1961); **PES-213** (May 1961); **LMS-117** (July 1961); **LMS-120** (Nov. 1961).

If any one of these components were lacking in a farm or ranch operation, total livestock numbers would be considerably reduced.

The contributions that high-altitude national forest ranges make in the total picture should not be overlooked. In 1960, 1,140,429 cattle and 2,523,138 sheep grazed under permit on the national forests. These relatively small range areas and the small percentage of the total feed needs supplied by them are important because the high-mountain national forest summer ranges form an essential link with the lower elevation spring, fall, and winter ranges in the chain of grazing use.

## COMPETITION FOR THE USE OF LAND

In determining the use of land and water resources, the livestock industry must have prominent consideration in planning procedures. The most important single factor in this respect involves the use of range and pasture land. Vast areas of such land probably have little use other than for cattle and sheep grazing. Significant other acreages of this land might eventually come under irrigation and involve only a shift in use of land from grazing to crop production. But even as this takes place, important amounts of the crops produced will be fed to livestock, perhaps to pigs, chickens, and dairy cows more than to beef cattle and sheep. By far the greater part of the area, however, will continue to be used for grazing by beef cattle and sheep.

About three-fourths of the land in the western half of the United States is used for grazing (4). The remaining one-fourth is in cropland, mountains, ungrazed forest, and other miscellaneous uses. Much of the grazing land is not useful for other purposes; some of it is. About three-eighths of the rangeland area of the West is federally owned (1). Use of this land is permitted and regulated under various programs by the federal government. The remaining five-eighths is, for the most part, privately owned. The rangelands are in varying states of productivity, depending on type of vegetation, rainfall, elevation, topography, use, and so on. Water is deficient on much of it, even for supplying livestock.

In recent times increasing pressures have been placed on the use of this land. These pressures will increase in the future. As an example, in response to increases in consumer demand for beef, cattle numbers have been increasing. On 1 January 1950, the number of cattle and calves on farms in the 17 western states was 25,321,000 head. On 1 January 1960, the number was 38,120,000, an increase of 50.6 percent. The number of sheep on farms on these same dates was 20,186,000 and 24,377,000, respectively, an increase of 20.7 percent (6). Although numbers of cattle and sheep kept by farmers and ranchers vary from year to year and according to livestock cycles, as affected by economic, climatic, and other conditions, the over-all prospect is that cattle numbers particularly, and sheep to perhaps a lesser extent, will increase. With the same amount of land, or even less, the recent increases in cattle and sheep numbers have put greater pressure on the land and

Table VI. Cash receipts from farm marketing in the 17 western states

| Item | Value (billions of dollars) | Percentage of total in U.S. |
|---|---|---|
| Meat animals | 4,405 | 41.6 |
| Livestock and livestock products | 6,374 | 33.6 |
| All commodities | 13,169 | 38.7 |

Source: *U.S. Dept. Agr. AMS* **LMS-117** (July 1961).

water resources. Future increases in cattle and sheep populations will impose even more pressure. These demands for land and water use, coupled with demands imposed by the increasing numbers of big game, by additional public parks, primitive areas, and forest reserves, by the closing of some of these areas to grazing, and by the removal of land for roads and urban developments, will limit or reduce grazing areas for cattle and sheep. Tighter control of forest grazing under permit may also limit the number of livestock that graze forest areas.

A real opportunity exists, however, to meet future needs for grazing lands for livestock production by increasing the productivity of the available land and water resources. Livestock producers and public agencies are at present actively initiating programs and practices that both protect these valuable land and water resources and make them more productive. Controlled grazing, improved livestock, reseeding, fertilization, weed and brush control, and dam-reservoir and waterway construction are but a few of the practices employed. These are only beginnings; much more can and must be done to extend these desirable practices and to initiate additional ones to increase productivity and at the same time conserve the natural resource base.

## GOOD RANGE MANAGEMENT IMPROVES PRODUCTIVITY

Greater range productivity per acre rests on augmented knowledge of how best to handle ranges for maximum sustained output. Research to date suggests many possibilities. In Colorado (2) and Montana (5) experiments, moderate grazing levels permitted gradual improvement of range forage production and simultaneously provided a maximum average yearly income from livestock. Texas (3) trials suggest potential increases in total productivity from concurrent grazing by two or more animal species. Brush removal and reseeding have shown high promise. By and large, however, research to date has merely scratched the surface of these problems.

The livestock producer must continue to adopt practices that will continually improve the yield and efficiency of the land he uses and the livestock he produces. At the same time, he must participate in a sound program of land and water conservation. In this endeavor he will need the backing of a strong educational-extension program and an intensified, far-reaching research program in the public-supported institutions that should furnish him with the information necessary to accomplish these objectives.

## REFERENCES

1. Bennett, J. B., *et al.,* "The heritage of our public land," *Yearbook Agr. (U.S. Dept. Agr.)* **1958**, 42-52 (1958).
2. Klipple, G. E., and D. F. Costello, "Vegetation and cattle responses to different intensities of grazing on short-grass ranges on the central Great Plains," *U.S. Dept. Agr. Tech. Bull. 1216* (1960).
3. Merrill, L. B., and J. E. Miller, "Economic analysis of year-long grazing rate studies on substation No. 14 near Sonora," *Texas Agr. Expt. Sta. Misc. Publ. MP-484* (1961).
4. Upchurch, M. L., "The role of land in western ranching," *Yearbook Agr. (U.S. Dept. Agr.)* **1958**, 167-174 (1958).
5. Woolfolk, E. J., and B. Knapp, Jr., "Weight and gains of range calves as affected by rate of stocking," *Montana State Coll. Agr. Expt. Sta. Bull. 463* (1949).
6. *Yearbook Agr. (U.S. Dept. Agr)* **1951**; **1960** (1951; 1960).

# Public Grazing Lands in the Economy of the West

*Economic Research Service, U.S. Department of Agriculture, Washington, D.C.**

Throughout the history of our national life, no question (save possibly that of national defense) has remained so long and so persistently in the public eye as the question of public land. The ledgers of the Congress abound with debates and decisions on acquisition, disposal, and management of the public domain. For most of the nineteenth century, disposal of the public domain was a chief public issue. Most of the land west of the Alleghenies was once in public ownership. It has been used to pay soldiers, to finance schools and other institutions, to build public improvements, and for many other purposes. For the last half-century or so, the chief questions relate to management of public land and they are still far from settled. With a shifting and growing population and with changing economic and social conditions, the question of public land is forever new.

In this paper, I shall discuss some aspects of the economics of public grazing land in the affairs of the western states. One approach to an evaluation of public grazing in the economy of the West would be to count the economic multiplier effects of wealth created by grazing domestic animals on the public land. Rather than attempt this in a short paper, I shall tell something of the nature and extent of the federal public grazing lands in the West and give my view on some economic facts relevant to current issues in the use of these lands.

My concern here is with federal lands used for grazing, most

---

* Now Staff Economist, Agricultural Economics, U.S. Department of Agriculture, Washington, D.C.

of which are in the 11 western states and are administered by the Bureau of Land Management, Department of the Interior, or the Forest Service, Department of Agriculture. I shall largely ignore the 120 million or so acres of state-owned public land, for this land is controlled and used under institutions that differ from those applicable to the federal lands. And I shall ignore the public land in our largest state, Alaska, for little of it is used for grazing.

The federal government actually owns 407 million acres of land within the 48 contiguous states, or about one-fifth of the total land area. Current estimates of land in federal ownership are from unpublished data compiled by H. H. Wooten, Farm Economics Division, Economic Research Service, U.S. Department of Agriculture. Of the federal real estate, about 240 million acres is used for grazing by farmers and ranchers under a system of permits and leases. If this land were all in one block, it would be a strip of country about 375 miles wide and 1000 miles long. In reality, it is found from the Canadian border to Mexico, from the Pacific to the Great Plains. It includes alpine meadows and Sonoran desert shrub, the short grass sod of the plains and the annual wild oats of the Pacific slope, the sagebrush range of the Great Basin, and the woodland grasslands of the mountains. The common traits of these diverse acres are their federal ownership and their use for grazing and associated purposes.

Despite the large acreage, production of livestock feed from this land is not large. The federal range produces 1.3 percent of the livestock feed that is consumed annually in the United States (Table I). The entire 240 million acres of public land produces an average feed equivalent per acre of about ½ bushel of corn or 1 bale of hay. To add perspective: in recent years we have idled in the Conservation Reserve at least 5 times as much feed-producing capacity as that of the federal range. Recently, we have been shipping abroad, through P.L. 480* and in other ways, more than twice as much feed as we get from public land. The 1961 feed grain program alone reduced our national feed supply more than the equivalent of the feed produced on all public land. Obviously, little of our national supply of livestock feed comes from

---

* Public Law 480, 83rd Congress (68 Stat. 454).

Table I. Feed consumed by class of livestock and by source, United States, 1959[a]

| Livestock | Total feed consumed in U.S.[b] (1000's of tons) | Percentage consumed from | | | | Total feed consumed from other pasture and range[b] (1000's of tons) | Percentage consumed from | | | | |
|---|---|---|---|---|---|---|---|---|---|---|---|
| | | Grain and concentrates | Harvested forages | Cropland pasture | Other pasture and range | | Private land | National forests[c] | Grazing districts[d] | Indian land | State land |
| All cattle | 218,089 | 23 | 29 | 17 | 31 | 67,338 | 93 | 2 | 3 | 1 | 1 |
| Dairy | 92,091 | 29 | 40 | 11 | 20 | 18,505 | 100 | | | | |
| Other | 125,998 | 19 | 21 | 21 | 39 | 48,883 | 90 | 3 | 4 | 1 | 2 |
| Sheep and goats | 12,277 | 9 | 9 | 29 | 53 | 6,506 | 90 | 4 | 4 | 1 | 1 |
| Horses | 7,276 | 22 | 32 | 16 | 30 | 2,156 | 96 | 1 | 2 | 1 | |
| Hogs | 57,331 | 95 | | 2 | 3 | | | | | | |

[a] Estimates from unpublished data by Ross Baumann and Earl Hodges, Farm Economics Division, Economic Research Service, U.S. Dept. of Agriculture.
[b] Quantities in terms of feed units. A feed unit is equivalent to 1 pound of corn.
[c] Includes national forests, national grasslands, land-utilization projects.
[d] Includes Taylor Grazing Districts and Section 15 leases.

federal grazing land; however, our national need for livestock feed from the public's domain does not tell the full story.

A regional view gives a different picture. Most of the federal rangeland is in the 11 western states. In the West, about two-fifths of all livestock feed comes from pasture and range other than cropland, and, of this, about one-third comes from the federal range (Table II). On the basis of volume of feed alone, the federal range hardly looms large even in the West, since it produces about one-eighth of the livestock feed consumed in the region. But again, this does not tell the full story.

The public grazing lands are important (i) as a source of livestock feed in some areas and for some ranchers, (ii) as a seasonal supply of feed to supplement other sources from private range- and cropland, (iii) in terms of who has access to public land grazing and the conditions under which grazing is permitted, and (iv) in terms of the joint use of public land for grazing and other purposes.

### DEPENDENCE ON PUBLIC LAND GRAZING

The acreage of public grazing lands is unevenly distributed over the West. In four western states (Arizona, Idaho, Utah, Nevada), more than half of the land grazed is in public ownership. In three others (New Mexico, Wyoming, Oregon), the proportion of public to private grazing land is nearly 50/50. In the other four (California, Washington, Montana, Colorado), the acreage of public grazing land ranges from less than one-fifth to about two-fifths of all land grazed.

Productivity, as well as acreage, varies by states. This variation could be shown by data on average carrying capacity or by acres required per animal-unit-month of grazing. A criterion that we might call an *index of dependence* on grazing land and on public grazing land may give us a measure with greater economic significance.

If we divide the gross sales of farm products between crops and livestock, we find that the percentage of sales from livestock varies from about 35 percent in Washington to 80 percent in Wyoming (Table III). If we divide income from livestock between range-

Table II. Feed consumed by class of livestock and by source, 11 western states, 1959[a]

| Livestock | Total feed consumed in U.S.[b] (1000's of tons) | Percentage consumed from | | | | Total feed consumed from other pasture and range[b] (1000's of tons) | Percentage consumed from | | | | |
|---|---|---|---|---|---|---|---|---|---|---|---|
| | | Grain and concentrates | Har-vested forages | Crop-land pasture | Other pasture and range | | Private land | National forests[c] | Grazing districts[d] | Indian land | State land |
| All cattle | 32,300 | 18 | 30 | 17 | 35 | 11,439 | 56 | 11 | 23 | 6 | 5 |
| Dairy | 7,800 | 17 | 48 | 32 | 3 | 219 | 100 | | | | |
| Other | 24,500 | 18 | 24 | 12 | 46 | 11,220 | 55 | 11 | 23 | 6 | 5 |
| Sheep and goats | 5,360 | 3 | 14 | 16 | 67 | 3,594 | 64 | 7 | 25 | 2 | 2 |
| Horses | 1,260 | 11 | 30 | 7 | 52 | 656 | 93 | 1 | 4 | 1 | 1 |
| Hogs | 885 | 96 | | 4 | | | | | | | |

[a] Estimates from unpublished data by Ross Baumann and Earl Hodges, Farm Economics Division, Economic Research Service, U.S. Dept. of Agriculture.
[b] Quantities in terms of feed units. A feed unit is equivalent to 1 pound of corn.
[c] Includes national forests, national grasslands, land-utilization projects.
[d] Includes Taylor Grazing Districts and Section 15 leases.

using and nonrange-using animals, we find that range livestock contribute from 30 to 95 percent in Washington and Wyoming, respectively.

Income from range-using livestock can be further divided according to the estimated proportion of value of feed obtained from range and from cropland and harvested crops. The contribution of range then varies from 55 to 80 percent by states.

Combining these three fractions gives an approximate index of the degree to which agricultural income depends on range and pasture land. As might be expected, Wyoming and Nevada show a high dependence on rangeland, with indexes of 60 and 55, while California and Washington show a low dependence, with indexes of 15 and 10.

One further calculation should be made: Of this dependence on rangeland, how much is attributable to private range and how much to public range? An estimate based on the relative quantities of feed obtained from each source can be made. Use of such an estimate gives us an index of dependence on public rangelands. This index ranges from 40 in Nevada to less than 5 in Washington. By states the numbers are: Nevada, 40; Wyoming, 25; Utah, 20; New Mexico, 15; Montana, 10; Idaho, 10; Colorado, 10; Arizona, 10; Oregon, 5; California, 5; Washington, less than 5.

One way to interpret this index is to say that roughly 40 percent of the farm income of Nevada is attributable to grazing livestock on the public land, and only 5 percent of the farm income in California is attributable to this source. Therefore, public grazing land for grazing is relatively more important to the farm economy of Nevada than to that of California. Let me emphasize that this is a very rough measure and is only one guide to the economic importance of public grazing land in the agricultural economy of the respective states.

These calculations are made on a state-by-state basis. Some areas, some communities, and some ranchers within states are more heavily dependent on the public range than these numbers suggest. In 1960, the Forest Service had nearly 15,000 permittees for grazing livestock on the national forests, national grasslands, and land-utilization projects of the West (3) (Table IV). The Bureau of Land Management issued about 18,000 permits for

Table III. Distribution of farm receipts by source and index of dependence on pasture and rangeland and on public range, western states, 1960

| State | Cash receipts from farm products | | Receipts from livestock | | Receipts from range livestock originating from | | Pasture and range receipts from | | Index of dependence on | |
|---|---|---|---|---|---|---|---|---|---|---|
| | Crops[b] | Livestock | Range[c] | Non-range[d] | Crop-land[e] | Pasture and range[e] | Private land[f] | Public land[f] | All pasture and range | Public range |
| Montana | 45 | 55 | 90 | 10 | 40 | 60 | 75 | 25 | 30 | 10 |
| Idaho | 55 | 45 | 60 | 40 | 45 | 55 | 45 | 55 | 15 | 10 |
| Wyoming | 20 | 80 | 95 | 5 | 20 | 80 | 60 | 40 | 60 | 25 |
| Colorado | 40 | 60 | 85 | 15 | 45 | 55 | 70 | 30 | 30 | 10 |
| New Mexico | 40 | 60 | 85 | 15 | 20 | 80 | 60 | 40 | 40 | 15 |
| Arizona | 65 | 35 | 80 | 20 | 30 | 70 | 55 | 45 | 20 | 10 |
| Utah | 20 | 80 | 50 | 50 | 25 | 75 | 30 | 70 | 30 | 20 |
| Nevada | 15 | 85 | 85 | 15 | 25 | 75 | 25 | 75 | 55 | 40 |
| Washington | 65 | 35 | 30 | 70 | 25 | 75 | 85 | 15 | 10 | g |
| Oregon | 55 | 45 | 50 | 50 | 20 | 80 | 60 | 40 | 20 | 5 |
| California | 60 | 40 | 45 | 55 | 25 | 75 | 75 | 25 | 15 | 5 |

[a] Percentages are rounded to the nearest 5 percent.
[b] Cash sales of harvested crops as a percentage of total sales of crops, livestock, and livestock products.
[c] Includes sales of cattle and calves, sheep and lambs, goats, wool, and mohair.
[d] Income from livestock and livestock products derived chiefly from resources other than dryland pasture and range, that is, poultry, dairy, hogs, bees, and so forth.
[e] Estimated proportion of value of range livestock and their products derived from harvested crops and cropland pasture and from all dryland pasture and range.
[f] Estimated proportion of value of dryland pasture and range from public land and from private land.
[g] Less than 5.

Table IV. Permits or leases and livestock using federal rangeland, 11 western states, 1960

| Land administration | Cattle and horses | | Sheep and goats | |
|---|---|---|---|---|
| | Permits or leases (No.) | Live-stock (No.) | Permits or leases (No.) | Live-stock (No.) |
| Forest Service | | | | |
| National forests | 13,860 | 1,091,084 | 1,968 | 2,512,936 |
| National grasslands | 731 | 44,787 | 66 | 26,705 |
| Land-utilization projects | 116 | 2,570 | 14 | 7,732 |
| Bureau of Land Management | | | | |
| Taylor Grazing Districts | 13,976 | 2,492,633 | 4,395 | 5,858,797 |
| Section 15 leases[a] | 9,242[b] | 745,306 | | 1,430,934 |

[a] Lands leased under authority of Section 15, Taylor Grazing Act.
[b] Number of lessees of Section 15 lands undifferentiated by type of livestock.
Source: From *Report of the Chief*, Forest Service, U.S. Dept. of Agriculture (1960) and from unpublished data of Bureau of Land Management, U.S. Dept. of the Interior.

grazing on its grazing districts and had nearly 10,000 leases for grazing on "Section 15" lands. ("Section 15" lands are outside of organized grazing districts and are leased under authority granted in Section 15 of the Taylor Grazing Act of 1934.) These numbers cannot be added to arrive at the total number of ranchers who use public land. Some ranchers have more than one permit on either BLM or Forest Service lands, and they may have permits from both agencies. However, more than 30,000 farmers and ranchers graze livestock on public land in the western states.

Public range contributes heavily to the feed supply of some ranchers. More importantly, it often provides a seasonal source of feed that supplements and complements other feed supplies. As a matter of fact, a rancher must have "commensurate" feed or water supplies to remain eligible for privileges to graze either national forest or Taylor District land.

One area in northeastern California may be cited to illustrate the interrelationship between public range and privately owned sources of feed (5). The area contains 558,294 acres, 58 percent of which is federal land in both national forest and grazing district administration. Of 43 ranchers in the area, 39 had permits to graze public land. Nine ranchers had permits on the grazing district only, 11 had both district and national forest permits, and 19 had national forest permits only. These ranchers got about two-thirds of the feed for their livestock from grazing privately owned land. The other one-third of their feed came about equally from grazing public land and from hay and concentrates. Although roughly about one-sixth of their feed came from public land, these ranchers were heavily dependent on their public land grazing allotments. The federal range furnished feed in a season when it made a valuable supplement to privately owned sources. At the same time, the private resources supplemented the federal range, which could not have been used for grazing domestic livestock without the private range- and hayland. Although this area is small, it is fairly typical of many ranching communities in the West.

In the aggregate, public rangeland supplies a minute part of the feed for our nation's livestock. Even in the West, feed obtained from this source is a small part of the total. However, it provides an important supplement to private resources. These facts should help us to understand the importance of grazing on public land and may sharpen our judgment in relation to two important issues, the issue of grazing fees and the issue of multiple use.

## PERMITS AND PRICES FOR PUBLIC GRAZING

Relatively few people use public land for grazing domestic livestock, and those who do use it as a supplement to other resources. This situation gives rise to two of the chief questions concerning public land management: Who may use public grazing land? How much should be paid for it? ?

The West was settled initially by people who exploited and used as their own the minerals, water, forests, and forage of the public domain. "Free grass" lured men to risk their wealth and their lives, to endure hardships and loneliness, and to establish institutional and cultural traits that still mark "the West" as a unique economic and cultural region.

The men who pursued free grass are only recently gone. They

were here when our forest reserves were established late in the last century. Some of them were here when the Taylor Grazing Districts were established in the 1930's. Their sons and grandsons are here now. The men who fought the Indians and the elements for free grass influenced greatly the shape of public land administration and how the land itself is used. They felt a proprietary interest in the land they helped to subdue, even though they had no title to it. When active government administration was established over grazing on the national forests between 1905 and 1910, this proprietary interest was reflected in the original rationing of grazing privileges. In a sense, preemption was recognized and institutionalized by the giving of priorities for grazing permits to people who had a history of using the public land. Similar principles were followed a quarter of a century later when active administration was established over public domain lands organized into the Taylor Grazing Districts. Both the Forest Service and the Bureau of Land Management recognize history of use as one basis for a grazing permit. Other factors relate to the permittee's dependence on federal range and his qualifications with respect to commensurate property.

Yet, people who have no permits demand them, and people who do have them want more. But there is not enough grazing to satisfy all demands. In many areas, even the present rate of use of the public range is excessive in terms of achieving conservation and improvement.

In private business, when a commodity or a resource is scarce, prices increase so that potential takers drop out of the market, and demand thus tends to equate with supply. This familiar principle of economics does not apply to grazing on public land for a number of reasons. First, the "seller" of the grazing is not a private firm that produces livestock feed for profit. The seller is the government, or a "public firm," and it permits livestock grazing as a privilege to those who meet established qualifications of eligibility and at the same time attempts to reconcile grazing use with other uses of the public resource for the greatest public good (1).

Second, there is no "market" for grazing permits in the sense of a free interchange between buyers and sellers competing for a homogeneous product. The product (range forage) is not homogeneous, the public agency is the only seller, and only one buyer or a very few buyers or potential buyers are situated so that they can use any one tract of rangeland. Although access to a grazing permit is frequently bought and sold through the commensurate land or the permitted livestock, the grazing privilege itself cannot be purchased.

Third, rarely is public rangeland used only for grazing domestic livestock. Its joint use for other purposes—big-game grazing, watersheds, timber, recreation, and others—argues against pricing the grazing privilege in the usual economic sense. Control over these nongrazing uses cannot be alienated by sale, as in transfers of real estate in fee simple between private firms.

For these and other reasons, price alone cannot equate supply and demand for public range grazing. Price alone will not ration the feed or choose the users. The problem of how to charge for grazing on public land remains a hardy perennial in the field of public resource policy. This problem has been given exhaustive study on a number of occasions, yet as recently as February 1961 President Kennedy asked the departments concerned ". . . to formulate . . . principles for the application of fees, permits and other user charges . . ." (2).

Some have advocated that a "fair market value" be charged for grazing on the public range. Those who use this phrase generally imply that the charges for grazing public land should be the same on an animal-unit basis as the prices paid for privately owned range. To me, the analogy between public and private range is questionable. Even though comparable pastures in public and private ownership may be found occasionally, the different circumstances of control and right of disposal of the resource makes equal pricing suspect. Also, in some areas private range may sell or lease at a high price because the price of public range is institutionalized at a relatively low level. Under such circumstances, arbitrarily setting the price of public grazing equal to that of private grazing would not make sense.

A "fair" price for grazing public land is needed, but fair to whom and under what circumstances? The original users of the public domain paid nothing for the privilege; that is, they paid nothing to the federal government. With the establishment of positive management and control of grazing on public land, initial fees were nominal. They have remained so, although they are higher now than originally. (The federal government now gets about 60 cents for each animal-unit-month of grazing on the national forests and about 20 cents for each animal-unit-month on the Taylor Grazing Districts.)

Federal range is always used in conjunction with private pasture, cropland, or water resources. Together, these resources are the land base of a ranch, a livestock-producing firm. As a unit they have a value. If one part of this input mix is underpriced, it is likely that other parts are overpriced. Thus when a ranch is sold, it is likely that the profit-producing capacity of the entire ranch is capitalized in the private property part of it. People who have bought ranches under these circumstances doubtless feel that they have paid "full value" for this profit-producing capacity, even though they did not pay the federal government for it.

How does the seller view this price problem? Does giving ranchers access to public range at 20 or even 60 cents per animal-unit-month seem as though the public is getting the worst end of a bargain, especially when private pasturage rents for $3 or more per animal-unit-month? Should the public get greater returns for the use of its resource?

In 1960, the Bureau of Land Management received nearly $3.5 million in grazing fees and leases (4). The Forest Service received $4.5 million. Receipts from grazing are a small part of the money received by both agencies—about 1 percent for the Bureau of Land Management and about 2.6 percent for the Forest Service. (A charge of only 5 cents per recreation visit in the national forests would have produced more revenue for the Forest Service.) Although estimates of the cost to these agencies of administering grazing are not available, it is likely that such costs far exceed receipts from grazing. If these agencies were operated as private businesses, they would have to raise their prices drastically or go out of the grazing business. If substantial federal revenues depended on income from grazing, there would be merit in striving for maximum income.

Maximizing income to the federal government is hardly the point. The point lies in the interpretation of "fair market value," a phrase often used in reference to grazing fees. A fair market value for the seller might mean some price above the costs required to make the grazing available to buyers. A fair market

Good forage for sheep is only one of several products of high-altitude lands like this. (Courtesy U.S. Department of the Interior, Bureau of Land Management)

value for the buyers means some price below the marginal net product of the range feed, taking into account the effect that the price of public land grazing has on prices of other inputs. I doubt that these two concepts of fair market value are compatible.

One way to arrive at the fair market value might be to sell public grazing permits at auction. Many states allocate the use of their state-owned land in this way. But the federal government is not just selling range forage to the highest bidder. Values other than grazing on public lands must be protected and preserved. Moreover, private land values and other aspects of the economic life of ranching communities have become adjusted to the institu-

tionalized prices now in effect for public land grazing. Drastic
and sudden changes in these prices would produce chaos. For
these reasons and others, public auction of grazing privileges must
be rejected.

Once a schedule of prices becomes institutionalized—be it grazing fees on public land, taxes, or rates charged for irrigation
water—to the extent that other prices and costs adjust to them,
there are strong arguments against change, at least against large
or sudden changes. Values of the commensurate property of
public range users have adjusted to the present schedule of fees.
Ranchers who have bought such property have paid full value
for the productive capacity of their ranches. An increase in grazing fees would, in effect, multiply the price they have already
paid.

## ISSUE OF MULTIPLE USE

The idea of multiple use of public lands is deeply embedded in
our land policy. It arises partly, perhaps, from a historical inability to prevent multiple use, partly from the notion that the
entire public should have access to the public resource, and partly
from the belief that several activities carried on jointly achieve
more efficient use of the resource.

The idea of multiple use as a policy goal was enunciated very
early in the history of the national forests. It has been confirmed
by numerous statements of Chief Executives since Theodore
Roosevelt, the latest being President Kennedy's special message on
natural resources (2). It has been confirmed also by many actions
and acts of the Congress, the latest being Public Law 86-517, "an
act to authorize and direct that the national forests be managed
under principles of multiple use . . . ."

Few would quarrel with the idea and policy of multiple use.
However, few would agree on exactly which combination of uses
on a specific tract of land would most completely fulfill the objectives of the policy. The local public land administrator has
only general rules and broad enunciations of policy to guide him.
These are not very comforting to him when he must choose
in his day-to-day decisions between fewer sheep and more deer
or between promoting recreation values at the expense of logging.

Economists have not been especially helpful on this question. Techniques of economic analysis have been developed to ascertain which combination of resources produces a given product at the least cost or which combination of resources and products maximizes profits. These techniques, however, have been applied chiefly to single firms or in the setting of a single firm. Multiple use of public land always involves a combination of firms—ranches, lumber companies, a group of sportsmen, an irrigation company, and so forth—each having its own set of input-product relationships. In this setting, each "firm" and each type of firm strives to maximize profits, and the efforts of one may be at odds with the efforts of others. The conditions of multiple use, however, imply a combination of uses and firms so that the aggregate of all their net revenues or satisfactions is the greatest over time.

I believe the complex economic problem of multiple use can be solved with modern techniques of analysis. With adequate input-output data, we now can calculate what intensity of a single use (cattle grazing) would maximize profits over time. We also can calculate the combination of uses (cattle and sheep grazing) that would maximize profits for a single firm. We have yet to quantify the values of the nonmarket uses (big game, recreation, and so forth) and to calculate the combination of uses and of firms that would maximize the aggregate of net profits or satisfactions. Until we do this, implementation of the policy of multiple use must remain a matter for intuitive judgment by administrators.

## SUMMARY

I have not tried to be exhaustive in this brief review of some of the economic aspects of public land grazing. Regardless of how we measure, grazing on public land is not large nationally or regionally, except in acreage covered, but it is important to some people and to some communities.

The chief issues are distribution of use among different people and to different uses and the charges for use. Now that grazing fees are institutionalized and values of other resources have adjusted to them, drastic changes would cause economic hardship until adjustments in the capital structure of ranches could be made. Moreover, revenues from grazing are a very small part of the revenues of public land agencies. Even if fees were doubled, revenues would still be small and would still be well below the costs of administering the grazing resource.

At present, the idea and policy of multiple use are implemented by the judgment of administrators. Economic analysis has not been helpful, because the techniques now generally in use apply chiefly to problems that involve single firms, whereas multiple use of public land involves many firms. Economic analyses can be made, however, to ascertain the combination of uses and firms that would maximize profits and satisfactions from our public grazing lands. Such analysis could provide a more substantial basis for future decisions.

### REFERENCES

1. Kelso, M. M., *Objectives of Public Resource Allocation, Economic Research in the Use and Development of Range Resources,* Rept. 2 (Comm. on the Economics of Range Resources, Western Agricultural Economics Research Council, 1958) (Univ. of California, Giannini Found.).
2. Kennedy, J. F., Special message on natural resources (The White House, 23 Feb. 1961).
3. U.S. Dept. of Agriculture, Forest Service, *Report of the Chief* (1960).
4. U.S. Dept. of the Interior, Bureau of Land Management, *Annual Report of the Director* (1960).
5. Upchurch, M. L., and T. S. Brown, *Land, Livestock and Deer in the Milford-Doyle Area of Northeastern California* (Office of the Farm Adviser, Agricultural Extension Serv., Susanville, Calif., Nov. 1951).

# Agriculture as a Competitive Segment of Multiple Use

B. Delworth Gardner

*Economics Department, Brigham Young University, Provo, Utah*

The earliest commercial uses of water in the Mountain States were in agriculture and mining *(1)*. Wherever state laws have defined beneficial use of water, "domestic use" tops the list *(10)*. This use enables a rural riparian owner to take water for himself, his family, and his stock. Irrigation ranks after domestic and municipal uses in those states where the law delineates preferred uses. Even without explicit statutory sanction, the courts have held that domestic and irrigation uses are beneficial in all western states. In fact, Trelease *(10)* remarks that "the use of water for the irrigation of land in order to supply the deficiencies of natural rainfall is so widespread in the western United States that 'water law' and 'irrigation law' have come to be substantially synonymous terms . . . ." Agriculture is firmly entrenched in water use as far as the law is concerned.

In 1950 irrigation was the most important nationwide use of water when 79 billion gallons were withdrawn for this purpose *(16)*. By 1955, however, withdrawals by industry had exceeded those by irrigation; but it must be pointed out that about 90 percent of the water withdrawn for industrial use can be recirculated in the same plants or returned to streams for other uses *(17)*. Irrigation is easily the nation's greatest *consumptive* use of water *(16)*.

Approximately 93 percent of the nation's irrigated acreage is in the western states, but most of the industrial withdrawals are in the East. From this, we can infer that irrigation is the most important use of water in the West in terms of gallons used and is likely to remain so for many years to come.

During the last several decades, population and industrial growth rates in the intermountain states have exceeded national averages. No doubt municipal and industrial uses of water have greatly increased. However, there is no evidence that the region's agriculture has suffered a great deal as a consequence of increased competition from these other uses. The total value of land and buildings on farms increased 278 percent in the Mountain States between 1930 and 1959, but nationally the increase was only 169 percent.* Also, in 1930 the Mountain States produced 5.2 percent of the total national value of agricultural products sold; in 1954 they produced 7.3 percent.† In the Mountain States in 1900, 23.3 percent of the region's population was engaged in agriculture; in 1950, 17.8 percent (2). The comparative figures for the country as a whole are 35 percent and 12.2 percent, indicating that agriculture lost relatively less population in the mountain region than in the country as a whole.

One of the factors that accounts for agriculture's strong position, even in the face of increased competition for water, is the large investment in water development and land reclamation. Agriculture and other resource uses have simultaneously benefited. But even with all the development, the net depletions of water in 1955 were dangerously close to the natural supplies available to the western region (5).

Despite the apparent solidity of agriculture's current position, both legally and quantitatively, the underpinnings may be weakening. It has been demonstrated often that the value of water may be much greater in nonagricultural than in agricultural uses (8). Where large economic disparities exist, the courts seem to be "beginning to show an awareness of the economic relativity of specific uses" (6, 10). As the competition for water increases in the years ahead, and as developmental project possibilities are exhausted, agriculture may be forced to relinquish its present preeminent position.

---

* U.S. Dept. of Commerce, *Statistical Abstract of the United States, 1962* (U.S. Govt. Printing Office, Washington, D.C., 1962), p. 614, Table 847 "Farms—value of land and buildings by states: 1930 to 1959."

† U.S. Dept. of Commerce, Bureau of the Census, *U.S. Census of Agriculture, 1930* and *1954* (U.S. Govt. Printing Office, Washington, D.C., 1930, 1954).

In the use of land resources, agriculture's position is even less secure. Encroachments from urban development and highways are taking some of our best irrigable land and rangelands. When this occurs, individual farm owners are compensated for these resource losses. On the other hand, some real wealth losses result when public lands are converted from agricultural to nonagricultural uses. In this instance, no compensation is paid for the loss of a valuable asset. The number of animal-unit-months of grazing currently taken from the national forests is only one-third of the 1918 peak level, and about one-half of the 1933 level. And the end is not yet in sight as pressures mount from hunters, fishermen, recreationists, conservationists, and others who would like to have their own particular uses increased.

In Utah and perhaps elsewhere, even the Bureau of Land Management, which has not reduced grazing quantities markedly in the recent past, seems determined to make a grazing cut to maintain range productivity. The stockmen probably will resist this move, and it should be interesting to see how much resistance does develop and how the BLM handles it. The livestock people have traditionally played a more significant role in range policy on the public domain than on the forests. This is true because in the multiple-use schema, livestock grazing is probably of minor importance on the forests compared with its position on the public domain.

Grazing permits have never attained the legal stature that water rights have, and this adds to the insecurity that ranchers feel with respect to tenure of grazing. The government agencies have made it absolutely clear that the grazing preference is not a property right (14). Furthermore, grazing quantities can and will be reduced as range condition warrants such action. Although "advisory boards" of stockmen may confer with, and advise, agency officials, sole authority to determine range condition and, if necessary, make the grazing cuts, clearly rests with the agencies. Considering the multiple demands for increases in competing uses and the agency authority to grant them if it wishes, it is difficult to be very optimistic about the future of livestock grazing on the public lands.

## EFFICIENCY OF RESOURCE USE

Any kind of policy consists of action (or lack of it) directed toward certain specified goals. What action is taken depends on the criteria for making decisions. Therefore, criteria are inseparably related to goals and constitute the primary guidelines that the decision-maker uses in policy formulation and execution. Sometimes the criteria are logically contradictory; sometimes, inefficient in reaching goals. The agricultural segment of multiple-use policy provides us with some interesting examples of both.

In resource use, the overriding goal of society is to maximize the value of the products that might be harvested from the resources over some relevant time period. Criteria for resource allocation should be consistent with this general goal. For our purposes in this section, criteria will be considered at two levels: those that affect the allocation of resources among the various *uses*; and those that affect the distribution of a given quantity of resources among the *users* within a specified use.

The scope of this paper will not permit a full-blown discussion of the complete gamut of criteria that relate to resource use. I shall discuss at some length just one criterion from the range area that goes far toward determining the quantity of livestock grazing from public lands that is allocated to western stockmen. However, all criteria for allocating resources should be reexamined as resource supplies shrink in relation to demand.

"The grazing capacity of a national forest range area is the maximum number of livestock the unit will support during the regular grazing period over a long series of years without injury to the soil, forage plants, watershed, or tree growth" *(14)*. This statement implies that the resources are to be used at that level where the product is maximized subject to the constraint that the resource base (forage-producing capacity, soil, and so forth) will not be injured. This principle has been called *sustained-yield* by people in range management and forestry. "The principles which should govern the administration of all federally owned rangelands whether on the national forests or in the grazing districts, including the public domain and other federal withdrawals and reservations are: (i) Management which will restore and maintain in perpetuity on a sustained-yield basis, and utilize all the resources of the land . . . ." *(13)* .

There are several difficulties with this kind of principle, the most obvious being that it is not clear at what forage level the range is to be sustained over time. Conceivably a sustained-yield level of forage could be anywhere from zero to some maximum level. The enunciation of the aforementioned criterion implies that the optimum level is some high-productivity level, for the forage is to be "restored" (presumably to its former peak level) and maintained in perpetuity at that level.

A maximum forage criterion might not be appropriate on a range that is grazed, since enough grazing to be economic may disturb the "ideal" composition and amount of forage. In the case of grazing, the desired ultimate product is pounds of meat or pounds of wool, and the forage has no value until it is converted. This may not be true with some other uses, such as watershed protection, or some forms of recreation where the forage need not be used up in order to yield a product that society desires.

The decision made by forest officials to reduce grazing quantities could indicate adherence to some maximum forage optimum. If so, *any* livestock grazing might be too much. On the other hand, it may be that some optimum less than maximum forage is advisable but is impossible to achieve at present grazing numbers. At any rate, Forest Service officials have strongly insisted since the 1930's that forest ranges are being overgrazed and depleted, and that livestock numbers must be reduced if range restoration is to be accomplished. Ranchers, on the other hand, have argued that forest ranges are not deteriorating in quality and that permit cuts are unjustified. At first blush, this looks like a straightforward problem capable of being resolved by the facts—either the range is in a depleted condition, or it is not; either it is deteriorating over time, or it is not. But on second glance, it is not so easy, because words like *depletion* and *deterioration* are tied up with the norm (criterion) that is used. Perhaps neither side in the controversy is "wrong." Each group desires its own criteria for determining optimum forage: the forest officials adhere to a "high-level" sustained-yield forage optimum, the stockmen want a sustained-yield optimum at lower forage production that would also permit livestock utilization. The high-level forage optimum may be appropriate in terms of maximum forage production and resource protection, but it may not always produce the maximum "economic" yield, unless the forage is converted into products that society values.

A very extensive report on grazing was prepared by the Department of Agriculture in 1936 (13). The Taylor Grazing Act had been passed in 1934, and little had been done to manage the public domain prior to that time. Grazing controls on the forests had been in effect for several decades.

With respect to forest grazing, the report makes the following assertion: "On the national forests a reduction in stocking averaging 6.5 percent is necessary to reach the grazing capacity of the range" (13). About 80 million acres of forest land was being grazed, and about 33 percent was being depleted.

The situation was much more grave on the newly created grazing districts. Nearly 70 percent of the land was being depleted, and 93 percent was on the downgrade. The stocking rate exceeded grazing capacity by 43 percent.

The report also estimated depletion of private rangelands. "Three hundred seventy-six million acres of western rangeland is in private ownership. During a few decades livestock grazing has depleted this area by 51 percent; 85 percent, or almost 318 million acres, is still going down; only about 12 percent, or 44 million acres, is in good or fairly satisfactory condition."

If range is overgrazed, the carrying capacity diminishes as time passes, assuming that rainfall and other exogenous factors are constant, unless grazing pressures are reduced. The 1936 report (13) made it unmistakably clear that reduced levels of grazing would be required to restore, or even maintain, the range, particularly within the grazing districts and on private lands.

Other inferences can be drawn. In 1936 forest ranges were in better condition than private or public domain ranges. If numbers of grazing stock were drastically reduced on the forests while being maintained or even increased on the public domain and private lands, then we would expect that either the public domain and private lands would be *further* depleted or that the forest ranges would be "undergrazed," judged by any criterion except the maximum forage optimum.

Actually the number of animal-unit-months of grazing in 1959 on the grazing districts was substantially the same as in 1937. Over the same time span forest grazing was reduced almost one-half. During the same time (1937–1959) the number of animal units of grazing animals (sheep, goats, and all cattle except milk cows) increased by 21 percent in the mountain region. This implies that grazing intensity has increased on private ranges, unless it can be shown that the increased livestock numbers are being sustained by feeds other than pasture. The total quantity of corn, wheat, barley, and oats grown on the farms of the region and fed to livestock fell by 8 percent, and the total number of animal units (horses, mules, all cattle, sheep, goats, and hogs) fed increased by 10 percent. At the very least, these figures strongly suggest that private rangelands might have taken the burden of the increased numbers of grazing animals. If so, and these private ranges are being overgrazed, then there should be evidence of declining range productivity and falling rangeland values.

First consider trends in land values. In the Mountain States a large fraction of total agricultural wealth is in land contained in ranch-type operations. Only about 3.5 percent of the total land in farms is irrigated (15), so a very large percentage of all the land in farms is rangeland. Building requirements are minimal in ranching. If private ranges are being depleted, less economic product will be capitalized into land values over time and they should fall, all other things being equal.

In the 11 western states, the relative value* of agricultural land and buildings in farms rose 124 percent between 1935 and 1959. This is above the national average. In California and Washington, ranching is minor in the total agriculture, so these states are not considered individually. In the other states, the percentage

---

* The census values of private land and buildings per acre were deflated with the wholesale price index to eliminate the effect of price-level changes. The 1959 deflated value per acre was divided by the 1935 deflated value per acre to obtain a percentage change.

increases are: Arizona, 280; New Mexico, 151; Montana, 96; Idaho, 77; Colorado, 73; Wyoming, 64; Oregon, 56; Nevada, 36; and Utah, 22. Clearly other factors besides forage production affect agricultural land and building values in the West, and their effects must also be accounted for before a definitive answer can be given. It seems unlikely, however, that land values in the West would rise more than the national average if the productivity base were being depleted over time.

Let us now look at range condition. The U.S. Department of Agriculture publishes monthly indexes of range condition through the grazing season for western ranges. Both privately owned and public ranges are included in the sample. Table I gives the decade and 5-year averages from 1920–1960. During this period the lighter stocking of forest ranges and probable heavier stocking of private ranges occurred. There may even be a hint of the presence of the maximum forage optimum in the reporting of these data, since presumably "normal" plant cover would produce an index of 100, and none of the individual year's observations, to say nothing of the averages, even approach this high level of range condition.

Apparently range condition is very closely related to rainfall. This is suggested by several years of "low" range condition in the 1930's and 1950's, when droughts occurred, and by several good years in the 1920's and 1940's, when rainfall was heavier.

The decade means fluctuate, but there is no trend. The 1920

Table I. Range-condition averages

| 10-yr period | Average | 5-yr period | Average |
|---|---|---|---|
| 1920's | 87 | 1925-1929 | 87 |
| 1930's | 78 | 1930-1934 | 77 |
| 1940's | 84 | 1935-1939 | 79 |
| 1950's | 78 | 1940-1944 | 86 |
|  |  | 1945-1949 | 82 |
|  |  | 1950-1954 | 78 |
|  |  | 1955-1959 | 79 |

Source: U.S. Dept. of Agriculture, *Agricultural Statistics* (1960). Area includes the 11 western states, as well as the range areas of North Dakota, Nebraska, Oklahoma, and Texas. Indexes are reported in terms of percentage of normal.

mean index was 87. The 1950 decade mean stood at 78, which was precisely the 1930 mean. The 1940 mean of 84 was substantially higher.

The 5-year averages show the same pattern. The two periods in the 1950's were almost identical to the two in the 1930's. Again, no trend is evident. The conclusion is that no significant deterioration of ranges occurred during the 1940's and 1950's when heavy grazing was continued on private ranges.

Unfortunately, the data apply to a composite of private and public rangelands. It would be desirable to have separate data for private and public ranges. However, farmers and ranchers report range condition for local grazing areas, which in most cases include some public, as well as private, land. They would surely give primary emphasis to ranges that they own in judging the productivity of the region. For this reason it is untenable to infer from the range-condition data that private ranges have declined in forage production.

Despite the evidence of land values and range condition, the 1936 report (13) may not be in serious factual error if the maximum forage optimum was the criterion for range depletion. Many range scientists were and are estimating range condition, and I have no doubt concerning their competence. My point is that the criterion may be faulty when it is used to determine optimum *grazing* quantities. For agriculture, the use of this criterion may be of crucial importance, since the allocation decisions that result will be biased in favor of nondestructive forage uses that cannot deplete the range, such as recreation, forage for watershed protection, and wilderness preservation. This may even explain the complete elimination of livestock grazing from so many multiple-use public ranges.

A criterion should be used that would maximize the value of the products produced by the resources. On multiple-use ranges where grazing is permitted, animal-unit-months of grazing should be maximized over time in combination with optimum quantities of other uses, if this is possible. It might even be well to have flexibility to increase grazing intensity when livestock prices are high and, then, to undergraze to increase productivity when prices are low.

Another criterion of doubtful validity that has widely affected the allocation of resources between uses is the principle of "the greatest good for the greatest number." The principle is a logical contradiction: the greatest good can never be secured for the greatest number of users. Much good can accrue to a few, or some good can accrue to many. The way it usually works out in practice is that the political process favors policies that confer small benefits on the greatest possible number of people. Thus, while livestock grazing has been reduced on the public lands, wild-game numbers have been markedly increased. There are many more hunters with licenses than ranchers with grazing permits. An "efficient" criterion must consider not only numbers of gainers and losers from a given change in policy but also the extent of the loss or gain. Only in this way can total losses be set against total gains.

This brings us to the question of estimating the values of the various uses. Resources will be efficiently allocated when the marginal value product of the resources is equal for every *use* and for every *user*. In a perfectly competitive market, the value of the marginal product (marginal physical product of the re-sources times the product price) will be equal to the resource price when markets are in equilibrium. Therefore, resource prices for the various uses will indicate efficiency of use and guide resource transfers.

The difficulty is that markets seldom allocate resources in the area under discussion. The courts and agency officials generally have made the important allocation decisions. Because the allocation problem is essentially an economic problem, estimates of economic values are prerequisite for *efficient* allocation decisions. This is true even if the decisions continue to be made by the same people as now.

Economists have tried various methods to estimate resource values (*12, 18*). Space does not permit an evaluation of these procedures. I regard the estimates of marginal value products or demand curves for the various uses as the most meaningful attempts to ascertain value (*3, 4, 7, 9*). Some estimates use price data from markets in other areas and sectors that allocate services of similar characteristics.

This general procedure holds much promise. In timber production, hunting and fishing, camping, boating, grazing, and so on, prices are set by market forces in private markets around the country. These services are quite similar (and any existing differences can be evaluated) to those offered by the government agencies. Values can be imputed to the public services by using the market-determined prices from the private sector.

A difficult conceptual problem is always present in this procedure and must be considered in each case. The imputation process requires the use of an assumption that may be heroic in certain circumstances. The supplies and demands of public and private services are not independent. That is to say, the price of the market-determined private services is affected by the pricing and allocating policies that operate in the public sector. In the case of public services that are sold below the value of the marginal product (in many cases they are free), the price of competing private services will be lower than would be the case if public services were market priced. Thus, suppose that the forest service fee is 65 cents per animal-unit-month and the market-determined private rent is $3 per animal-unit-month. Now if the forest fee increased to say $2 per animal-unit-month, there would be a shift in demand toward the private grazing, and the market price per animal-unit-month of private grazing would rise above $3. It is clear that policies used to price public services affect market-determined prices of private services. When public services are underpriced, the prices of private services will be lower than the price that would be established if all services were priced in a free market.

Another crucial area in which our empirical estimates are woefully inadequate is the estimation of physical production relationships among the various uses. Often the presumption is that uses are competing and that increasing one use necessarily involves decreasing another. For example, the average hunter and rancher believes that livestock and game are competitors for forage—at least most of the public statements made by these groups indicate as much. On the other hand, many range-management experts believe that over wide levels of range productivity these uses are supplementary or complementary. We need research on these and other basic production relationships, followed by wide public education on these matters.

So far our discussion has been confined to allocation problems between agriculture and other uses. I and others have argued elsewhere that some severe allocation problems may exist *within* agriculture (7, 11). Essentially, the reason is that the resources have been "underpriced"; as a result, there has been excess demand, and some sort of rationing (allocating) scheme has been used to determine which potential users get the services. In the case of water, it is necessary to file for a "right," and if this is granted water use may in practice be tied to some "beneficial" use specified in the law. In many instances the irrigation or domestic-use right would be tied to some private property. In the case of livestock grazing, permits are issued to "preferred" applicants who meet certain noneconomic prerequisites, such as (i) being prior users of the range, or (ii) owning "commensurate" base property and livestock. Too often, as the years come and go, these rationing criteria tend inflexibly to tie the use of the resources to particular private users, thus preventing their transfer to more efficient users, who in a free market could and would bid the services away. Economists, politicians, and government-agency officials should work out ways to free the system of these transfer impediments.

## WEALTH TRANSFERS

The allocation procedures are inseparably connected with wealth distribution, both among industries and within industries. Because the water supply is so limited in the West, total private agricultural wealth will always be affected by the total amount of water allocated to agricultural uses. In large measure, who holds the wealth will depend on who holds the rights to use the water.

Net wealth will be created for individuals to whom the right is issued if, when the right originates, the water is priced below its value. This differential between water cost and value is capitalized into the value of the right if it is transferable, or into the value of appurtenant property if it is not. In any case, if some differential exists, a windfall wealth gain will accrue to the original right-recipient *only*. If the right changes hands, the purchaser will have to pay the capitalized value of the differential to acquire it. Therefore, the purchaser receives no windfall, assuming that water quantities permitted by the right are not affected in the transfer and that estimates of future water costs and benefits do not change.

The same phenomenon exists in grazing. The fee charged by the government agencies is below the value of the grazing services. The differential has become partially capitalized into permit values, since they sometimes may be transferred to other "qualified" ranchers. In 1957 in northwestern Colorado, the forest permits were being exchanged at an average value of about $16 per animal-unit-month, and Bureau of Land Management permits were worth about $11 per animal-unit-month (7).

Each time a grazing permit is reduced or a water right is canceled, the individual holding the asset suffers a wealth loss, because he is deprived of the future use of the resource. If it were simply a matter of offsetting a windfall that had been reaped previously by the same individual, these equity considerations might not be so important. However, as is indicated earlier, the windfalls were captured by the *original* recipient of the right or permit, and enough time has elapsed so that very few of these same people hold them when the *use* is shifted. Therefore, if resources move without compensation, the holder loses an asset that he has already paid to use. If transfers must be made, it would seem to be important to consider the use of some scheme to compensate the losers.

## SUMMARY

Although agriculture's current position is very strong in the use of water and land resources, some diminution of use is likely in the years ahead. Two factors are primarily responsible for this probable change in use patterns: (i) sharp increases in numbers of people who demand greater quantities of other uses, and (ii) the greater economic values of competing uses.

Before transfers of resources to other uses take place, however, several questions should be raised and answered: (i) Is the transfer clearly in the public interest; that is, is it clear that society values the new use more than it values the old? (ii) Are the allocating criteria and procedures efficient? (iii) Are the shifts in wealth that accompany resource movements identifiable, and, if so, what should be done about them?

With respect to the first question, basic research is needed to give us the physical production relationships among uses. Moreover, society must have a way of expressing its relative preferences for the various uses. This is most easily accomplished in a market situation. If the market solution is not feasible, then values must be imputed to the various uses. This will require ingenuity and painstaking research.

Fuzzy criteria, such as "the greatest good for the greatest number," should be abandoned. In the case of land use the sustained-yield, maximum-forage optimum for determining grazing quantities should be reexamined for its appropriateness, especially on lands where grazing is a major use.

Finally, whenever resources are transferred from one use to another, sizable wealth losses are suffered by someone. The size of these losses should be ascertained, and perhaps it may be desirable to compensate the losers.

## REFERENCES

1. Arrington, L. J., *From Wilderness to Empire,* Monograph 1 (Inst. of American Studies, Univ. of Utah, Salt Lake City, 1961).
2. ———, "Industrial structure of the mountain West, 1850-1950," a series of mimeographed tables (distributed by Dept. of Economics, Utah State Univ., Logan, 1961).
3. Clawson, M., *Methods of Measuring the Demand for and Value of Outdoor Recreation,* Reprint 10 (Resources for the Future, Washington, D.C., 1959). Out of print.
4. Dawson, J. A., "The productivity of water in agriculture," *J. Farm Economics* **39**, 1244-1252 (1957).
5. Fox, I. K., *Water Supply, Demand and the Law,* Reprint 15 (Resources for the Future, Washington, D.C., 1960).
6. Fisher, J. L., *Our Resource Situation and Outlook,* Reprint 22 (Resources for the Future, Washington, D.C., 1960).
7. Gardner, B. D., "Transfer restrictions and misallocation in grazing public range," *J. Farm Economics* **43**, 50-63 (1962).
8. Gertel, K., and N. Wollman, "Price and assessment guides to western water allocation," *J. Farm Economics* **42**, 1332-1344 (1960).

9. Tolley, G., and V. S. Hastings, "Optimal water allocation: the North Platte River," *Quart. J. Economics* **74**, 279-295 (1960).

10. Trelease, F. J., "The concept of reasonable beneficial use in the law of surface streams," in *Ground Water Economics and the Law*, Rept. 5 (Comm. on the Economics of Water Resources Development, Western Agricultural Economics Research Council, Berkeley, Calif., 20-21 Dec. 1956).

11. ———, "A model state water code for river basin development," in *River Basin Development* issue of *Law and Contemporary Problems* (Duke Univ. School of Law, Durham, N.C., spring 1957).

12. Trice, A. M., and S. E. Wood, "Measurement of recreation benefits," *Land Economics* **34**, 195-207 (1958).

13. U.S. Congress, *The Western Range*, S. Doc. 199 (24 Apr. 1936).

14. U.S. Dept. of Agriculture, "Range management," *Forest Service Manual* (U.S. Govt. Printing Office, Washington, D.C., 1941), vol. 3, title 8.

15. ———, "Water," *Yearbook Agr.* **1955** (1955).

16. ———, *Water Facts* (U.S. Govt. Printing Office, Washington, D.C., Aug. 1957).

17. ———, *Water for Farm and City* (U.S. Govt. Printing Office, Washington, D.C., Dec. 1960).

18. Wallace, R. F., *An Evaluation of Wildlife Resources in the State of Washington*, Bull. 28 (Bur. of Economics and Business Research, Washington State Univ., Pullman, 1956).

# Managing Private Lands in Relation to the Changing Uses of Public Lands

N. Keith Roberts

*Department of Agricultural Economics, Utah State University, Logan*

Public and private land-use relationships have always been dynamic. Earlier in our history the shift of land from public to private ownership dominated land policy. Today, the pressure in the western part of the United States is to shift public and private lands from an established single use to a different use or to more than one use. Increased urbanization, recreation, and conservation demands on the public-private land complex have upset the recent historical land-use balance. What can be done by users of these lands and by society to ease the economic confusion that accompanies changing land-use patterns?

Public and private lands in the West are economically related in two general ways. First, both are integral parts of firms, of which livestock ranchers are the dominant type. Second, economic development by a firm on public or private lands influences the use and value of lands of opposite ownership located nearby, although these may not be part of the firm. Only the intrafirm relationship is discussed here.

Except for small, highly specialized areas, grazing consistently has been the major economic use for large areas in the West, and it will probably continue to be so for some time to come. For decades, ranchers have used both public and private lands in their operations, but over the long run the number of animals grazing public ranges has decreased. In the continuing process a relatively stable relationship has developed between use of public and private lands.

The livestock economy of the intermountain West is dominantly a range economy, although the degree of dependency on range forage, of course, varies by area. Some feed is produced on privately owned irrigable lands for winter-breeding herds and to fatten some range-started calves, steers, and heifers, and privately owned rangelands supplement public ranges during grazing seasons. Without public ranges as a source of feed, however, the western livestock industry could not survive as we know it today. A 1961 survey of sheep and cattle ranchers in the middle intermountain and mountain states who use both private and public ranges in their operations indicated that these ranchers depended on public ranges to the extent of about 45 percent of their total feed requirements.

After World War II, society began to view the West as something more than desert and mountains. People became aware of something westerners had known all the time; the West held many attractions for living, playing, and working. It could satisfy many of society's desires.

Growing pressures for change in the use of public lands in the West have been reflected in the increased uncertainty ranchers face with respect to grazing privileges and costs of forage. More than ever before, ranchers have come to realize that permits to graze public lands are not rights that they own but only privileges administered by others.

A decision to raise the price of forage on public land or to reduce the permitted use of public land produces economic shock, not only for each ranch affected, but throughout ranching communities, ranching states, and the nation's livestock economy. However, economic shocks cannot be arbitrarily classed as bad or good. The results of stimuli for change in the economy must be judged in relation to the degree to which social goals are or are not achieved.

The seeds of conflict between ranchers and social interests are found in the divergency of goals. The planning horizon for society is much further in the future than it is for individual ranchers (11). Also, ranchers use combined public and private lands to make their living, while nonranch segments of society use public lands to achieve their next higher level of goals in the means-ends continuum (5). Nonranchers make a living in other pursuits and hope to realize more value by spending their dollars in using public lands than they could by keeping the dollars or spending them for anything else. These subjective utility estimates enter into decision-making with respect to the use of public lands and, consequently, also affect decisions about the use of related private lands. A broader understanding of the differences between ranch and social accounting schemes would facilitate a more rational reconciliation of the conflicts between ranchers and society at large over the use of public lands.

When ranchers and their communities face an economic shock not of their making, how can they adjust the use of privately owned resources to minimize the undesirable effects on their ability to make a living? Also, how can society be made aware of the entire social bookkeeping process that is involved in a policy or program that includes social costs, as well as social benefits? Answers to these two questions may be less controversial if we review how the present land-use problem developed and seek to understand the issues facing ranchers, as well as the social issues.

## CHANGE IN PUBLIC LAND USE

Changes in land use in an area are associated either with shifts in the demand for the products and services of the land or with changes in production advantage owing to technological advances. Pressures for changing public land-use patterns in the West have not been initiated by the agencies that administer public lands. Agencies change policies and programs only after society indicates a desire for change. Our land agencies administer laws developed by policy-makers at the legislative level, who, in turn, are supposed to represent the thinking in our society.

Some of the most obvious influences that now affect thinking with respect to public land use in the West are (i) population increases and shifts, (ii) increased income per capita, (iii) increased leisure time, (iv) improved transportation facilities, and (v) increased demand for extensive recreation.

**Population changes**

National population has been increasing in recent years at about 1.6 percent per year. By 1980 the population of the United States could approximate 244 million (8). The shift to the West is also significant. Population increased about 24 percent in the United States between 1940 and 1955. In the West the increase was 66 percent; in the Mountain States population increased 43 percent over the same period. This shift to the West is expected to continue. Between 1955 and 1975 the over-all United States population is expected to increase 34 percent, in the West 68 percent, and in the Mountain States 62 percent (12).

The population shift from rural to urban life affects land-use demands. This movement has been going on for some time and is expected to continue. Some projections indicate that 77 percent of the people in the United States will live under urban conditions by 1980, in contrast with 56 percent in 1940 (2). The general population growth in the United States and the shift to the West and to cities will continue to increase the demand for nongrazing uses of public lands.

**Increasing income**

One forecaster predicts that by 1980, the gross national product will exceed $1.1 trillion measured in 1959 dollars, compared with $532 billion for 1960. This is an increase of about 3.5 percent per year. If the level predicted for 1980 is realized and the ratio between consumption and investment remains about the same as in 1960, real per-capita consumption will increase about 79 percent by 1980 (7). Such a change in real consumption means an increased demand for all the products and activities related to public lands in the West.

**Increases in leisure time**

The number of working hours per week has decreased historically. The trend will probably continue. A general 4-day

week and 7-hour day may not be far off. Even more important
to public land use in the West is the increase in numbers of
workers who are given annual paid vacations. These paid vacations allow 1 week or more in which people can travel to the
West. More and more people are looking for uncrowded areas
where they can spend their leisure time. Public lands in the West
provide a refuge from crowded city life.

### Improved transportation facilities

Not very long ago, crossing the deserts and mountains of the
West posed a real threat to life, and only the hardy ones considered
such a trip. Less than 100 years ago the railroad pushed through
America's "waste" land to connect the oceans. The twentieth
century has brought, in order of appearance, automobiles, hard-
surfaced roads, buses, propeller-driven airplanes, and jets.

Deserts and mountains now can be crossed while a traveler takes
a short nap. On the road it takes longer, but the old dangers
have all but been eliminated. Millions of people travel to and in
the West each year. Some even reach the most remote and inaccessible areas with little fear of physical harm. The West is viewed
by some as a huge playground for people who are cramped up in
cities most of the year.

### Extensive recreation

More than ever before, the public wants to use its land for extensive recreational activities. It has been estimated that such
activities will increase 40 times between 1956 and the year 2000
(2). Much of this increase logically will involve the use of public
lands in the West. If this happens, further shifts in use of public
lands are inevitable, and the same is true for related private lands.

### Demand exceeds supply of land

All these pressures tend to increase the demand for land in the
West. In some areas of the country, land appears to be in ex-

cess supply when it is measured by the "surplus" of dominant crops. Some advocate taking such land out of production and reallocating the associated capital and labor resources in order to solve the surplus problem. In the range areas of the West no surplus land problem exists when the land is measured by the same criterion. No large carry-over of beef and lamb exists. Practically all public and private lands open for grazing are used to current capacity in the production of livestock products.

If a large economic surplus of beef and lamb existed, then it could be argued with more assurance that society would be better off to shift public land use away from grazing. In reality, however, society is in a dilemma. The resources are wanted simultaneously for meat production and for other uses. Any adjustment in historical use patterns on public lands in the West could create a burden on society through higher meat prices, higher land values, and, thus, higher opportunity costs for other products desired from the resources.

To restate the predicament that society faces, the demand for public land in the West for other than grazing uses is increasing, but the supply is fixed and already used at its capacity to produce livestock products, which also face increasing demand. Given the present state of technology and demand pressures, the only answer is higher land prices and higher product prices. But, to assume the present state of technology in either livestock production or other uses is a reactionary attitude. Technology in all lines of endeavor in the United States has changed rapidly in the last 100 years; there is no evidence that the rate of technological change is slowing down.

Ranching in the West has felt the influence of technological change, but it is still the nearest thing to an extensive use of land resources that exists in the United States. This is especially true in the use of public lands. Because of serious climatic, topographic, soil, and water deficiencies in large areas of the West, the output response of rangelands to technological change might not be as dramatic as for some agricultural situations. It might be enough, however, to make it profitable to intensify ranch management practices. If so, society might escape the dilemma and end up by having its fun and meat too.

## RANCHING ISSUES

With public lands in the West being used at capacity for grazing, any change in land use will be felt first by ranchers in the form of either an increase in cost of public forage or a decrease in permitted use. What can ranchers do to minimize the undesirable effects that may accompany either of these changes?

### Adjustment to increases in grazing fees

A change in grazing fees for use of public lands will change both ranch operating costs and capital structure.

*Impact on costs of operation.* Raising grazing fees on public lands will simultaneously increase the costs of operation for ranchers and decrease their net ranch returns. Ranchers whose cost-returns structures cannot withstand increased costs over the long run must make operational adjustments in order to stay in business. Adjustments may mean changing size if economies or diseconomies of scale exist. Other adjustments can be classed as intrafirm and are discussed later.

*Impact on ranch capital structure.* An increase in public land grazing fees will generally result in a decrease in the value of complementary private capital assets. This occurs because public grazing fees have been lower historically than the marginal value product of the forage. The tendency is for nonranchers to say that ranchers are subsidized by low fees. Ranchers claim that this is untrue because the overvaluation of private resources more than compensates for any undervaluation of forage on public lands.

If the latter interpretation is true, ranchers have an artificial capital structure today because of past public land fee policies. The difference between the marginal value product of range forage in the production of livestock products and the fees charged has been capitalized into the value of private property, or is reflected in a value for public land permits used by the rancher, or both. At any rate, if fees are increased to reflect more nearly the marginal value product of range forage, the rancher faces a loss in the value of his private property, or his permits, or both. The shock to a rancher's capital structure from an increase in fees is felt when he wants to sell his ranch, and it may also be reflected in his ability to borrow money.

Public land grazing permits have value over and above the fee charged. This has been verified many times in the West. In Utah, permits to graze land administered by the Bureau of Land Management sell for $8 to $12 per animal-unit-month; permits to graze land administered by the Forest Service sell for $18 to $24 per animal-unit-month.

There is further preliminary evidence that part of the difference between the marginal value product of range forage and public grazing fees is capitalized into the value of private ranch property. If this were not so, the market value of an animal-unit-month permit $(S)$ plus the capitalized value $(C)$ of the grazing fee per animal-unit-month $(B)$ would equal an estimate of the capitalized value of an animal-unit-month of grazing $(V^1)$, which could be converted to an estimate of grazing use value per acre $(V_1)$ by dividing by the carrying capacity $(A)$. Also, the capitalized value $(C)$ of private grazing fees per animal-unit-month for comparable rangeland $(F)$ divided by the carrying capacity $(A)$ less the per-acre value of nonland assets, services, and assessments $(L)$ not found on public lands would be an estimate of rangeland value per acre $(V_2)$. The two estimates should be equal for ranges of the same quality. Ideally, then

$$V_1 = \frac{S}{A} + \frac{B}{CA}$$

and

$$V_2 = \frac{F}{CA} - L$$

and if

$$V_1 < V_2$$

then public land for grazing is undervalued, or private land is overvalued, or both.

A study made in Utah in 1960 indicated that the difference between estimates of public and private grazing-land values based on capitalized lease fees ranged between $1 and $6 per acre in favor of private lands. The conclusion must be drawn that forage on public lands is undervalued and that part of the undervaluation is capitalized into the value of private ranch lands.

### Adjustment to permit changes—animals or time

If changes in public land use take the form of reduction in the number of livestock permitted to graze, a rancher faces several adjustment alternatives in the short run. He can (i) sell breeding animals, (ii) purchase feed, (iii) lease private grazing land, or (iv) produce more feed. Of course, he may use some combination of these alternatives. If changes in public land use take the form of reduction in the time permitted on the range, selling part of the breeding herd will not solve a rancher's problem. He would still have to care for the balance of his herd during the time lost on public land. The other alternatives for adjustment offer real possibilities, however, and involve adjustments in the use of private lands. In the long run, the rancher may change size or, at the extreme, go out of business. Only the intrafirm adjustments are discussed here.

*Sale of breeding animals.* If a rancher sells animals because of a reduction in the number permitted on public lands, it is not inevitable that his gross annual income will fall. It is true that he will market fewer animals each year; however, his ranch costs will decrease as charges related to number of animals fall. Also, he will have excess feed to sell or less to buy. Whether or not net ranch income will decrease if breeding stock are sold to adjust to a cut in permitted use of public ranges will depend largely on the existence of economies or diseconomies of scale (measured by number of animals) and on product and factor price relationships.

A recent survey of ranchers in the intermountain West indicates that most of them are small. A size distribution is highly skewed to the small end of the size scale, with the modal class of cattle ranches 25 to 50 cows and the modal class of sheep ranches about one summer band. Chances are that these small ranches would face such economies of scale that a decrease in herd size would result in losses of net ranch income.

*Purchase of feed.*  A rancher could try to compensate for a cut in either the number of livestock allowed or in the time permitted on public lands by buying feed.  The reduction in total fees paid would surely be offset by the increase in money spent to purchase feed.  Thus, net ranch returns would fall.

*Lease of private rangeland.*  A rancher could try to compensate for a reduction in numbers or in time permitted on public lands by leasing more private range.  Costs would increase and net ranch returns decrease.  Private range fees in most of the areas of the West are higher than public land fees.  A 1960 survey in Utah revealed that private fees ranged from $1.50 to $5 per animal-unit-month for private ranges and pastures, compared with 22 cents for BLM permits and about 65 cents for Forest Service permits.

*Shifts in private land use.*  Ranchers may be able to change established private land use in order to compensate for losses of permits on public lands.  Although a change in the status quo is always upsetting, it does not follow that such change is either always economically disastrous or automatically beneficial.

What adjustments can be made on privately owned land to compensate for decreases in public land grazing?  Farmers have proved time and time again that nature can be improved upon.  The idea that man must not upset nature's balance on rangelands is as impotent as the sun-bleached bones of a dead range bull.  Introduced crop varieties and improved livestock breeds, as well as other intensive management practices, increased agricultural output per unit of all inputs almost 75 percent between 1910 and 1960 and about 22 percent in the decade of the 1950's.  During the same decade, farm output per acre increased about 26 percent.  Intensive management, resulting in more output per unit of land and labor input, is expected to be practiced more in the future.  Ranching is still a relatively extensive type of agriculture.  Ways to increase ranch output per unit of input should be examined by ranchers.

Evidence from research that encourages the initiation of some types of range improvements is growing.  One such study was concluded in 1960 in Nevada.  The study tested four techniques for improving meadowland (3).  When improvements consisted of leveling, draining, reseeding, fertilization, controlled irrigation, and well development, annual forage production increased almost 3.4 tons per acre, and the return on the investment amounted to 18.5 percent when forage was priced at $16 per ton. For meadowland improved as before except that no wells were developed, forage production increased about 2.3 tons per acre; and, when

A typical irrigated valley of the intermountain area with a dominant livestock enterprise based on the joint use of private valley lands and publicly owned mountain lands. (Courtesy U.S. Department of Agriculture, Soil Conservation Service)

forage was priced at $16 per ton, it returned 26.8 percent on the investment. When improvements consisted of controlled irrigation, limited drainage, reseeding, fertilization, and partial leveling, forage production increased about 2 tons per acre and returned 46 percent on the investment. When the only improvement practice was change from wild flooding to controlled irrigation, forage yields increased about 0.58 ton per acre and returned nearly 293 percent on the investment.

These data, which came from operating ranches, suggest a capital-forage production function that increases rapidly but at a decreasing rate. Also, the return to improvement capital in each alternative studied was far above the market rate of interest for capital, indicating a profitable venture.

Unfortunately, all ranchers do not have meadowland of the type studied in Nevada. How will other types of rangeland respond to more intensive management? The Utah Experiment Station has published some information on reseeding (9). Ranges in western Utah with a carrying capacity of approximately 10 acres per animal-unit-month were reseeded with crested wheatgrass. The carrying capacity for seeded areas studied rose to an average of 3.8 acres per animal-unit-month. Yearling steer and heifer gains on unseeded ranges averaged 1.2 pounds per day, whereas on seeded ranges the average was nearly 2 pounds per day. If a rancher has the type of private range that responds to reseeding, as did those studied, instead of 10 animal-unit-months of forage on 100 acres he would have slightly more than 26 animal-unit-months of forage with considerably more marketable product. When response to seeding is like that found in the Utah study, 100 acres of improved private range could replace 16 animal-unit-months formerly obtained from unimproved public range during the season. This adjustment would compensate for the loss of about 160 acres of public rangeland.

On range areas in Idaho where reseeding was practical from a physical standpoint, the return to the required capital was found to be considerably higher than the market rate of interest (1). Thus, for the conditions under which the study was made, reseeding paid.

A recent study of northwestern Colorado ranches indicated that, on the average, reseeding returned 15 percent on reseeding investment, 9.5 percent on sagebrush-spraying investment, and 4.8 percent on sagebrush-beating investment (4). Only the latter was questionable as far as competition from other external uses of capital was concerned.

Researchers in New Mexico discovered that clearing sagebrush and seeding to crested wheatgrass where physically feasible could improve the carrying capacity from 70 acres to 2.5 to 7 acres per animal-month of grazing. Annual forage production increased from 50 pounds of native grass per acre to 600 to 1400 pounds per acre. Average cow gains per day increased from 1.3 pounds per head on native range to 2 to 4.3 pounds on reseeded range. Daily gains of calves increased from 1.1 pounds to 2.2 to 2.3 pounds. Where crested wheatgrass could be grazed intensively at 2 to 3 acres per animal-unit-month, returns to capital investment over native range use increased $23.65 per animal unit for a cow-calf operation grazing yearlong. This differential was influenced by a 7.5-percent increase in calf crop, the higher grade of marketable animals, and better rates of gain for the cows (10).

The ability of a rancher to compensate for loss of public land permits through improved management of private lands will depend on the level of management at the time the permit cut is realized. An implicit assumption in this discussion is that private ranch land has not been used at its economically optimum intensity. If private resources are being managed at their optimum before public range permits are decreased, then adjustment of the use of private ranch resources, given the same ranch enterprises as before the permit cut, will only help to minimize losses.

New enterprises on ranches can add flexibility. In one area in Utah, ranchers facing a loss of public range permits introduced turkeys into their program. Others shifted from a cow-calf operation to a cow-calf-feeder steer operation. In both cases cropping patterns on private lands changed also.

The possibility that ranching may be compatible with non-agricultural uses of private lands should also be studied. In areas that have a high recreational potential, services provided for vacationers may prove to be supplemental, rather than competitive, for labor and land. Many a wildland enthusiast wants to pay someone to take the responsibility for his security, enjoyment, and comfort. He wants to "rough it" but appreciates a soft bed, plumbing, electricity for his razor, and guide service. Ranchers already located in an area to be developed for recreation could provide the services that will be required, rather than wait for outside capital to do the job.

## ISSUES SOCIETY MUST FACE

Society must realize that changes in old land-use patterns on public lands will result in social costs as well as benefits.

### Demand for meat

With population burgeoning at an annual rate of 1.6 percent and purchasing power at 2 percent, the demand for beef will continue to increase (8). Under past public land-management policies the West has had a relative advantage over other parts of the country in the production of range beef and sheep. Young stock produced from range forage are fed mostly in feedlots in other parts of the country to a finish desired by consumers. If society decides to use the range area for recreation instead of meat production, it must realize that meat will cost more if the previous range contribution has to come from other sources. The additional cost of meat resulting from a shift in production areas should be charged to new uses of public lands in the West. Of course, this is no argument against change if society wants it, but the public should understand that shifts in land use will be accompanied by social costs as well as benefits.

### Land-use relationships

Are rangeland uses necessarily competitive? Some think not. Uses may be supplementary. A new use that permits a fuller use of a resource without detracting economically from the old is an example of a supplementary use. Perhaps extensive use of public lands in the West for recreation is supplementary to extensive livestock grazing. It is my contention that only after recreation, or grazing, or both reach a much higher degree of intensity of resource use than is in effect at present will they become economically competitive. The point where real competition develops between grazing and other uses can be determined by research. Society should insist that the marginal rates of substitution among uses be determined before large-scale changes in established land uses are made. Any time a supplementary use is eliminated, society loses something or pays in some way. Even after uses become competitive, some combination will generally benefit society the most unless, of course, the uses are perfectly competitive.

It is even possible that, during the early stages of substitution, uses may be complementary. If so, a new use made of a given resource will increase the benefits received from another use. At some point the substitution of a new use will reduce benefits received from the old use, however, and then the uses become competitive. Society would indeed be foolish to eliminate an old use that has a complementary relationship with a new one. It has been suggested that such a relationship exists, within limits, between deer and beef cattle on the range (6). Deer prefer shrubs to grass. They keep shrubs grazed down, thus permitting more grass to grow for cattle.

To what extent complementarity and supplementarity exist among uses of rangelands is not well established. Society would be well advised to get answers to these questions by supporting research.

### Social responsibility in change

Changes in public land use are inevitable. Total benefits to society may increase as a result. It is likely, however, that a relatively small segment of society will be hurt by such changes. Still, net social benefits may increase. Does society have some responsibility for that portion of the whole which is upset by social change? The answer has been *Yes* in many cases throughout our history.

If a man owns property through which society wants to build a road, his means of making a living are not taken from him without compensation. Permits to graze public lands are as important to a rancher's livelihood as is his private property. Any reduction in permitted use upsets his means of making a living. Is it any less reasonable for him to expect to be compensated for loss of permits than for loss of private property? Since he cannot buy public land except under unusual situations, he has no alternative but to use public range on a permitted basis.

Whether or not the use of public ranges by ranchers is a privilege or a right is a matter of legal definition. In either case, a firm is organized to produce socially acceptable products, and it is economically dependent on public land use for its existence as organized. The compensatory principle seems consistent with social adjustments made in other segments of the economy, and it at least partially fulfills society's responsibility to those who are made worse off by social action.

## SUMMARY

Can landowners shift their use of private land to compensate fully for the changing uses of public lands? The answer is not obvious. Some possible ranch adjustments may compensate, to a limited extent at least, for changes imposed upon ranchers.

Should society subsidize the users of public lands? A dogmatic *Yes* or *No* is not an enlightened answer. Whether or not ranchers are subsidized has been questioned; whether or not extensive recreational uses of public lands should be subsidized must be questioned.

Will the social benefits realized by changing the use of public lands exceed the social costs, including those suffered by ranchers and ranching communities? Society should examine closely the cost side of social benefit-cost accounting. Many important answers needed for wise decisions are not now available. Some are. More research on the potential combinations of various uses of public and private lands is needed. Let us not have ranchers or society fight changes to the point of ignoring alternatives beneficial to both.

## REFERENCES

1. Caton, D. D., and C. Beringer, "Costs and benefits of reseeding rangelands in southern Idaho," *Idaho Univ. Agr. Expt. Sta. Bull. 326* (1960).
2. Clawson, M., "Potential demand for nonfarm products and services provided by agricultural lands," in *Dynamics of Land Use— Needed Adjustment* (Iowa State Univ. Press, Ames, 1961), chap. 4.

3. Fulcher, G. D., "Economics of meadow improvement in northern Nevada," *Nevada Univ. Agr. Expt. Sta. Bull. 215* (1960).
4. Gardner, B. D., "Costs and returns from sagebrush range improvement in Colorado," *Colo. Agr. Expt. Sta. Bull. 511-S* (1961).
5. Heady, E. O., *Economics of Agricultural Production and Resource Use* (Prentice-Hall, Englewood Cliffs, N.J., 1952), chap. 1.
6. Hopkin, J. A., "Economic criteria for problem solutions in research relative to use and development of range resources," in *Economic Research in the Use and Development of Range Resources—a Methodological Anthology*, C. B. Baker and C. V. Plath, Eds. (Comm. on the Economics of Range Use and Development, Western Agricultural Economics Research Council, Montana State College, Bozeman, 1957).
7. Knowles, J. W., "Growth prospects for the American economy," in *Dynamics of Land Use—Needed Adjustment* (Iowa State Univ. Press, Ames, 1961), chap. 2.
8. Koffsky, N. M., "Potential demand for farm products," in *Dynamics of Land Use—Needed Adjustment* (Iowa State Univ. Press, Ames, 1961), chap. 3.
9. Lloyd, R. D., and C. W. Cook, "Seeding Utah's ranges—an economic guide," *Utah State Univ. Agr. Expt. Sta. Bull. 423* (1960).
10. Pingrey, H. B., and E. G. Dortignac, "Economic evaluation of seeding crested wheatgrass on northern New Mexico rangeland," *New Mexico Agr. Expt. Sta. Bull. 433* (1959).
11. Roberts, N. K., and E. B. Wennergren, "Economics of acquiring and managing state lands for surface uses," *Utah State Univ. Agr. Expt. Sta. AES 61-4* (Oct. 1961).
12. Thomas, W. P., "Industrial and population growth in Utah," *U.S. Dept. Agr. AERS* (Mar. 1959).

# Evaluations of Dryland Environments by Societies at Various Levels of Technical Competence

HOMER ASCHMANN

*Department of Geography, University of California, Riverside*

Anyone who surveys the entire history of human cultural development, most of it known only archeologically, must be impressed by how much of the early record comes from drylands in the lower and lower middle latitudes. It is in such areas that we find the earliest evidences, in both the Old World and the New, of the discoveries and inventions that created neolithic cultures and led on to city-building, metallurgy, writing, and eventually the formation of states and empires. The accident of preservation does not provide a fully adequate explanation for the preeminence of the records of civilization in the drylands. We know historically that Egypt and Mesopotamia in the third millennium B.C. had cultures far more elaborate than those in nearby humid lands, both north of the Mediterranean and in East and Central Africa; and at the beginning of the Christian Era the arid coast of Peru was enormously more advanced than the humid eastern two-thirds of South America.

Although they are not capable of supporting as many people as certain humid lands, the world's drylands seem to have made a heuristic contribution to man's cultural development, to have stimulated discoveries that increased man's control over both his physical and his cultural environment. This paper endeavors to identify sets of physical conditions peculiar to lands of deficient precipitation that may have had this stimulating effect, or that seem to correlate causally with the characteristic features of desert civilizations as we know them, now or historically. It also shows that, once a new level of technology or social organization had been achieved, certain aspects of the physical environment, which had previously been neutral in their effect on man, became vital concerns that encouraged or even demanded further adaptive modifications in technology or sociopolitical structures.*

## HUNTERS AND GATHERERS IN THE DRYLANDS

Despite their low floral density, the drylands offer considerable attraction for the human populations that possess simple technologies. Many xerophytic plants concentrate nutrients rich in starches and proteins so effectively in their fruits, seeds, and roots that they are food even for the small-capacity, low-efficiency human digestive apparatus (8). The sparse vegetation made the relatively abundant game of the steppe regions visible and accessible to hunting and, at the same time, permitted the identification and evasion of dangerous beasts. Like other predators, man profited from the concentration of animals around the limited number of water sources as the dry season advanced.

In steppe regions all over the world, the economic activity of primitive societies has tended to focus on hunting organization and technology. As their capabilities increased, however, the hunters of the steppes quickly began to deplete their food resource. Fire drives and the concentration of animals around waterholes in the dry season made mass killing of animals too easy. In many steppe regions it is likely that the development of a more effective hunting technique permitted a florescence of the human population for only a generation or two before a declining game supply forced movement into other regions and caused a decrease in the wealth and number of the local human population. There is little, if any, record of a hunting culture that persisted long at a high level of prosperity in any dry region. A focus on hunting seems to have precluded a subsequent development of the attributes of civilization by a particular society.

In truly desert areas, however, the animal resources are ordinarily too meager to be relied on as prime sources of human sus-

---

* C. O. Sauer (10) and J. Steward (11) provide general and highly relevant references on the subject of this paper.

tenance. A parallel exploitation of the vegetable resources was necessary, and it had to be a comprehensive one. One or a few kinds of plants were not sufficiently abundant, or their season of availability was too short or irregular, to be fully sustaining. The ethnobotanical data that I know best are from the Central Desert of Baja California and the Southwest (2, 3), although a comparable situation seems to have existed in Australia and Southwest Africa, and a particularly striking feature of these data is the great number of species that were utilized and played a significant part in the food economy. Also notable are the variety and ingeniousness of the techniques for preparing these diverse plant foods for consumption, a matter of little concern in connection with foods of animal origin. These are potentially progressive sorts of cultural foci with obvious leads toward the use of domesticated plants, a trend reinforced by the native tendency of many dryland plants to overreproduce and, thus, be efficient creators of food suitable for man.

The seasonality of life and the focus on highly localized sources of water, the number and distribution of which are subject to severe reduction in times of drought, have important implications for the human social organization. Although the high mobility required by the seasonally variable and sparsely occurring food resources characterizes virtually all nonagricultural dryland societies, there is no record of a freely nomadic society, and it is improbable that one could have existed. Man was tied to a limited number of known water sources and, in years of severe drought, to the still more restricted number that did not fail. Undoubtedly many groups became extinct in the process of acquiring this intelligence. Although in much of the year efficient exploitation of desert food resources required wide-ranging social units of minimum size, on two sorts of occasions the assembly of much larger social units was either essential or feasible.

When water sources had been reduced to minimal numbers by a prolonged drought, all the people in the region came to them or died promptly. There they had to remain in intimate contact until the drought broke. An ordering of social relationships on an extended scale, government if you like, was necessary to survival. We can recognize a problem of protecting the food resources of these favored localities that they might be available to support an augmented population during such emergencies and not be dissipated in ordinary times. To what extent this problem was recognized and faced by preagricultural societies has not been examined widely, to my knowledge, but many aspects of totem and taboo in central Australia seem, when viewed from this standpoint, to possess a rationality that would enhance prospects of group survival.

The marked seasonality of vegetative growth in drylands also was likely to present a brief period of abundance and easy availability of some foodstuff. The fall ripening of the fruit of the pitahaya dulce (*Lemaireocereus thurberi*) in southern and central Baja California, at which time as many as 1000 people are reported to have assembled for ceremonial and social purposes (6), is a good example. Thus, both of necessity and because of opportunity, the dryland environment, despite its sparse total population, did not produce social isolation, but at certain times of the year it placed large numbers of people in fairly intimate social contact. Where a major oasis was created by an exotic river, such as the preagricultural Nile Valley, we may infer intensive social contact among quite large numbers of people. This is a situation that is conducive to cultural elaboration and appears to give the drylands an advantage over forested ones where social isolation seems to be the rule among primitive groups.

The ecology of contagious disease in drylands as opposed to humid ones is a problem that merits investigation from many standpoints, and the following comments are intended to be provocative, rather than conclusive. Three distinct situations can be distinguished: open country without permanent water sources, small isolated springs or waterholes, and major extensive oases such as a slowly flowing exotic river.

In open country a disease could be maintained during the annual dry season only through its human vectors. Should they die, the disease would disappear promptly.

At waterholes, however, insect vectors and aquatic worm parasites or vectors could persist for longer periods, and diseases could be introduced to new and distant waterholes by man and, perhaps, by other agents. A particular water source might acquire a reputation as a pesthole and long be avoided on any of several sorts of rationales. On the other hand, if the disease organism required a human host in its life cycle, it would ultimately disappear unless it were mild enough in its effects not to exterminate or even scare man away from the water source.

Where a major oasis existed, man and his diseases would stay together and achieve some level of mutual adaptation, perhaps lowering man's efficiency, biologically and otherwise, but never eliminating the human species. From his diseases the surviving dweller at a major oasis received a sort of protection. He could be conquered but not replaced by outsiders. The 5000-year stability of the Egyptian physical type can be explained better in these terms than in any other I know. Until modern sanitation and antibiotics were available, involving perhaps the last 100 years, immigrant conquerors had little biological future in the Nile Valley. Each major oasis—the Nile, Mesopotamia, and the Indus Valley, for example—would tend to develop both its own disease varieties and a resistant human population. With the rise of historic empires and interoasis travel and conquest, some exchanges of infection could occur. Such developments have explanatory potential in accounting for cyclic declines in oasis civilizations known historically and, at the same time, help to account for the long-maintained cultural identities in each of the great Middle Eastern oases and the several coastal sectors in Peru.

In humid tropical areas the environments for diseases and their vectors were generally favorable, and there was a tendency for diseases to have broad and continuous distribution. Humid areas with cold seasons were less favorable to diseases, but again disease-spread was likely to be continuous and not to serve as a mechanism for isolating a moderately extensive culture area.

## BEGINNINGS OF AGRICULTURE

The logic of environmental interpretation, the distribution of the postulated ancestors of the earliest domesticated plants and animals, and, most recently, dated archeological finds, all indicate that small-grain, seed agriculture had its earliest beginnings in a steppe region or regions, probably in the more humid sectors near

the forest margin, between the Indus Valley and Anatolia (*12*).
Jarmo still looks typical of the initial stage of neolithic agriculture,
although it may not have any temporal priority. The system
spread quickly over extensive areas. Digging-stick or hoe preparation of land for planting was involved. Soil fertility and yields
had to be high on a per-acre basis to maintain the neolithic farmer,
so slash-and-burn seminomadism was more appropriate to lands
of adequate rainfall where soils lost their initial productivity
quickly. The drier steppes, where crop loss from drought threat-
ened regularly, were not suitable for dry farming until the plow
permitted the planting of extensive fields and the accumulation of
large surpluses in good years. The barrenness of the overgrazed
landscape around Jarmo makes us forget that it receives annually
about 18 inches of rain, concentrated in winter, which is just the
right time for the small grains grown there.

Although the shift from hunting and gathering to neolithic
farming undoubtedly increased the total population that an appropriate area could support, and although the areas under cultivation might be shifted regularly and fairly rapidly, we would err
to imagine that the scope of social contacts was increased for the
early farmers. It probably decreased. The neolithic farming
community, although not fixed in residence, was less mobile than
its gathering predecessor. It also needed to, and was able to, exploit less territory. Finally, it was more completely self-sufficient,
and in regard to its prime resource, space for farming, it was
directly competitive with its neighbors.

To leave the forest steppe or forest areas with their reasonably
assured moisture supplies from seasonal precipitation and carry
neolithic farming into more arid lands, new techniques of varying
difficulty and generality of applicability had to be developed.
These techniques may be grouped into two sets: dry farming and
irrigation. Successful dry farming depends on substantial surpluses being produced in good (that is, wet) years and stored for
drought years. Although excellent soil characteristics in some
dryland districts might provide greater than normal yields, hoe
or digging-stick tillage, especially difficult in steppe sods, sets such
a severe limitation on the amount of land an individual can plant
that surpluses sufficient to counteract major and frequent climatic

risks could not be accumulated. Dry farming could become important only when domesticated draft animals and the plow permitted an order of magnitude increase in the area cultivated and planted. The great florescence of agriculture in the American, Argentine, and Russian steppes is entirely modern and is based on mechanically derived power.

Irrigation affords more immediate benefits, especially in truly arid localities that are watered by exotic rivers. Although the requisite preparatory work might have been greater than that for farming based on rainfall, crop yields that were both bigger and more secure could be obtained, and, barring local difficulties with soil depletion or salinity, a given plot could be tilled indefinitely.

The quality of the soil resource is the most important asset common to irrigated valleys that have become centers of desert civilizations. Because of seasonal variations in riverflow that have a ratio of 10/1 in a normal year and much more in extreme years, the deposition of alluvium at flood stage will be extensive wherever the valley is not an actual canyon. Where there is a long river, heading in a humid region and entering or passing through a dry one, the alluvial material will have been sorted and will consist of a mixture of sand, silt, and clay, rather than the coarse cobbles and boulders that cover the upper slopes' alluvial fans on short steep watercourses fed by local rainfall. The riverine alluvium in drylands possesses a full supply of the soluble minerals needed for plant nutrition, and these minerals are renewed by the regularly recurring flood deposits. If an adequate water supply could be assured, crop yields of unprecedented size and security, and available on a continuing basis from the same field, could be obtained from soils of nearly ideal texture, having high soluble-mineral plant-nutrient content, and natural restoration of fertility.

The economic advantage to be derived from irrigated farming in a limited but considerable number of favored desert valleys was revolutionary in its scope. Neolithic shifting cultivation, although it undoubtedly increased the number of human beings a given area could support, rarely yielded a substantial food surplus. Virtually the entire labor force of a community was engaged most of the time in producing the sustenance for that community. In a favored irrigated valley a true surplus of food—that is, more than the producers could eat—could easily be garnered. Julian Steward has indicated that two-fifths of the labor force was able to feed the whole population in the irrigated valleys of coastal Peru, and this was without energy from other than human muscles.* A similar situation probably existed in the predynastic Nile Valley, before population pressure required cultivation so intensive that labor was uneconomically used.

In all probability flood farming was the earliest irrigation activity, and the historically known system of the Yuma and Mojave Indians of the lower Colorado (5) may have existed for a long time prehistorically in several of the Old World valleys. The Yuma and Mojave effectively dissipated their potential for producing a food surplus by a systematic pattern of individual indolence, coupled with a war pattern that was sufficiently violent to prevent population growth and to forestall any pressure to develop a more encompassing scheme for exploiting their agricultural opportunities (9). Elsewhere canal systems for diverting and controlling irrigation water were developed, thereby expanding the area available for planting and making its yield more certain. The utilization of schemes like this, varying slightly in their technical details, characterizes every culture area where what we can properly call a desert civilization flourished.

The self-renewing character of dryland soils that made possible fixed agricultural settlement encouraged investment of a community's labor, which was unneeded for food production, in immobile property. The investment could go into dwellings and monuments to enrich the quality of life, or into capital structures to increase the productive capacity of the locality, such as canals for irrigation and transportation, land clearing, leveling, and draining, and embankments for protection against uncontrolled flooding. In an arid environment such investment does not decay or erode as rapidly as it would in a humid land. The capital investment by one generation could benefit, and be added to by, subsequent generations for an indefinite period into the future. In desert oases, for the first time in all of human history, a generation received from its parent something more than life with a

_____
* Personal communication.

cultural inheritance of knowledge and a few mobile tools and art objects; it received productive capital in the form of a developed agricultural landscape that needed only maintenance to yield ample food for less than the maximal labor investment.

Although the Nile Valley, once cleared and canalized, has proved its almost indestructible agricultural potential for 5000 years, serious deterioration afflicts most of the other major developed oases. Where heavy local rainfall occasionally occurs, as in Mesopotamia, the 100-year storm may wreck a canal system, and lesser storms may damage it by siltation. A vigorous society could repair the damage promptly, but one in social and political decadence might lose, even permanently, the assets that had been laboriously constructed by preceding generations. Even with modern chemical understanding, the problem of increasing salinity in irrigated desert lands remains intractable. In the simplest terms, the problem will arise whenever irrigation water with a moderate content of dissolved salts—and this is almost a universal property of the waters in dry parts of the world—is applied to fields and allowed to evaporate or be transpired by plants. The dissolved salts will be left behind and will accumulate to intolerable concentrations. The problem can be avoided only if an excess of water is applied to afford some runoff that will flush out the excess salt.

Except in the delta, the sharply demarcated valley bottom of the Nile does not provide enough accessible flatland to use all the water at flood stage. Some has always flowed to the sea and served as a flushing agent. In the Indus Valley there is more potentially irrigable land than water to irrigate it. Waters have been led from the river to distant fields and never returned to the river. Hundreds of thousands of once-irrigated acres are now alkali wastes, and the expansion of these wastelands and the forced abandonment of farmland is a vital problem in modern Pakistan (1).

## GRAZING ACTIVITIES AND THE DRYLANDS

Although it is developed on theoretical and deductive grounds, Eduard Hahn's 65-year-old thesis (7) that the domestication of large herbivores was carried on by the rich societies of the irrigated river valleys for ceremonial purposes, for milk and blood sacrifices, rather than for utilitarian ones, maintains its general validity. The economic utilization of such animals was derivative and came later.

In truly desert Egypt, plowing with oxen contributed little to the economy, but in steppe lands like northern Mesopotamia and the Punjab the possibility of thus multiplying the acreage planted made marginally dry lands capable of being farmed and yielding a surplus. This was especially true if large and highly organized societies could store surplus grain and distribute it to localities that had suffered crop failure from drought. With their more efficient digestive systems, the domesticated herbivores could also be maintained by grazing still drier steppe lands or rocky uplands that yielded no crops for man. In broken terrain with small plots of land of varying quality, a given community or village might both farm and keep animals economically, and such a pattern spread from Persia and Anatolia to the Mediterranean peninsulas of Europe. But when broad plains graded from steppe to desert far from large oases with irrigable land—as happens east of the Syrian littoral, south and west of the Tigris Valley, north of the Caucasus, and east of the Caspian Sea—specialized pastoral economies were developed. None of these were fully independent of planters, but their trade relationships were infrequent, coming after long treks from the pasture lands. An inevitable concomitant of a grazing economy is that ranges become overstocked in no more than a human generation.

Military and political power tended to gravitate to the herdsmen whenever they competed with steppe farmers. Their wealth was as mobile as they were; the size of their herds could be expanded in favorable seasons, and at times of drought they might protect at least some of their animals by migration. Direct and violent struggle for grazing lands was a normal part of their lives. Ordinarily a major center of intensive irrigated agriculture could protect itself against the herdsmen, although conquests of great civilizations by small groups of warlike pastoralists are a familiar theme in history. Most such conquests occurred when internal political disorganization had afflicted the irrigation civilization.

The steppe lands that were marginally suited for dryland farming, if it was supported by the plow and draft animals, tended to be conquered by pastoralists and used for grazing. This clearly constituted a regressive form of land use, since it permitted fewer people to be supported by a given area. The regularity of this development is perhaps best emphasized by noting one major exception. At the height of Roman power, when reasonably effective order was being maintained in the steppe margins south and east of the Mediterranean, the frontier of tillage was advanced in places like Cyrenaica and central Syria far beyond its present limit.

The ability of pastoralists to take over the nonirrigated steppe lands of the Old World had direct environmental consequences that their occasional conquests of irrigated areas did not have. In the latter case the agricultural system persisted or was soon restored, and it is possible to consider the military conquests as beneficial in that they introduced new political ideas. In the steppe lands, however, overgrazing and the deliberate removal of brush and timber produced a cycle of soil degradation and removal by erosion, a phenomenon especially apparent in the limestone hills and plateaus that rim much of the Mediterranean. The utter barrenness of the landscapes south and east of the Mediterranean does not accord with the recorded precipitation values. Mosul and Kirkuk get more rain than the Sacramento or Salinas valleys of California, and the bleak, rocky Judean hills are fully humid lands, receiving annually 25 to 35 inches of rainfall.

In the irrigated valleys of the Old World, domesticated animals were of ceremonial and esthetic significance but of relatively little economic importance. On the forested lands of northern Europe, with their relatively poor soils, animal-oriented agriculture and careful use of manure made possible a permanent, nondepletive, and reasonably productive agriculture. But throughout the lands of steppe climate, which they might have benefited, grazing animals and their herders have proved to be destructive of the earth's resource capital. In the warmer Old-World drylands, the term *steppe* is relatively insignificant. They contain irrigable farmland and overgrazed pasture land that is little more productive than true desert.

## DRYLAND CIVILIZATIONS

Karl Wittfogel's theme of hydraulic civilizations and the rise of oriental despotism assumes that the management of complicated irrigation systems required a central authority to control water for the welfare of the entire community dependent on irrigated agriculture (13). This bureaucratic, often priestly, authority then arrogated to itself absolute power over the community. The sociopolitical implications of this theme are beyond the scope of this paper. The rigidity of the socioeconomic patterns in the several great irrigated valleys of the Old World, however, and the capacity of these patterns to endure almost unchanged for millennia—facts that Wittfogel points up—are enormously significant elements in human culture history. I should like to apply a less particular theory to the economic structure of irrigation civilizations: namely, the classical theory of rent operating in a specific sort of environment.

Once the gallery forest was cleared and canals constructed for irrigation, the land that could thus be farmed was enormously productive. The 5000 square miles of irrigable land in the Nile Valley alone probably supported more people than the whole of contemporary Europe in the third and second millennia before the beginning of the Christian Era. Furthermore, to do this, only about half of the labor force had to be engaged in food production. Roughly comparable situations existed in Mesopotamia, the Indus Valley, and the coastal valleys of Peru. In other words, the productive energy of nearly half of large populations, living so close together that effective organization was easy, could be diverted to other activities. These activities ultimately produced the domestication of large herbivorous animals; monumental constructions, both utilitarian and ceremonial; complex priestly and religious traditions, as well as governmental bureaucracy and law, institutions that often led to a system of writing, metallurgy, and magnificent refinements of arts and crafts: in sum, the objective attributes of civilization. The surplus productive capacity of irrigable land that supported these activities may be thought of as rent.

During the initial stages of land clearing and canal construction, the procurement of productive land was the reward to labor, applied in an organized and rational fashion to gain a deferred benefit. Because of the restrictions set by the terrain and the total amount of water available, a point would ultimately be reached where additional labor invested in clearing, leveling, and canal-building would yield no more productive land. With minimal maintenance labor costs, however, the developed land would continue to support far more people than were needed to farm it.

By the beginning of the third millennium B.C., virtually all the irrigable land in Egypt was being irrigated. The valley bluffs still form a sharp boundary between wonderful farmland and absolute waste; only in the eastern delta was there room for a limited expansion of irrigation when a strong government could approach a rational maximum in water use. Within a few yards one could go from land where a family could farm an acre and feed itself and another family, land that *could* pay 50 percent of its product in rent, to land of which a square mile would not support a goatherd. Rather promptly the human population grew to a point where it could exploit optimally all the irrigable land. Further investment of labor would yield only diminishing returns, and within all of Egypt there was no additional place to invest this agricultural labor.

Irrigable land was an absolutely finite and almost infinitely valuable resource. Individuals, even big landholders, could not afford to fight for it because the irrigation structures were too fragile. Only an all-powerful central authority or state could allocate water and land to assure its continuing productive use. An effective government would also collect the surplus as taxes, which were really rent, and employ it for public purposes, however conceived. A weak state might protect landlords and permit them to dispose of their rents as they chose, the situation that prevailed in Egypt for several centuries prior to the present decade. Characteristically, the private landowners did little to increase productivity and sought to use their rent yields to protect their holdings or to acquire more already productive land. Bobek (*4*, pp. 279-287) identifies this system as *Rentenkapitalismus,* noting that it leads to a constricting, rather than an expanding, economy, with rising prices and rents and lowered wages as the number of land-less increases. Should the mass of the populace not like the way the rents were used they might revolt. The existing bureaucracy, however, supported by its great income, did its best to make this difficult, and revolts ordinarily succeeded only with external sup-port. But the conquerors or revolutionary victors could only re-new the old monolithic pattern. There was no marginal land on which a simpler system of control would serve, where the landless might eke out a bare living on even less productive land and ex-periment with other political and economic systems.

Initially, the general Mesopotamian and Syrian pictures were far more complicated. Here, as in European farmlands, there were several grades of land, some of which would barely or not quite support those who farmed them, but others graded to highly productive districts. In the classic Ricardian sense, potential rents ranged from nothing through minuscule to great. There was some possibility for a small community to try to exploit marginal land. Or an individual or group could work on better and more pro-ductive land, expending its surplus or rent on protection, usually in the form of taxes to a government. Some easily irrigable land, especially in Sumer, could be made as productive as the Nile Valley. Other areas required major canal construction that had to be maintained at greater labor cost, reducing the rent yield. Because of a limited water supply, some lands could be irrigated only briefly except in unusually wet years, so their yields fluc-tuated drastically. Finally, dry farming was feasible in extensive areas, but it gave lower yields for more work; in other words, it yielded little or no rent. Abraham could leave Ur of the Chaldees and try marginal dry farming and herding in the Judean hills if he did not like the government. In these terms, the kaleidoscopic political history of the region, seldom repeating earlier patterns as it seemed to do in Egypt, is expectable. Similarly, with varied societies organizing their economies in diverse fashions, one would expect a longer and more creative period of cultural in-ventiveness, an expectation that the historical record supports.

The tenth century may mark the last major period of cultural creativity from this Syro-Mesopotamian region, and even the pre-ceding 1500 years seem to have been relatively stagnant. The growing dominance of pastoralism in the steppe areas may have been a major contributory factor. The cumulative effects of overgrazing and soil erosion had made more and more of the marginal lands submarginal, so that there was ever less intermediate terrain that might support an agricultural population while yielding little or no rent. As the division between the haves and have-nots grew sharper, the power of the state had to be increased proportionately. Opportunities for technical and organizational experimentation in districts too poor to be organized and heavily taxed by a central state had virtually disappeared by the time of the Abassid Caliphate, although they were diminishing from the time of imperial Assyria.

In pre-Columbian America, environmental alteration caused by overgrazing was not a problem; but in the extreme environment of coastal Peru, which had only irrigable land and sterile waste, a rational and rigidly stable organization of society was developed early in each irrigable valley. In Meso-America, or more peripherally in the American Southwest, where there were many gradations in the productivity of the arid and semiarid lands, more open societies, a more fluid history, and, most of us would agree, greater cultural attainments were achieved before indigenous developments were cut off by the Conquest.

## CONCLUSION

Today the great river valley oases that nourished the irrigation civilizations of the past continue to sustain concentrated masses of humanity but in a deplorably impoverished state. Their bordering steppe zones, terribly overgrazed, support herding groups even more miserably. For 1000 years these lands, which once contributed so much to mankind's cultural progress, have failed either to support their inhabitants comfortably or to give evidence of cultural vitality. Despotic governments or irresponsible landlords extract high rents or taxes from overly abundant cultivators, but no advance in the general welfare is evident.

However, in the New World and in Soviet Central Asia, where labor is scarce and expensive because there are alternative demands for it, mechanization and other technological applications permit the drylands to exploit their distinctive environmental advantages. Competing with the agricultural production of humid regions within the same politicoeconomic units, they contribute to inter-regional trade and provide good living standards to the productive local populations. The demonstrated capacity of an irrigated oasis to support many people over long periods of time tends to make land reclamation through projects that extend irrigation a popular panacea for the ills of overcrowded lands, such as Egypt or West Pakistan. Significant benefits will be gained, however, only if per-capita production is increased. An irrigated acre may feed a family, but it will not long satisfy the rapidly increasing wants of even the humblest peoples. Unless agricultural labor is to be used sparingly and efficiently on the lands to be irrigated, as we now know it can be, the capital needed for such projects might better be directed into other, more productive channels.

## REFERENCES

1. Ahmad, N., "Soil salinity in West Pakistan and means to deal with it," in *Salinity Problems in the Arid Zones, Proc. Teheran Symp., Arid Zone Research* **14**, 117-125 (1961).
2. Aschmann, H., "The Central Desert of Baja California: demography and ecology," *Ibero-Americana 42* (Univ. of California Press, Berkeley, 1959).
3. Barrows, D. P., *The Ethno-Botany of the Coahuilla Indians of Southern California* (Univ. of Chicago Press, Chicago, Ill., 1900).
4. Bobek, H., "Die Hauptstufen der Gesellschafts- und Wirtschafts-entfaltung in geographischer Sicht," *Die Erde* **11**, 259-289 (1959).
5. Castetter, E. F., and W. H. Bell, *Yuman Indian Agriculture* (Univ. of New Mexico Press, Albuquerque, 1951).
6. Clavigero, F. J., *The History of [Lower] California,* transl. by S. E. Lake and A. A. Gray (Stanford Univ. Press, Stanford, Calif., 1937), pp. 33-35. (Original ed., Venice, 1789).
7. Hahn, E., *Die Haustiere und ihre Beziehungen zum Menschen* (Duncker and Humblot, Leipzig, 1896).
8. Haudricourt, A. G., and L. Hedin, *L'Homme et les Plantes Cultivées* (Gallimard, Paris, 1943), pp. 68-74.
9. Kroeber, A. L., "Handbook of the Indians of California," *Bur. Am. Ethnology Bull. 78* (1925), pp. 729-731; 751-753.
10. Sauer, C. O., *Agricultural Origins and Dispersals* (American Geographical Soc., New York, 1952).

11. Steward, J., *et al.*, "Irrigation civilizations: a comparative study," *Social Sci. Monographs 1* (Pan American Union, Washington, D.C., 1955).

12. Vavilov, N. I., "The origin, variation, immunity and breeding of the cultivated plants," transl. from the Russian by K. S. Chester, *Chronica Botanica* **13** (1949-1950).

13. Wittfogel, K. A., *Oriental Despotism: a Comparative Study of Total Power* (Yale Univ. Press, New Haven, Conn., 1957).

# Costs of Space in the West

MAURICE M. KELSO

*Department of Agricultural Economics, University of Arizona, Tucson*

I feel that I must open my remarks with a banality if my discussion is to be in proper perspective. The banality is that space is a fundamental and necessary condition for human activity, necessary even for the very notion of existence. But so are air, water, and food necessary conditions; and just as air, water, and food may exist in quantities not optimum to the needs of man, so may space.

## SPACE AND HUMAN ACTIVITY

The *economic* problems of space arise, not because it exists, but rather because its magnitude in relation to human needs and aspirations may be out of balance. It is a problem when it is too limited as well as when it is too extensive; the problems of unspaciousness are as acute and, in extreme cases, more acute than the problems of spaciousness.

As is clearly implied by the title of this paper, we are here concerned with the problems of spaciousness. Spaciousness implies much space in relation to man. It is also banal to remark that much space—that is, spaciousness—is as likely to be a benefit as a problem. But we are concerned here only with the problem aspects of spaciousness, not with all of its relationships to man, good and bad alike. As a problem, spaciousness implies too much space for the optimum satisfaction of man's wants.

What then are its economic connotations—its economic dimensions? Spaciousness, like floodwater, means that there is too much of a good thing, too much in the sense that man must sacrifice—in economic terms, must incur costs—to overcome the redundance.

For purposes of economic evaluation, *space* defined in the generic, general sense as the mere presence of "nothingness" has no usefulness. Space for economic purposes must be expressed in "units of space," units that must be identifiable and definable in a geographic sense. These units also must be either (i) subject in some meaningful way to control by a decision-maker over the activity that takes place within them, or (ii) expressible as a measurable obstacle between other determinable spatial units— an obstacle that can be bridged only at some sacrifice. Such units of space have dimensions that may be large or small in relation to man's wants. Let us examine what may make them large.

Spatial units may be relatively large in situations where the possession of space by persons has value in itself and where those persons possess the resources to cover the sacrifices it entails. Spacious suburban living is an illustration. But so also is the man who lives in ranching or dryland farming country because he likes the "elbowroom" around him. For such reasons, larger units of space may be more valuable than smaller units and may be actively sought after for the sake of the space they contain.

On the other hand, large spatial units may arise, not because they are sought after as space per se, but because their size is a by-product of the economic productivity of the land resources they encompass or to which they give access. When the land resources available through or within the confines of the space unit are of low economic productivity, a relatively large volume of these resources will be required for optimum combination with the associated labor and capital of the human agent. In such circumstances, it will take relatively large space units to provide enough of the land resource for optimum economic use, or much space in relation to people.

The problems of spaciousness arise when either or both of these two forces—a preference for space or the low economic productivity of land resources—generate spatial units so expansive and people in relation to space so sparse that both the private and the public costs for overcoming spatial resistances become too large for optimum satisfaction.

*Too large* in this context is definable and measurable in terms of an economic choice criterion so structured that it can compare either the satisfactions obtainable from equal alternative sacrifices or the sacrifices required to attain equal alternative satisfactions. The economic choice criterion always implies a comparison between alternatives and never specifies an absolute value. In assessing the economic problems of spaciousness, then, it will be appropriate and revealing to compare areas of much space in relation to people—our West, for example—with areas of little or, at least, less space in relation to the people—the North Central and New England areas, for example—in terms of comparative costs for equal benefits or with regard to comparative benefits from equal costs. This type of economic evaluation is attempted in this paper.

The economic problems of space will arise as an "open-country" phenomenon, as distinguished from an urban or urbanization phenomenon, in two instances: (i) when land resources are of low productivity per surface unit under conditions of optimum economic use so that the surface area per capita must be relatively large (ranching, for example); and (ii) when bodies of particularized land resources are highly localized, of relatively small magnitude in each locality, and widely dispersed spatially (some types of mining, for example).

That land resources of low economic productivity per surface unit will produce large spatial areas per capita utilizing those resources would appear to be self-evident. The reference to some types of mining may be a little more obscure. Imagine a typical small ore body exploited by a mining enterprise large enough to support a small town; imagine that similar ore bodies, each exploited by a similar mine surrounded by a small town, are located in a widely dispersed pattern over the landscape. The economic problem of space arises in such instances because, although persons are concentrated at village spots, such villages are too small to support private and public services at costs equal to those in urban areas, yet the several village units are so widely dispersed that they cannot cooperate toward the common rendering of such services. In other words, although the population is concentrated in local spots, the over-all distribution of population in relation to surface area is as sparse as when the people are dispersed as families on ranches or large dryland farms.

Space becomes a "cost" (synonymously, an economic problem)

when population dispersions that result from one of the aforementioned "open-country" instances are so sparse in relation to
space that satisfactions must be sacrificed to live in, and exploit,
the resources inherent in the spatial units so affected. When
population dispersions that result from one of the "open-country"
instances are sparse in relation to space, one or more of the following three conditions must arise: (i) local processing and fabrication of primary products produced in the area are uneconomi-
cal, necessitating the moving of raw materials out and finished
products in (this is the "colonial" case); (ii) the volume of
traffic per mile of total transport facilities is low, resulting in
high costs per unit of traffic moved; (iii) many services furnished
by private businesses or public bodies are either very "thin" per
capita (at comparable cost) or very costly per capita (for comparable quality). In each case, the fact that space exists in excess
quantity per capita means that additional sacrifices (that is, costs),
by comparison with the sacrifices entailed in more thickly settled
areas, must be incurred in order to overcome the excess of space.

The absence of local processing and fabrication, which arises
because of the sparsity of production in relation to space, reinforces the scarcity of population in relation to space. If processing
and fabrication could occur in the area, secondary industries with
their collateral service industries would also develop, thus leading to urbanization and enhanced populations in relation to space.
The absence of local processing and fabrication also reinforces
the high cost of transportation of the area's raw-material exports
and finished-product imports when the cost is measured against
the area's aggregate and per-capita income. Transportation of
goods will be relatively costly, not only because of the necessity
for moving raw materials out and finished products in, but also
because the volume of commodities moved per unit of distance
will be smaller. The services enjoyed by people resident in the
area, whether such services are rendered by private or by public
agencies, either will cost more for equal quality or will be of
poorer quality at equal cost, owing to the higher cost per unit of
service rendered as a result of the insulation of space that sur-
rounds the people served.

The higher costs of space generated under the conditions described may be borne *internally* by the area affected, in the sense that those who live in the area and do the exploiting of the area's resources may be those who make the requisite sacrifices. Such costs of space may be borne *externally* to the area, however, in that these costs may be shifted outside in whole or in part by "subsidies" (private or public) to freight rates, highway construction, school costs, and so forth.

## SPACIOUSNESS AND THE WEST

The preceding remarks are an abstract analysis of spaciousness as an economic problem. It remains for us to discover whether the abstraction can be actually observed in the West.

The data for this study of the problems of space in this region are available largely only as state unit data; therefore, for purposes of the empirical analysis that follows, the West, as it is defined in this paper, embraces the western tier of Great Plains states from Montana to New Mexico and the intermountain states extending to, but not including, the Pacific states from Washington to California. The area is generally designated in the census (and other) statistics as the *Mountain States.*

This West is not a uniform entity of spaciousness in relation to people. The conurbations of Denver, Salt Lake City, Phoenix, and other cities of smaller size experience costs of space that differ little from those of similar aggregations of people in conurbations in the more thickly settled parts of the country. Using, as I must in this paper, empirical evidence of the cost of space based on state unit data, the presence of these urban entities within the West reduces the apparent magnitude of the costs of space in the West, as compared with the more thickly settled parts of the United States. These city concentrations, themselves, help to carry the costs of space for the more sparsely settled portions of their states; what we have in the state data is simply the average costs in relation to the over-all population density.

An attempt is made early in this paper to set forth an analytical framework to facilitate the approach to the economic problems of spaciousness. From that framework the following hypotheses may be deduced.

1) The aggregate personal net income generated per unit of area in the region will be low.

2) Net personal income per capita, however, need not be low but can be equal to, or even higher than, that in other less spacious areas.

3) The tonnage of freight moved per mile of transport arteries (railroad plus road mileage) will be low.

4) Total road mileage per capita (reflecting the cost of roads) will be high, or the proportion of unsurfaced miles (reflecting the poor quality of roads) will be large, or *both* conditions may exist.

5) The cost per capita for health and medical care will be high, or the number of physicians and hospital beds per capita will be low, or both.

6) The per-pupil cost of education will be high, or the proportion of pupils in "ungraded" schools (as a reflection of quality) will be high, or some combination of both.

7) A large proportion of the total personal income will be generated in primary industries. The proportion of personal income generated in secondary industries (that is, fabricating and processing industries) will be low in relation to that generated in primary industries.

8) The "real" level of living per *dollar* of personal income will be low; whether the real level of personal income per *capita* will be relatively low or high will depend on (i) whether the dollar amount of personal income per capita is enough more to offset its lower worth per dollar, or (ii) whether the unmeasured and unmeasurable satisfactions of "room, lots of room" are enough greater than the sacrifices that such a condition necessitates to offset any lower real level of living based on dollar amounts alone.

Let us now review the empirical evidence that is available to test the validity of these hypotheses, which at this stage are advanced only as propositions.

### Personal income per square mile and per capita

It is hardly surprising that the empirical evidence supports the proposition that personal income generated per square mile is low in the West compared with the more thickly settled areas. In

New England, almost $400,000 of personal income is generated per square mile of surface area. In the Great Lakes area, it is almost as large, being $350,000. But in the West, the comparable figure is only $16,500—one-twenty-fifth, or 4 percent, as much as the income-generating power of "space" in New England.

Any service, the cost of which is related to area in some degree (transport of people, things, or messages, for example), will be expensive in relation to aggregate income in the West, as compared with the more thickly settled regions.

This does not mean, however, that the costs of such area-connected services will also be more expensive per capita in the area. If the per-capita incomes generated in the West are enough larger than those generated elsewhere to make up more than the difference in such costs, the higher cost of such services is not a burden on the persons resident in the area (although it may be on the society as a whole). But, contrary to our hypothesis that per-capita incomes in the area will be no lower, and may be higher, than those elsewhere, Table I shows that per-capita incomes in the West are lower than those in the more thickly settled industrialized regions to the northeast ($2078 compared with $2471 in New England and $2373 in the Great Lakes region). Why they are lower is not explored in this paper. Whether or

Table I. Personal income per square mile and per capita by regions, 1960

| | Personal income | |
| | Per sq mi | Per capita |
| Region[a] | ($) | ($) |
|---|---|---|
| *United States* | *110,650* | *2233* |
| New England | 388,970 | 2471 |
| Great Lakes | 347,681 | 2373 |
| Great Plains | 61,781 | 2071 |
| West | 16,594 | 2078 |

[a] *Region* as used in this and the following tables represents (unless otherwise noted) those groupings of the states used in recent censuses of the United States. *New England:* Maine, New Hampshire, Vermont, Massachusetts, Rhode Island, Connecticut. *Great Lakes:* Ohio, Indiana, Illinois, Michigan, Wisconsin. *Great Plains:* Minnesota, Iowa, Missouri, North Dakota, South Dakota, Nebraska, Kansas. *West (Mountain):* Arizona, New Mexico, Colorado, Utah, Wyoming, Montana, Idaho, Nevada.

not they are lower *because* of spaciousness is not answered here, although I would advance the hypothesis that they are not. Insofar as the space-affected costs of services per person for those who live under conditions of spaciousness are higher, however, the economic burden of that spaciousness per person is greater still because those higher costs must be paid from smaller incomes.

Let us next examine the costs of characteristic services of various kinds and compare the cost burden of those services in the West with those in the more thickly settled regions. First, consider the third hypothesis, namely, that freight tonnage moved per mile of transport arteries will be comparatively low.

## High cost of transportation

Unfortunately, empirical data for testing the validity of the third hypothesis are not available. Railroad and truck tonnages moving in interstate commerce are reported not by states but by broad ratemaking areas. Consequently, this proposition will have to remain hypothetical, although I cannot conceive how it could possibly be other than true.

It is possible, however, to examine the burden of road mileage as a cost to the economy of the West when it is compared with other parts of the nation. Table II shows that road mileage per

Table II. The burden of highways and spaciousness by regions

| Region | Highway expenditures by state and local governments (per capita) 1959 ($) | Total road mileage[a] per 1000 persons 1960 (mi) | Proportion Surfaced (%) | Unsurfaced (%) |
|---|---|---|---|---|
| United States | 54 | 46.6 | 68.7 | 31.3 |
| Great Lakes | 55 | 37.8 | 89.4 | 10.6 |
| Great Plains | 71 | 81.8 | 68.2 | 31.8 |
| West | 77 | 115.1 | 37.3 | 72.7 |

[a] Mileage of rural roads in relation to population outside of metropolitan areas (census definition).

1000 persons in the West is 115 miles compared, for example, with 38 miles of road per 1000 persons in the Great Lakes states. Each occupant of the West is responsible, therefore, for 3 to 4 times as many miles of road as is a resident in the Great Lakes states. Even more striking, however, is the proportion of that road mileage which is surfaced and unsurfaced as between the several regions. For example, in the Great Lakes states almost 90 percent is surfaced, whereas in the western region only a little more than a third is surfaced. The generally poorer quality of the much larger mileage of roads per person in the West could result in expenditures per capita for roads in the West no greater than in the thickly settled areas. However, Table II reveals that per-capita costs of roads in the West are 35 percent higher than in the nation and in the Great Lakes states, and about 8 percent higher than in the Great Plains states. As is indicated in our theoretical analysis, the cost of space may show up as higher costs for equal quality or poorer quality for equal costs. Highway costs of space would seem to involve both—higher costs and poorer quality.

### High cost of health care

Another service that may be "space affected" is health and medical care. The fifth hypothesis states that costs of such care will be high, or the quality of the services as exemplified by numbers of physicians and hospital beds will be low, or both.

Empirical evidence on the number of physicians and hospital beds per capita was not available to me; consequently, this measure of quality must be left as an assertion without proof. The overall cost of health and medical care to farm families is greater in the western region than it is in the more thickly settled regions, as is shown in Table III. In 1955 health-care cost per farm family in the West (assuming that farm families adequately represent people living under relatively sparse settlement conditions) was $299 compared with $241, or 24 percent more than the same cost, in the more thickly settled northeastern regions. This might reflect a "higher level" of medical care in terms of either quantity or quality in the western region, compared with the more industrialized Northeast. Although I have no evidence on the

Table III. Health-care costs per family and per person by regions, 1955

|  | Health-care cost | |
|---|---|---|
| Region | Per farm family ($) | Per family member ($) |
| Great Lakes, North Atlantic, New England (combined) | 241 | 64 |
| West | 299 | 75 |

point, this seems doubtful. I cannot conceive, from my own experience in the areas, that the level of health and medical care in the West is higher than that in the industrialized Northeast. In fact, it seems more probable that the relationship runs in the other direction. Nevertheless, the evidence indicates that expenditures for such care are higher in the spacious West than they are in the much less spacious industrialized Northeast.

**Costs of local government**

Some activities of local governments must be carried on, regardless of the size of the area served. When the costs of these activities are spread over fewer people under conditions of sparse settlement, they will be greater per capita.

Table IV, which combines the costs of state and local governments, shows that such costs per $1000 of personal income in the West are about $30, or 23 percent higher than similar costs in

Table IV. Costs of local government in relation to income and population by regions

|  | Local government cost | | |
|---|---|---|---|
| Region | Per $1000 personal income ($) | Per capita ($) | From federal sources (%) |
| Great Plains and Great Lakes (combined) | 132.82 | 257.68 | 15.3 |
| West | 161.51 | 333.41 | 23.2 |

the combined regions to the east; per-capita costs are about $80, or 30 percent, higher in the West than they are in the more populous regions. It is interesting, however, to note that the proportion of these costs of local government that is shifted outside the region onto the federal government is about 50 percent higher in the West than it is in the more heavily populated regions. This supports my earlier contention that the costs of space need not be borne internally but may be shared externally to the spacious region. Although Table IV does not indicate this, it is true, nevertheless, that the costs of local government borne within the region per capita are higher in the western region

Table V. Costs of education[a] and sizes of schools by regions, 1959

| Region | Per-capita cost ($) | Per-pupil cost ($) | Pupils per school (No.) | | Teachers per school (No.) | |
|---|---|---|---|---|---|---|
| | | | Elementary | High school | Elementary | High school |
| *United States* | 98 | 341 | 255 | 463 | 9.0 | 21.4 |
| New England | 78 | 358 | 264 | 477 | 9.7 | 25.2 |
| Great Lakes | 98 | 359 | 297 | 528 | 10.8 | 23.2 |
| Great Plains | 97 | 337 | 98 | 250 | 3.7 | 13.9 |
| West | 125 | 342 | 216 | 441 | 8.2 | 20.1 |

[a] Primary and secondary schools.

than they are in the more populous northeastern areas, in spite of this "subsidy"—that is, only part, not all, of the excess cost is shifted "outside."

## Cost of education

Education is an important public service, and we have hypothesized that costs of such education will be higher under conditions of sparse settlement than elsewhere, or that the quality will be lower, or both. It is striking, however, as is shown in Table V, how far we have gone in the United States toward standardizing our educational efforts. The cost *per pupil* in primary and secondary education is strikingly uniform among the several regions. The *per-capita* (as distinguished from the *per-pupil*) cost of education, however, is significantly (25 percent) higher in the West than it is in the country as a whole.

One might further hypothesize that the education provided in the West, although no more costly per pupil, is of poorer quality. Measuring the quality of education is difficult, but one indication of relative quality might be the number of "one-room" schools or the number of one- and two-teacher schools. Evidence bearing directly on this point is not available, but Table V does show the average number of pupils and teachers per school in the different regions. It is noticeable that the numbers of pupils and teachers per school in the West compare quite favorably with those in the more populous industrialized areas.

The small numbers of pupils and teachers per school in the Great Plains states compared with the other regions is worth noting and leads me to speculate a bit. Rural settlement in the Great Plains area is distributed rather uniformly over the surface of the region. In the West, on the other hand, rural populations tend to be concentrated more in small mining towns, in irrigated areas along stream courses, or in mountain valleys. Consequently, the effect of sparsity on such things as size of schools may be offset in the West by the tendency of populations to live in relatively compact rural agglomerations, although the over-all average of residents per unit of total area may be low. This might explain why the size of school units (as an index of quality) is smaller in the Great Plains than in the even more sparsely settled West.

### Dependence on primary industries

In a spacious area, we have theorized, the total personal income will be heavily proportioned toward the primary industries. This is inevitable under conditions of the colonial case and, in fact, defines it. Table VI bears out this hypothesis.

In 1960 in the West, personal income generated by primary industries was almost 14 percent of the total personal income generated from all sources in the region. In the United States as a whole, the comparable percentage is only 6 percent, and in the more populous northeastern areas it is only 2 percent and 4 percent. If processing and manufacturing industries are the chief

Table VI. Primary industries[a] as a relative source of personal income
by regions, 1960

| Region | Income (%) |
|---|---|
| *United States* | *6.0* |
| New England | 1.7 |
| Great Lakes | 3.8 |
| Great Plains | 13.8 |
| West | 13.9 |

[a] Agriculture, forestry, fisheries, and mining.

builders of urbanization and the chief stimulants to increases in
population and incomes and, hence, to the overcoming of spaciousness, then another way to indicate the spaciousness of the
West is to show the amount of personal income generated in
secondary industries for every dollar of personal income generated
in primary industries.

Table VII shows this difference strikingly. In the New England
region, for each $1 of income generated in primary industries,
$22.40 is generated in secondary industries. In the West, on the
other hand, for each $1 generated in primary industries, only 95
cents is generated in the secondary industries. This is eloquent
evidence of the "colonial" situation, in which primary products
are exported and fabricated products are imported. Whether this
is good or bad is beside the point of this paper. What is significant
is that economic development, with its accompaniment of increasing urbanization, increasing numbers of people, and rising incomes
and levels of living, is associated with the expansion in the fabricating and processing industries in an economy. In this respect, the

Table VII. Personal income in secondary industries in relation to
personal income in primary industries by regions, 1960

| Region | Income ($) |
|---|---|
| *United States* | *4.90/1* |
| New England | 22.40/1 |
| Great Lakes | 10.40/1 |
| Great Plains | 1.60/1 |
| West | 0.95/1 |

West is still a "colonial" area, and the number of people in relation to its vast spatial areas is small and will continue to be small as long as this condition obtains. The costs of spaciousness in the West will continue large as long as it remains a primarily "colonial" area.

### "Real" level of living

A final conclusion is that the "real" level of living per dollar of personal income will be low in an area such as the sparsely settled, spacious West. Evidence on this point is found in Table VIII, which shows that expenditures per farm family for living in 1955 were 22 percent higher in the West than in the more

Table VIII. Expenditures for family living and the level of living attained, by regions

| Region | Expenditures per farm family for living, 1955 ($) | Level-of-living index, 1954 (farm families) |
|---|---|---|
| Great Lakes, North Atlantic, and New England (combined) | 3512 | 164[a] |
| West | 4300 | 155 |

[a] Estimated from state unit data.

populous northeastern areas, but that the level-of-living index for farm families in the region was 6 percent lower than that for the industrialized Northeast. The implication is that people in the West spend more money for family living, but that the level of living they attain with this money is somewhat lower.

I am fully aware of the shortcomings of the Department of Agriculture's level-of-living index. It indicates the extent to which certain gadgets of modern living have been acquired and does not reflect other, and possibly more meaningful, measures of the quality of living. As an index, however, it probably does denote the extent to which people can live more richly or more poorly in relation to the environment they must cope with. On this basis, it seems evident that larger incomes and expenditures are necessary in the western region, at least on the part of farm families, to acquire a level of living even approximately equal to that of farm families who live in more populous, urbanized areas. This again is evidence of the earlier assertion that the cost of space can be stated either as higher costs for equal quality, or as lower quality for equal costs, or as some combination of both.

### Spaciousness has benefits too

All of the hypotheses advanced in this paper and the evidence presented to test them still do not warrant the assertion that the spaciousness of the West is a problem in the sense that it does not permit an optimum adjustment of people to their surroundings. This is a value judgment. Many individuals would say vehemently that, in spite of the higher economic costs, the benefits of "room, lots of room" are worth the costs. This is not the point of contention here. The point of this analysis is that the benefits, whatever they are and however much they are worth, incident to having "room, lots of room" entail costs that must be borne by someone—either by the person who enjoys the spaciousness or by others external to the area. The dweller in the spaciousness of a rural area of the West makes some sacrifices for that privilege. He also is subsidized in part by his fellow-citizens who live in the urbanized areas of his own state and, in part, by other citizens who live in the more thickly populated regions of the United States. But, again, note that the determination of what is an optimum relationship of man to space is a value judgment; all we can assert on the basis of the reasoning and evidence presented here is that space as we know it in the West is a costly benefit in comparison with similar costs of space borne by residents in the more populous industrialized areas.

### Can the costs of spaciousness be reduced?

The economic problems of spaciousness, as they are revealed in this paper, are not immutable. Technological change and economic development may reduce them. Improved techniques of production can increase the level of real income in the region by increasing the dollar amounts of income, even though the real worth of each dollar is not changed. In other words, a more economically efficient exploitation of the resources of the region may lead to incomes sufficiently higher to offset, in whole or in part, the higher costs of services incident to the spaciousness of the region. Technological improvements in transportation, in communications, and in relevant institutions can also reduce the economic problems of spaciousness.

The import of technological change in transportation and communication in relation to reduction of the costs of space is self-evident, but the significance of institutional changes may be more obscure and warrant a brief discussion. The institutional structure by which private and public services are rendered in the West was carried over from the structure that evolved in, and was—and still is—more applicable to, areas of closer settlement. Institutional adaptations to meet the problems of spaciousness are within the hands of man. They might involve such different, even radical, ideas as expansion in group health and medical care; the consolidation of schools with more pupil transportation to larger schools, which, in turn, requires a denser network of improved roads; and the development of closed-circuit television teaching from centralized lecture centers to decentralized classrooms. Dramatic institutional developments, such as the Flying Doctor Service in Australia, which combines airplanes, group hospital-medical care, radio, and television for improved "local" medical care, education, and communication under conditions of extreme spaciousness, might also be initiated.

The West is spacious in relation to the needs and wants of those who occupy it. It is a primary producer (in the "colonial" sense) with lower levels of real income per dollar and also, probably, with lower levels of real income per capita. The costs of this spaciousness are borne not only by the area's occupants but in part by people external to the area. It also is a region of "magnificent distances," solitude, elbowroom, outdoors, and "room, lots of room," all of which are noneconomic values and may offset the economic costs (or sacrifices) its spaciousness imposes. But such noneconomic justification of its spaciousness does not support, by that value judgment alone, any conclusion that the costs of space are "worth it" and that nothing should be done to reduce them.

The invention and adoption of new institutional devices or arrangements may reduce the costs of space without in any way reducing the noneconomic values that flow therefrom.

## SUMMARY

Space is an obstacle to be overcome—at least, to a point. As an obstacle, it entails costs when there is too much of it in relation to population and income. In the West, by comparison with more populous (less spacious) areas to the east, the level of personal income per square mile and per capita is low; costs per unit of, and per capita for, transportation, health and medical care, and education are high; and the "real" level of living per dollar of income and per capita is low.

Such higher costs may be more than offset by high, although intangible, satisfactions derived from spaciousness. However, invention and adoption of new or modified institutions may reduce the costs of such spaciousness without impairing the benefits derivable from it.

# Recreation as a Competitive Segment of Multiple Use

Marion Clawson

*Resources for the Future, Inc., Washington, D.C.*

An unprecedented demand for natural resources to be used for outdoor recreation pursuits is evident to everyone who is even moderately familiar with natural resource use. A rapid and continued rise in demand for resources for some particular purpose naturally raises the possibility of a larger allocation of resources to that purpose.

Postwar increases in usage of public outdoor recreation areas have been approximately 10 percent *annually* for land areas and much more for water areas. The number of visits to major public outdoor areas in 1948 and 1960 are shown in Table I.

I have pointed out elsewhere that the four major factors underlying these large increases have been (i) growth in total population, (ii) increase in real income per capita, (iii) increased leisure, and (iv) improved transportation facilities (*2, 3*). Other factors might be added, but, in my judgment, these are the major ones. The trend in each factor has been almost steadily upward since World War II; hence, it is impossible to determine the relative effect of each. As nearly as we can estimate, the trend in each of these basic factors will continue upward, and at something like the present rate, for a generation or more into the future. Further massive increases in demand for outdoor recreation areas therefore appear certain to come (*7*).

## INTANGIBLE-VALUES ARGUMENT

Some conservationists, outdoor recreationists, and others will argue against trying to evaluate recreation in monetary terms in order to measure it against other competing demands for natural resources. Their arguments usually include all or some of the following points.

1) Outdoor recreation provides human satisfactions of a psychic or nonmaterial kind, to which it is wholly impossible to assign a monetary value. Another aspect of this argument stresses the great emotional, moral, and public values of outdoor recreation.

2) It is difficult or impossible to put monetary values on outdoor recreation opportunities, even if this were desirable. Public outdoor recreation is usually provided free or at a nominal price, and such a price obviously does not measure the true worth of outdoor recreation. In this regard, the problem of measuring the

Table I. Visits to major public outdoor areas

| Area | 1948 | 1960 |
|---|---|---|
| | (millions of visits) | |
| National forests | 24 | 93 |
| National park system | 30 | 66 |
| State parks | 105 | 259 |
| Army Corps of Engineers reservoirs | 26[a] | 109 |
| TVA reservoirs | 11 | 42 |
| Total | 196 | 569 |

[a] 1952.

monetary value of something not sold is generally cited. Those who use this argument often fear that efforts to place a monetary value on outdoor recreation will result in figures so low that their position will be worsened.

3) Historically, the establishment of public parks and outdoor recreation areas has been achieved through political struggles, in which comparative costs and returns were not seriously considered. This will probably continue to be the means whereby natural resources are allocated to recreation. In this case, comparative values, even if calculable accurately, are largely irrelevant.

One may have considerable sympathy with each or all of these viewpoints, yet they are *not* very helpful to the manager of natural resources that are being operated on a multiple-use basis, or to a legislator who is trying to decide how much public money should go into natural resource development for various purposes. An advocate of larger recreation areas may, indeed, refuse to make estimates of economic values, preferring to let the political process run unhampered by such calculations. But this is scarcely responsible behavior for the research man, whether he is publicly or privately supported.

## DIFFERENCES OF DEGREE, NOT OF KIND

The premise that it is both possible and desirable to estimate the monetary value of natural resources when they are used for outdoor recreation is basic to the remainder of this paper. Although such estimates are difficult and, at the present stage of research development in this field, may have an undesirably large margin of error, yet it is asserted that major advantages lie in making the best possible estimates. Monetary values of natural resources, when they are used in different ways, provide administrators, legislators, and the general public with some highly useful guides to natural resource policy. Decisions need not be based wholly on comparative economic values—public decisions rarely are—but such values do constitute one significant fact or set of facts (1).

All commodities and services are valued, in an economic sense, because people value them—because people are willing to exchange scarce dollars to buy or rent them. A commodity or service is valued, not solely because of any intrinsic characteristic, but only because people find it necessary to expend part of their limited funds to acquire what they want. The earliest economists were puzzled because, in the relatively simple society of their day, water was everywhere free; yet water was obviously critical to life itself. In placing an economic value on natural resources used for outdoor recreation, we are simply measuring how people act; we are not evaluating some intrinsic feature of the resource (6).

In public resource management and development, we typically place values on resources not sold in the competitive market.

Federal water-resource programs are full of this: flood reduction is not sold, it is provided nearly free to recipients, as is improved navigation; and irrigation water is neither competitively sold nor made available only on a full cost basis. Other examples are possible in public resource programs. We do not assume that value is zero because price is zero. On the contrary, elaborate calculations are made in an attempt to show that proposed projects are "economically feasible." Such calculations are under well-nigh universal suspicion of being seriously biased upward; however, even if true, this is insufficient ground on which to condemn the whole process.

Conservationists and recreationists might well ponder, as a practical fact of life, that the old esthetic and emotional arguments for setting aside parks and recreation areas may not suffice in the future. The competition for land and water grows increasingly keen. The rising demand for outdoor recreation will require substantially increased new areas if the old areas are not to be trampled and crowded past real usefulness. But new areas can be won only with difficulty. Rational argument may have to supplement emotional appeal.

## WHOLE RECREATION EXPERIENCE

One reason that past attempts to measure the economic value of natural resources used for recreation have been so barren of results is that nearly all studies have focused on only a part of the economic process involved. Typically, attention has been directed at the recreation site only. But the experience at the recreation site is only part of the whole—and, in terms of cost, a minor part.

An outdoor recreation experience, such as a day's outing in a state park or a visit to a national park, always includes five rather distinct phases (although the proportions among the phases may vary), as follows.

1) *Anticipation* or planning is the stage during which the family or the person contemplates various alternative outdoor recreation opportunities and chooses among them. The process

may be methodical or haphazard, well-informed or random, prolonged or impulsive, and otherwise variable. The basis of decision and the later reality may differ widely. Yet, I submit, this
is the crucial part of the whole experience, for on it depends
everything that follows. Moreover, as I shall show later, as a

Outdoor recreation is steadily increasing in importance as a competitor
for natural resources. (U.S. Department of Agriculture, Forest Service)

practical matter this is the most significant phase, for more than
half of all expenditures for outdoor recreation take place during
it.

2) *Travel to* the recreation site is involved in almost all outdoor recreation experiences; use of larger land and water areas
typically involves a good deal of travel. As much as, or more,
time is likely to be spent traveling to the recreation site as is
spent at the site itself. Substantial costs are incurred for this

travel. There is grave suspicion that the typical recreationist places a negative value on this travel—something unavoidable, to be gotten over with as quickly as possible, in order to enjoy the outdoor area of his choice.

3) *On site* outdoor recreation experiences are generally familiar. A myriad of activities is included in this general term; they differ greatly in the area of land or water required and in their appeal to persons of differing age, sex, and interest. For our present purpose, we need not consider these many variations; for recreation area administration, they are often critical.

4) *Travel back home* has many points of similarity with travel to the site. Yet it may involve different routes and different costs in time and money and, possibly most important of all, is likely to be undertaken in a different frame of mind.

5) *Recollection,* or the reliving of the experience, may include a substantial part of the total satisfactions. Like anticipation, it may not bear an exact relationship to the experience as it was realized. Unpleasant experiences may provide conversation, and hence a kind of enjoyment, for months. It has long been observed that fish grow longer as the time since their catch lengthens. Above all, it is the recollection of the recreation experience that will largely affect future experiences.

Any economic analysis of outdoor recreation must consider this entire recreation experience. *All* the costs of the whole experience must be counted; each is necessary, and no single item of expense is determinant. Also, *all* the satisfactions (and dissatisfactions) must be considered. It is not enough to know what the visitor thought of the view from the vista point, or of the swimming facilities, or of any other feature at the site; his reactions to the restaurants, hotels, rest rooms, and so forth, en route may be equally significant. The costs are a package deal; the benefits are a package deal; and meaningful economic analysis must start with these significant economic entities.

If the whole recreation experience is accepted as the unit of economic analysis, cost-quantity relationships common to all demand curves exist for outdoor recreation (*4*). Both cost and quantity need careful definition; and, as in other demand curves, factors such as income may affect the location and shape of the cost-quantity curves.

Cost of the whole outdoor recreation experience can be expressed in one or a combination of three forms: money, time, and travel. Money must be spent for gasoline, restaurant meals, motels, and a host of other items required for outdoor recreation; and, sooner or later, it must be spent for purchase of a new automobile or other necessary equipment. The whole outdoor recreation experience requires time; some may be pleasurable, especially that spent at the site, while some (perhaps travel) will not be. In any event, time spent for outdoor recreation cannot be used for productive employment or for enjoyment of other activities. Some travel is nearly always involved in outdoor recreation; occasionally, a great deal is necessary. The costs in money, time, and travel are likely to be highly correlated. That is, the person who visits a distant outdoor recreation area must expend much money and much time and must perform much travel, while the visitor to a nearby area spends much less of each. If money, time, and travel were perfectly correlated, then cost would be expressed in any one of these measures; money would presumably be the best, since most costs in demand analysis are in these terms. Under some circumstances, money is the limiting factor; under others, perhaps limitations of time impose the chief constraint; and perhaps at times travel will be dominant. Within some limits, money can substitute for time; and money can certainly ease travel.

The quantity of outdoor recreation use, in demand-curve analysis, amounts to the number of visits per 1000 total population in the tributary area. Thus, if there were 50,000 visits by people living within 20 miles of the recreation area, and 1000 people resided in this zone, the use factor is 50; similarly, for 100,000 visits by people 20 to 40 miles away with 5000 people living in this zone, the use factor is 20; and so on.

When money (or distance) costs per visit are related to such use factors, for every area for which I have been able to find adequate data, there is a familiar cost-quantity (demand) curve relationship. By and large, the demand curves for different areas are consistent; and demand is generally elastic. The number of visits per 1000 base population varies inversely with cost per visit, but not exactly proportionately so.

*Total usage* of an outdoor recreation area depends not only on cost per visit but also on size of population in the different distance zones. Recreation areas with large populations in tributary zones will have large total visitation, other factors remaining equal; areas with small tributary populations will have smaller total visitation. Alternative outdoor recreation areas, particularly if they are equally attractive and equally close, will draw off some of the potential visitors. Higher incomes, more leisure, and better roads each lead to more visits (costs per visit and population in the base zone remaining constant); their opposites mean fewer visits. All of these relationships can be illustrated graphically or statistically by using hypothetical data in each case, or by using actual data in some cases. Space does not permit an exposition of these illustrative and hypothetical relationships.

## EXPENDITURES ON OUTDOOR RECREATION

The foregoing discussion of the nature of the whole recreation experience may be illustrated by some estimates of total expenditures for different purposes and at different locations. Using available data concerning number of visits, length of stay, and expenditures per day, I have calculated the total expenditures involved in using the national park system, national forests, federal wildlife refuges, Army Corps of Engineers reservoirs, TVA reservoirs, and state parks, in 1960 (5). The estimates include all expenses for the whole recreation experience: travel, including meals and lodging en route to and from; expenses at the site; and, most important, an allowance for equipment, including automobile, used in the recreation experience. Although the estimates are necessarily approximate, given the paucity and variability of expenditure data, it is felt that they are reasonably accurate with regard to general magnitude and relative proportion among items.

In 1960, total expenditures by all visitors to the aforementioned public outdoor recreation areas slightly exceeded $11 billion. Of this sum, about one-third was spent to visit national forest areas, somewhat less was spent for visits to state parks, and progressively lesser amounts for visits to the national park system and to federal reservoir areas. Total expenditures are determined by total numbers of visits, length of each visit (including travel), and expenditures per day.

Of these total expenditures, slightly more than half of the total was spent in the home community of the recreationist. Most of these expenditures were made during the anticipation phase of the total experience, although a smaller part may have occurred during the recollection period also. Nearly all equipment was bought in the home community; it is here, for instance, that almost all automobiles were purchased. More than 40 percent of the gas and oil was also purchased in the home community; the family that goes on a single day's outing is likely to "fill 'er up" before leaving and after returning but not to buy gasoline en route. The same will be true of groceries for picnics and even for longer trips. On the other hand, expenses for hotels, motels, and restaurant meals were made primarily en route to the recreation area or in its vicinity. Of the total expenditures, about one-fourth was spent in or near the recreation area and somewhat less en route to and from. The latter was more or less evenly divided between the travel-to and travel-from phases of the total recreation experience. The proportions spent in the home community, en route, and at or near the site differed considerably among the various types of public areas. The shorter the trip, the more spent in the home community; the longer the trip, the more spent en route.

No data are available on the admission charges to these public recreation areas, but they probably did not exceed $10 million in 1960. Data are not available on expenditures by public agencies for management of outdoor recreation on these areas; indeed, for the agencies practicing multiple use it would be hard to estimate the share of total expenditures chargeable to outdoor recreation. Using such data as there are, however, it seems probable that in 1960 the expenditures for the enumerated public areas did not exceed $500 million. Thus, for a total public expenditure of roughly $500 million, private business connected with outdoor recreation of more than $11 billion is generated.

## REVENUE-PRODUCING CAPACITY OF NATURAL RESOURCES
## USED FOR OUTDOOR RECREATION

The foregoing analysis, even if presented in detail, would not in itself provide an estimate of the monetary value of natural resources when they are used for outdoor recreation; but it can provide the foundation on which value calculations can be made. We have shown that moderately large sums, even for modern America, are spent in order to enjoy the major types of public outdoor recreation areas. Visitors to these areas must certainly believe that they get their money's worth, for each year they come in increasing numbers. Yet it is also true that in order to come they spent most of their money for gas and oil, motels, restaurants, food from grocery stores, equipment such as autos, camping gear, and the like. Very little of their total expenditure went to pay for use of the land and water resources, because these were provided free or at nominal cost by public agencies.

The pertinent question for our purpose is: How much would the visitors have paid, if they had been forced to pay; and what is the maximum total fee revenue that could have been secured? Some, of course, would have been unwilling to pay any entrance fee; total costs of the whole recreation experience were so large, in relation to the pleasures and satisfactions derived from the whole experience, that any entrance fee whatsoever would have tipped the balance against visiting the area. At the other extreme, some visitors derived such large satisfactions from visiting the area that they would have paid large entrance fees—perhaps unwillingly, but paid nevertheless—rather than forego the whole experience.

One basic assumption in all demand-curve analysis is that large blocks of consumers, reasonably similar with respect to income and other socioeconomic characteristics, will react in generally similar ways to price changes of various commodities. By use of this assumption, the aforedescribed quantity-cost, or demand, curves can be translated into fee-gross revenue curves.

This process cannot be traced in detail in this paper, but an illustration may help. Assume that people within 20 miles of a park make 150 visits per year per 1000 base population, at an average cost per visit of $1.50. If an entrance fee of 50 cents per visit is imposed, the total cost per visit is now $2. Some people will no longer come, arguing that the cost exceeds the value. Assume further that people living 20 to 25 miles distant incur costs of $2 per visit even when entrance fees are zero, but that only 100 visits per 1000 base population are made from this zone. On our assumption about comparability of groups and rationality of behavior, the 50-cent entrance fee would reduce visits from the under-20-miles zone from 150 to 100 per 1000 base population. But it would also produce a fee revenue from this group of $50. A similar process could be carried out for each zone within the tributary area. In each case, the illustrative fee would cut usage but would raise some revenue. In order to calculate total revenue, consideration would have to be given also to total population within each zone.

The same process could be repeated for higher entrance fees—in our example, for $1, $2, $3, $5, and so on. In each case the effect of the fee on costs per visit and, thus, on number of visits from each zone could be calculated. The amount of fee revenue that could be realized from visitors from each zone of origin and, thus, the total can also be calculated. In the end, one can construct a simple chart, with varying entrance fees on the horizontal scale, and the resultant total fee revenue on the vertical scale.

Such calculations have been made for as many outdoor recreation areas as had data available. (Space does not permit a detailed presentation of the results here.) In general, maximum fee revenue is obtained at volumes of visitation that are equal to less than half, and sometimes as little as one-fourth, of the volume of visitation when no entrance fees (or nominal ones) are imposed. Also, the entrance fee required to produce maximum fee revenue is much higher than most administrators would probably guess—something in the rough magnitude of $3 to $5 per visit for day-use areas, and of $10 to $25 per visit for outstanding park and forest areas. Studies to date are primarily illustrative; much better data must be collected, from a wide variety of areas, before we can have much confidence in the results.

Several observations on this procedure are necessary even in a brief paper, to avoid major misconceptions.

1) As the foregoing remarks indicate, it is a *gross-revenue* approach. To obtain net benefits from recreation usage, administrative costs should be deducted. This would not be difficult on areas managed solely for recreation but would be very difficult on multiple-use land and water areas.

2) The kind or intensity of management applied to an area might materially affect the demand for it. By spending more money in annual administration, maximum fee revenues might be increased materially, for instance.

3) As is described earlier, this is essentially a static analysis, with population pattern, incomes per person, transportation facilities, leisure, and other factors assumed to be given or fixed. These would vary over time, and the demand curves would shift. Allowance can be made for this variation in the scheme of analysis.

4) This method also assumes that fees and costs at alternative outdoor recreation areas remain unchanged. Some of the people who will not pay the higher fee will go elsewhere; one reason they refuse to pay a higher fee at one recreation area is that they know they can indeed go elsewhere. If a state raised the entrance fees at all its parks, or if all public agencies in a given district or region raised the fees at all areas, then the substitution factor would be much less. As a result, usage would fall off much less as fees were raised, and maximum total fee revenues would be much higher.

One further major point must be made regarding this method of estimating the value of outdoor recreation. It is not concerned with stating what entrance fees *should,* as a matter of policy, be imposed. We are here concerned with estimating the maximum net fee revenue that could be raised from a particular natural resource used for outdoor recreation. This is closely akin to estimating the total benefits from given flood-control measures. As a matter of policy, the nation, state, or locality may decide to provide these benefits free or nearly so; in fact, this is the practice with respect to flood control. In my opinion, a good case can be made for charging entrance fees to public recreation areas at a level much above the present one. But this is another, separate issue. The *value* of outdoor recreation can be estimated without the *price* being necessarily established at that point.

On the basis of the system of analysis outlined sketchily in this paper, it is possible to measure the value of land and water resources used for outdoor recreation and to compare this value with the value of the same resources used for other purposes. A direct monetary comparison is possible, although it is not easy, and careful detailed studies are necessary. It cannot be claimed that the resulting estimates will not contain an element of uncertainty. On the contrary, *all* calculations of future resource value (which is what we are concerned with) involve debatable estimates of future magnitudes of population, income, and other critical factors. But, resource values for outdoor recreation can be estimated with as much accuracy as can values for other purposes, if we are really willing to expend the necessary effort.

## ALLOCATION OF NATURAL RESOURCES TO OUTDOOR RECREATION

After the completion of a sufficient number of careful, detailed studies, it would be possible to indicate the present and probable future allocation of natural resources to outdoor recreation on a purely economic advantage basis. A national forest supervisor could measure the amount and quality of resources to be devoted to outdoor recreation, as compared with timber production, grazing, or any other potential use of the same resources. The manager of a multiple-use water project could do the same, contrasting recreation with power production, irrigation, or other uses. The value of land if used solely for recreation, as in a state park, could be contrasted with its value if used for agriculture, and so on for other situations and other uses.

To my knowledge no such studies have been made; certainly they do not now guide the allocation of natural resources between outdoor recreation and other uses. As is noted earlier, such studies would not be easy, yet they are practical. Perhaps we are unwilling to abide by the results of such studies; perhaps we prefer to make our allocations of natural resources to recreation on the basis of judgment, argument, emotion, and political pressure. Until we have reliable information, we can do little else. In the absence of the necessary studies, all estimates of how much land and water should be allocated to outdoor recreation are necessarily very rough. I have argued in several places that future demands for outdoor recreation will indeed rise very much above present levels. My estimates have been among the largest appearing in print; yet they assume a much slower rate of future than of past growth, in spite of continued future increases in basic relevant factors at approximately past rates. Even much more conservative estimates than mine nearly all accept the premise of major future increases in demand for outdoor recreation.

If the major prospective increases in demand for outdoor recreation are to be met, even at a much intensified degree of crowding, large additional areas of land and large additional quantities of water must be allocated to recreation. Every resource manager will face this problem in the next several decades.

## SUMMARY

A mounting demand for outdoor recreation suggests a larger allocation of natural resources, in a multiple-use management program, than has previously been the case. This requires some estimate of the economic values involved, however, if it is to be done well. Although it is an admittedly difficult undertaking, I have outlined briefly a method for making dependable estimates of economic values of resources for outdoor recreation use. The values obtained by this method are comparable with values for other uses, as they are customarily calculated.

The values of natural resources used for outdoor recreation are often substantial, even though precise measurements have generally not been made in the past or at present.

## REFERENCES

1. Beazley, R. I., "Some considerations for optimizing public forest recreational development and value," *J. Forestry* **59**, 644-650 (1961).

2. Clawson, M., R. B. Held, and C. H. Stoddard, *Land for the Future* (Johns Hopkins Press, Baltimore, Md., 1960), chap. 3 especially.
3. ———, *Crisis in Outdoor Recreation*, Reprint 13 (Resources for the Future, Washington, D.C., 1959). [Originally appeared in *Am. Forests* **65** (3; 4), 22-31, 40-41; 28-35, 61-62 (1959)].
4. ———, *Methods of Measuring the Demand for and Value of Outdoor Recreation*, Reprint 10 (Resources for the Future, Washington, D.C., 1959). Out of print.
5. ———, "Private and public provision of outdoor recreation opportunity," in *Economic Studies of Outdoor Recreation*, ORRRC Study Rept. 24 (Govt. Printing Office, Washington, D.C., 1962).
6. Milstein, D., "Prospective research contributions of economics to outdoor recreation," in *Outdoor Recreation in the Upper Great Lakes Area, U.S. Dept. Agr. Forest Serv. Lake States Forest Expt. Sta. Paper 89* (1961). This article contains an extensive reference list.
7. Outdoor Recreation Resources Review Commission, *Outdoor Recreation for America* (Govt. Printing Office, Washington, D.C., 1962). A report to the President and to the Congress.

# Modifying Management and Vegetation of Watershed Areas to Improve Water Yields

Fred H. Kennedy

*Forest Service, U.S. Department of Agriculture, Albuquerque, New Mexico*

During the early years of national forest administration, emphasis was placed on watershed protection, and the primary aim was maintenance of water quality. The fundamental principle involved utilization of a cover of trees, grass, and brush to hold the soil and to facilitate water storage within the soil.

Too frequently in the past watershed protection and watershed management have been assumed to be synonymous. Over time, however, watershed management has come to have a much broader meaning, at least to the Forest Service, than just protection. Protection is essential but alone is insufficient. We must be concerned also with the amount and timing of water yield, with quantity as well as quality. Maximum protection of watersheds does not necessarily produce maximum yields of water.

An increasing awareness of the need to consider management of watersheds for their maximum production of usable water has become apparent in the southwestern part of the United States. If any resource on the national forests in Arizona or New Mexico could be labeled the most important, it would be water. Most of the water that originates or passes through these two states is used many times by agricultural, domestic, municipal, or industrial interests before a compact-defined outflow is released to other states or Mexico. The water of the Colorado River, for example, which drains practically all of Arizona and a part of New Mexico, is almost entirely consumed in some way or other. Contrast this with the Columbia River system in the Northwest where only about 5 percent of this great river is consumed before it enters the ocean.

The Southwest's rapid increase in population, which is about 2 to 3 times the national average, is placing ever-increasing demands on its water resources. The water tables in practically all of the river basins of both states are being constantly lowered. Few if any are being recharged at a rate that will maintain them.

The Salt River Valley in Arizona, one of the important agricultural production areas in the nation, has been overpumping its ground-water resources for many years. Pumping has been at a rate many times greater than the rate of recharge, and the water table within the pumping area has been lowered at a rate of between 5 and 15 feet per year. In addition to being an important agricultural center, this area is the home of well over a half-million people in and near metropolitan Phoenix. Phoenix jumped in population from 98th place among the cities of the United States in 1950 to 29th place in 1960—a climb unequaled by any other major city in the nation.

All of the water that maintains the Salt River Valley and its people comes from the Salt and Verde rivers, a drainage comprising about 8,320,000 acres of mostly mountainous land with elevations ranging from a low of about 1100 feet at Phoenix to a high of 11,600 feet on Mount Baldy in the Apache National Forest. Exclusive of the arable land, a broad classification of the vegetative types on the watershed would divide them as follows: 30 percent ponderosa pine, 21 percent pinyon-juniper, 25 percent chaparral, 21 percent desert shrub and grass, and 3 percent mixed-conifer. Annual precipitation for these types is about as follows: desert shrub, 8–18 inches; chaparral, 16–24 inches; pinyon-juniper, 12–20 inches; ponderosa pine, 20–28 inches; and mixed-conifer, 28–35 inches. About 55 percent of the precipitation occurs in winter, 45 percent in summer. Winter precipitation is usually general in character, with snow in the higher elevations and rain in the lower. Summer storms, the majority of which come in July and August, are very sporadic and often in the "cloudburst" category.

Adequate storage facilities are available on both the Verde and the Salt rivers. The recorded runoff on both drainages for the period 1910 through 1959 has never exceeded the present available reservoir capacity. The average annual yield of water of the

Verde and Salt rivers for the period 1889 through 1959 was 1,227,278 acre feet. This yield ranged from a low of 291,000 acre feet in 1900 to a high of 5,200,000 acre feet in 1905. In 1956 the runoff was 340,654 acre feet. These records emphasize the wide range in precipitation and water yield that can be expected in the Southwest. Prior to 1958 the entire Southwest experienced a decade or so of extreme drought and generally low water yield. This was especially true for the Salt and Verde drainages. During the 16-year period from 1942 to 1957 the runoff equaled the long-time, 71-year average only during 2 years—1949 and 1952.

## MANIPULATION PROGRAM

Research studies by the Forest Service at Coweeta, North Carolina, Fraser, Colorado, San Dimas, California, and Sierra Ancha, Arizona, indicate that certain changes in vegetative cover do have a favorable effect on water yield. With these findings as a basis, the Forest Service decided late in 1956 to undertake a pilot-test watershed-management program in the Salt and Verde rivers drainage. This drainage involves a number of national forests and is ideal for expanding some of the research findings by pilot testing. Also, if water yields can be increased by manipulating the vegetative cover on a practical scale, the needs and demands of the area dependent on these rivers would certainly justify expanding the pilot test to an action program. The primary objective of the pilot testing is to determine the practicability of developing and initiating such a program.

To date, the pilot testing has been started in the pinyon-juniper, ponderosa pine, and mixed-conifer types. Nothing is contemplated for the desert-shrub type, which yields little water. The chaparral type will be considered for pilot testing as soon as a practical method has been developed for eliminating the shrubs in this type on a selected-species basis. An intensive research program is underway to obtain the needed answers.

The Beaver Creek drainage in the Coconino National Forest was selected for the pilot testing in the ponderosa pine and pinyon-juniper types. It comprises about 276,000 acres. Pilot testing in the mixed-conifer type will be done in other watersheds on the

Apache National Forest. Both projects are in the Salt and Verde rivers drainage.

In the pinyon-juniper type on the Beaver Creek pilot-testing project, the aim was to determine what effects on water yield would follow complete removal of the pinyon and juniper. For the ponderosa pine type, several treatments were undertaken: proper silvicultural harvest and thinning; complete conversion of the tree and shrub cover to grass; and controlled or prescribed burning. Measurements were made for each to be compared with similar untreated stands. The treatments to be tested in the mixed-conifer type have not been developed in detail. The aim has been to determine which treatment of the cover would give the most favorable water yield and which treatment would be the most desirable from the timber-production angle. Then a conclusion could be drawn on which treatment or combination of treatments might be the most desirable from all angles.

### Description of areas and treatments

In the Beaver Creek project two drainages were selected, one of about 16,000 acres and one of 30,000 acres. The 16,000-acre area was left untreated, and the 30,000-acre unit was treated by removing the pinyon and juniper, placing the pine in good silvicultural condition, and converting the poorer pine types to grass. Precipitation and runoff are being measured in all cases. So much variation in condition was found to exist that it was impossible to compare directly the water-yield results from treated areas with those from the untreated. In order to evaluate the effect of the treatments, three undisturbed, comparatively small drainages within the over-all area being considered were selected in the Utah juniper type, three in the alligator juniper type, and eight in the ponderosa pine type. The relationships between runoffs from the drainages in each set will be determined before any of these drainages are treated. These small watersheds range in size from about 200 acres in the pinyon-juniper type to 2000 acres in the ponderosa pine type. Stream gages, as well as precipitation stations, have been operating for most of the drainages since the latter part of 1957.

## Impacts

Treatment on a large scale was necessary to establish other needed answers in addition to the one on water yield. Other resources of the national forests also are important. The effect of the treatments on these uses or resources should be known and will be determined as the pilot testing progresses. Relative costs for different treatment methods under varying conditions also must be considered. For example, before the pine thinning was begun we estimated that precommercial thinning would cost $25 per acre. After thinning some 4000 acres in the Beaver Creek area, we have learned how to do the job for about $6 per acre. Juniper control on the better soil types in the region was being accomplished for about $3 to $4 per acre. When we attempted a complete job on the Beaver Creek for all soils except the steeper slopes, the costs jumped to $10 to $12 per acre. Eradication of oak (*Quercus gambelii*) in the ponderosa pine type immediately posed a game-habitat problem. What effect will this have on turkey and deer? This is being determined with the help of the Arizona Fish and Game Department. Also, it is no simple task to eradicate oak. The larger, mature trees have been effectively killed by use of ammate, but this treatment did not control the sprouts that materialize at the base of the killed mature tree.

Converting an area of about 200 acres of ponderosa pine to grass costs about $60 per acre. At the beginning of the testing project, we had no reliable data on the cost of clearing areas of this magnitude. Less expensive methods can be developed if this practice proves desirable from the viewpoint of over-all resource effects as well as from that of benefit to water yield. The pulp industry, which has just commenced in Arizona, will also be a factor in determining the economics or desirability of such conversion.

Positive, as well as negative, economic values must be determined before an action program can be considered. This cannot be done on a dependable basis unless some pilot treatments are applied on a rather large scale. Grazing-capacity studies are being made to determine the effects on livestock and game production of the several treatments applied to each type. In other words, a good many facts will have to be in hand before the water-yield evaluation job is completed for vegetative treatments in the several climatic zones.

Also, is the recreation-seeking public going to support large-scale treatments—clearings, conversions, burnings—of their national forest land, changing it into something besides the natural forest they are used to? Land treatments of any kind are not lovely to behold until the complete change has been made and the surface of the watershed is again productive. We already have met some resistance to our juniper-clearing programs, which do improve forage production on rangelands. And all kinds of groups and individuals are getting more and more interested in the public heritage of the national forests. This is another resource aspect that must be considered and evaluated in advance of an action program.

The installation and operation of the devices for measuring the runoff, precipitation, and other weather factors on the Beaver Creek project have not been small undertakings. Forty precipitation stations and three complete weather stations have been established. Fourteen stream gages have been installed on the upper drainage watersheds and four on the lower drainages. The majority of the gages on the upper drainage will be used in evaluating several treatments. The lower ones will aid in ascertaining total runoff from the project and will assist in determining how much of the water produced on the upper part of the watershed reaches the main Verde River in the valley below. It is one thing to produce water near where it falls and something else to deliver it 100 miles or more downstream for use. This has to be a part of the over-all testing.

**Treatments**

For the ponderosa pine areas being thinned to optimum silvicultural condition, a basal area of 80 square feet per acre is contemplated on the Beaver Creek project. The trees being cut in the precommercial thinning are those under 6 inches in diameter. One-man "bow" and "circular" power saws are being used to do this job. To date, about 4000 acres have been precommercially thinned. Pulp-size trees (6 to 12 inches in diameter) that have to be removed will be taken for pulp on a commercial basis. Mature saw-log trees are being sold to commercial mills and cut. The majority of the trees that remain form an even-age stand from 40 to 60 years old.

Anchor chains dragged between two tractors clear scrub brush to permit more desirable plant cover to develop. (Courtesy U.S. Department of the Interior, Bureau of Land Management)

To date, the area of ponderosa pine converted to grass has been limited to one drainage of about 200 acres. The commercial trees were sold, and the remainder were "bulldozed" into windrows and later burned. The area was then seeded to yellow sweet clover and a mixture of orchard, crested wheat, and intermediate wheatgrasses. Oak sprouts are a problem in the cleared area. In addition to an original cost of about $60 per acre for clearing, about $2 per acre each year will be required for the 4 or 5 years of follow-up necessary to control the oak sprouts. No additional clear-cutting will be done in this type until one of the evaluation drainages is treated in this manner to determine the effect of the treatment on water yield. To estimate the possibility of applying this treatment and other treatments on a larger scale in the testing, a complete soil survey that includes the necessary interpretative phase of the soil inventory is being made of the Beaver Creek area. This will help to separate the good timber-producing sites from the poorer ones and to indicate which areas may be justifiably cleared for water-yield purposes.

To date, about 12,000 acres of juniper and pinyon have been treated in the Beaver Creek project. Most of the area was cleared by pulling about 150 feet of 3-inch cable between two D-8, or comparable, "cats." This removed most of the larger trees. The large ones remaining were "pushed" with a single "cat"; those too small to be pushed were cut by hand. The disturbed soils were seeded with grass. Sand dropseed, Lehmann, and other love-grasses were used on the lower elevation or Utah juniper types. Crested and intermediate wheatgrasses, side-oats, and blue grama were seeded on the higher elevation or alligator juniper types. Sweet clover was seeded over the entire area. The treatment averaged about $11 per acre in cost.

No prescribed burning has been done in the Beaver Creek area to date. Some burning, both broadcast and of individual slash piles, has been done merely to dispose of the debris left by other treatment operations. Prescribed burning is being done outside the project in the ponderosa pine type to learn how to do the job and to determine what effect it will have on resources other than water. A set of three drainages in the project will be calibrated for water yield and will later be used to determine the effect of pre-scribed burning on water yield.

Two additional large areas in the ponderosa pine type of about 10,000 acres each will be calibrated for water yield. One of these eventually will be given "full watershed treatment" by applying what has been learned from the work already underway. The other will be left untreated as a control. The comparison of areas of this size should help to provide the needed information about, or actually prove to be, the step between the pilot testing and an action program. This will implement the results from the smaller calibrated drainages on a larger scale—a much needed step in developing any action program.

## Results

To date, water-yield results from the Beaver Creek project are largely in the tentative stage. None of the test watersheds have been fully calibrated to determine the runoff relationships among them. After the 1961 runoff data for the six drainages in the Utah

Table I. Annual runoff and precipitation in untreated drainages

| Year | Runoff (in.) | Precipitation (in.) |
|---|---|---|
| | *Utah juniper type* | |
| 1958 | 0.8 | 23.0 |
| 1959 | 0.0 | 13.0 |
| 1960 | 0.6 | 19.0 |
| | *Alligator juniper type* | |
| 1958 | 4.6 | 29.0 |
| 1959 | 0.3 | 14.0 |
| 1960 | 3.9 | 24.0 |

and alligator juniper types are analyzed, it was anticipated that one drainage in each would be treated in 1962. The runoff, as determined for these untreated drainages, and the average annual precipitation for the type for the water years (1 October to 30 September) 1958 through 1960 are shown in Table I.

As has already been indicated, two of the ponderosa pine drainages where streamflow records are being taken were treated ahead of the water-yield calibration. Eight drainages in this type have been left in an untreated condition for calibration purposes. Although the testing procedures and over-all study have not been in operation long enough to warrant any conclusions about what effect the treatments have on runoff with this type of vegetation, it is interesting to compare the results of the two treated drainages with a somewhat comparable untreated drainage. Table II makes such a comparison.

The runoff data from Table II for these three pine-type drainages appear to support the finding from the several research projects in other areas that complete removal of tree cover increases the water yield. From observations of the various watersheds in both the juniper and the ponderosa types, it has been concluded that the character and timing of storms, as well as the condition of the soil when the storms come, also have an important bearing on the amount of runoff. In some instances these factors seem to overshadow total precipitation. The amount of precipitation is

Table II. Annual runoff and precipitation in treated and untreated drainages

| Year | Runoff (in.) | Precipitation (in.) |
|---|---|---|
| *Untreated (drainage No. 10 in ponderosa pine type)* | | |
| 1958 | 4.0 | 37.0 |
| 1959 | 0.2 | 17.0 |
| 1960 | 3.8 | 26.0 |
| *Treated—thinned (drainage No. 7 in ponderosa pine type)* | | |
| 1958 | 5.4 | 37.0 |
| 1959 | 0.1 | 17.0 |
| 1960 | 2.9 | 26.0 |
| *Treated—clear-cut (drainage No. 11 in ponderosa pine type)* | | |
| 1958 | 5.2 | 37.0 |
| 1959 | 0.9 | 17.0 |
| 1960 | 4.8 | 26.0 |

certainly important, but the other factors must also be considered. Research evaluation teams are studying all factors that might affect runoff, and we plan to have the answers before definite decisions are made on the type of treatments that will be extended to a possible action program. There are still a lot of unknowns with regard to why watersheds perform as they do in providing water yields. Because of drastic climatic fluctuations, this is especially true for the many drainages on which streamflow measurements are being taken throughout the national forests in the Southwest.

## MIXED-CONIFER TYPE PILOT-TESTING PROJECT

The pilot testing in the mixed-conifer type that is being done on the Apache National Forest primarily involves calibrating the runoff for selected watersheds and learning how to treat them after the calibration. The three drainages selected are about 300, 500, and 800 acres in size, respectively. Stream gages and precipitation stations have been installed on these drainages. No treatment of the cover will be attempted until calibration has been completed and methods for treatment have been developed.

The prescription for maximum water yield is being determined by type-conversion experiments at the Sierra Ancha Experimental Forest and other research centers. The prescription for attaining maximum timber production in this type is being determined on Burro Creek, another watershed in the mixed-conifer type on the Apache National Forest. Seven areas, ranging in size from 20 to 100 acres, are being cut or treated under different methods along upper Burro Creek. These treatments range from selection of individual trees for cutting through various intensities of timber harvest to complete clear-cutting of the trees and disposal of slash. Clear-cut areas are planted to ponderosa pine or limber pine in some cases; to grass and sweet clover in others. The effects of the various methods on tree, shrub, and grass vegetation are being studied. Without going into detail, I will say that from this study we hope to determine a practical method for harvesting the saw logs and pulp and at the same time to insure regeneration of a productive crop on valuable high-precipitation land.

Two grass-covered drainages of about 400 acres each, in the mixed-conifer zone of the Apache National Forest, are being calibrated for streamflow. Future treatment involving snow manipulation will be applied in this test. Also, several downstream gages are being installed just below the mixed-conifer type to ascertain the total water yield from this type, which is relatively limited in area in Arizona but provides the highest water yields in the state.

## SUMMARY

The pilot testing is designed to assist in developing methods, management policies, and techniques that could be used in the management of important water-yielding lands in the national forests in Arizona, as well as in other parts of this region, that have conditions comparable to those of the testing areas. Water, as I have indicated, is the most important single resource, but many other uses or resource values are also important. The testing as a basis for determining future management practices must consider the needs and relative importance of all uses. An action program is contemplated as a result of the testing, but this will not be activated until we know where we are going and what we are likely to gain from our efforts.

# A Meteorologist Looks at Hydroclimatology

Paul R. Julian

*High Altitude Observatory, Boulder, Colorado*

This paper deals with the two broad aspects of the behavior of the atmosphere as it is related to water supply. The first topic involves a summary of some aspects of the general circulation of our atmosphere. By the *general circulation,* a meteorologist means the large-scale, global distribution of wind, pressure, and temperature. A discussion of this is included because climate is determined by the general circulation. The second topic is the forecast problem. The solution of current and future problems associated with water-resources planning would be facilitated in obvious ways if long-range—beyond a month or so—weather forecasts were possible. These two topics are related because a thorough understanding of the general circulation and the part played in it by water in all its phases is necessary if the long-range forecast problem is to be solved.

There seems to be little point in setting down here what can be found about the hydroclimate in a textbook on climatology, although I do not mean to belittle the efforts of the climatologists in classifying climate. Also, various individuals and agencies have done an excellent job of summarizing our water resource. It is possible, for example, to read that out of an annual average precipitation of 30 inches in this country (range, 10 to 51 inches) about 9 inches is available for man's use (range, 1 to 19 inches), and that an average of 3 inches is ultimately used. It is possible to find estimates of the rate of ground-water recharge and the rate at which pumping depletes reserves. It is possible to estimate that the hydrologic efficiency, or the percentage of incident precipitation that finally runs off in the larger rivers, ranges from 9 to 60 percent.

With these facts duly noted as examples, I have chosen to approach the subject of water and climate from the point of view of a meteorologist who is interested in the general circulation of the atmosphere. The mechanism of the general circulation is, in the last analysis, the mechanism that determines the supply of water from the atmosphere and the variability of that supply.

## WATER AND THE GENERAL CIRCULATION OF THE ATMOSPHERE

Water vapor is one of four physical quantities that can be studied on a global basis with the objective of quantitatively accounting for its distribution and flux. Energy, in the form of internal heat energy and kinetic energy of motion, and momentum are, in a sense, easier to handle; and most of the budgetary studies of the general circulation have been concerned with these quantities. By applying very fundamental physical reasoning to the observed structure of the atmosphere, it can be shown that a source of both energy (kinetic energy and sensible heat) and momentum occurs in tropical latitudes and a sink occurs in higher latitudes. Both energy and momentum, therefore, must be transported from low to high latitudes by some mechanism that involves circulation of the atmosphere. Empirical studies of sources and sinks and of the transport of water vapor have shown, too, that a source exists in low latitudes and a sink exists in higher latitudes. The same circulation mechanism that transports heat and momentum poleward also can be invoked to transport water vapor. Water-vapor transport is, of course, a form of energy transport, because of the latent heat of condensation. I do not want to give space to a discussion of the evidence for the various schemes that have been suggested whereby the necessary meridional transports of momentum, energy, and water vapor are effected. I think it has been fairly well ascertained empirically, however, that in our latitudes the transient disturbances that are known as extratropical cyclones account for nearly all of the required transport. The integral place of these storm systems, which contribute most of our hydrologically important water, is thus evident in the over-all scheme of the atmosphere's circulation.

With this point made, I want to return for a moment to the

water budget of the globe. Fundamental empirical investigations by Wüst, an oceanographer (9), and Jacobs, a climatologist (2), have agreed that evaporation from the sea surface exceeds precipitation within the area stretching from the intertropical convergence zone or the meteorological equator to about 45°N and S. The principal regions of evaporation excess, and therefore the source regions for water vapor, are the subtropical high pressure areas in summer. These same areas plus the relatively warm ocean areas immediately off the eastern shores of the major landmasses are the water-vapor sources in winter. Combining these data with the distribution of precipitation over land and ocean, it is possible to arrive at a water budget for all the earth. These estimates (Table I) may be as much as 10 percent in error, since we have only the crudest notion of the precipitation over the oceans. Even such crude indications, however, suggest that the oceans are the major source of moisture for the earth's storm systems. The figures in Table I represent something like a lower limit to the magnitude of the oceanic source, because estimates of precipitation over the oceans are thought to be too high.

Table I. Water budget of the earth

| Place | Precipitation (cm/yr) | Evaporation (cm/yr) | Outflow-inflow (cm/yr) |
|---|---|---|---|
| Ocean | 90 | 100 | +10 |
| Continent | 67 | 42 | −25 |
| Earth | 83 | 83 | |

Various studies on the latitudinal distribution of the sources and sinks of water vapor seem to agree fairly well with respect to the broad picture. Table II sets out the precipitation minus evaporation quantities in centimeters per year as computed by three separate studies. The last two columns on the right are not strictly independent, since similar methods were used. Evaporation was estimated by both shipboard pan measurements and by the local energy-budget method. The two left columns are the result of Starr and Peixoto's studies (7) on the hemispheric balance of water vapor using aerological data only. The quantity

listed was computed by averaging the water-vapor flux divergence
about the hemisphere between latitude bands. The agreement
in all except the extreme polar latitudes is encouraging.

It should be pointed out that the average residence time for
water vapor in the atmosphere must be about 10 days. This is
so because the range of precipitable water values in an air column
at any given time is about 1–4 grams per square centimeter, and
from Table I, the mean evaporative rate is about 0.1 to 0.3 centimeter per day. Such a fact is important because it suggests that
long-term storage of water vapor in the atmosphere must be very
small indeed, and, in these terms at least, the precipitation mechanism is a remarkably efficient one.

To return to the study of Starr and Peixoto, a few remarks concerning the importance of their computations are in order. By
collecting aerological soundings for the calendar year 1950 from
stations distributed over all the Northern Hemisphere, they computed the horizontal moisture flux and the flux divergence
(Fig. 1). Such a study is, of course, fundamental. It may be surprising in view of the irregular and unsatisfactory distribution of
radiosonde stations, the wide diversity of equipment, in particular, humidity sensors, and the difficulty in computing the divergence of such a quantity that any reasonable results emerged.
But water-vapor flux divergence is seen to occur in the regions
occupied by the subtropical high cells, as well as over the major

Table II. Precipitation-evaporation (cm/yr)

| Latitude | Starr-Peixoto | | Conrad (Wüst) | Benton (Wüst) |
|---|---|---|---|---|
| | Winter | Summer | | |
| 90–80 | −8.0 | −9.6 | +8 | +16 |
| 80–70 | +20.0 | +15.7 | +22 | +14 |
| 70–60 | +26.5 | +32.5 | +25 | +25 |
| 60–50 | +27.3 | +53.2 | +32 | +22 |
| 50–40 | +8.7 | −11.5 | +32 | +19 |
| 40–30 | −13.2 | −30.2 | −19 | −24 |
| 30–20 | −57.8 | −30.5 | −48 | −35 |
| 20–10 | −77.4 | +27.2 | −37 | −34 |
| 10–0 | +35.4 | +50.3 | +43 | +46 |

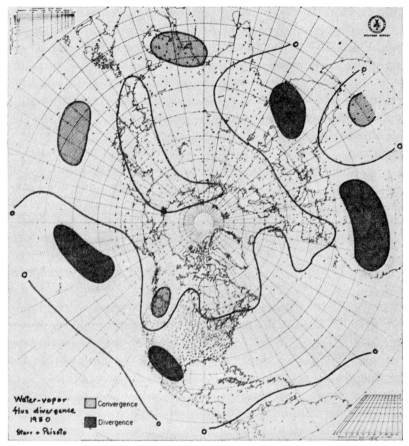

Fig. 1. Schematic rendition of the water-vapor flux-divergence computations of Starr and Peixoto (7).

desert regions of the continents. Flux convergence occurs over the areas of the tropics that receive heavy precipitation, in mid-latitudes in the Pacific Northwest of the American continent, and over western Europe.

Over a more limited region, that of our contiguous United States and Canada, Benton and Estoque (1) have conducted a similar experiment. They calculated the horizontal moisture flux for the calendar year 1949, separating the flux into a time-mean and an eddy-flux. Their most important conclusions are the following. (i) The North American continent acts as a moisture sink in winter but as a weak source in summer. (ii) Space-time eddies transported about 40 percent of the total meridional flux, thus emphasizing the importance of transient disturbances in transporting the necessary moisture poleward. (iii) High values of moisture flux are a necessary but not a sufficient condition for excessive precipitation. (iv) Examination of mean monthly moisture flux patterns made obvious the importance of the relationship between the major sources of moisture (the Gulf of Mexico and the eastern Pacific) and circulation anomalies—that is, deviations of the monthly average flow patterns from the long-term average. (v) Potential evapotranspiration computed from Thornthwaite's empirical formula agreed within reason with the calculated value of evapotranspiration from the continuity equation (estimating the flux divergence, precipitation, and change in precipitable water).

Starr and White (8) have summarized the energy budget of the Northern Hemisphere, again utilizing the aerological data for a calendar year. Table III, taken directly from their report, is a grand summary of the work. Shown on the left are the results of two different studies giving the necessary poleward energy flux across latitude circles, as is demanded by radiative balance considerations. Columns 3 and 4 give the meridional energy transport by the horizontal eddies for sensible and latent heat, and the final column gives their sum. The results of Starr and White's work indicate that, except for the lower latitudes, the horizontal eddy circulations or the extratropical cyclones to which I referred earlier are capable of transporting all the needed energy poleward. Since the ocean circulations also carry sensible heat

Table III. Eddy-energy flux across latitude circles (units: $10^4$ cal $sec^{-1}$)

|  | Required flux | | Observed flux | | |
| Latitude | London | Gabites | Sensible | Latent | Sum |
| --- | --- | --- | --- | --- | --- |
| 70 | 1.9 | 3.7 | 3.3 | 0.8 | 4.1 |
| 55 | 4.7 | 8.1 | 5.8 | 2.3 | 8.1 |
| 42.5 | 6.4 | 10.3 | 5.6 | 2.7 | 8.3 |
| 31 | 6.2 | 9.3 | 2.8 | 3.1 | 5.9 |

poleward, to the extent of something like 10 to 20 percent of the required transport, a satisfactory energy balance seems marginal at this time.

## PREDICTION PROBLEM IN METEOROLOGY

In a certain sense, then, we have a good idea of the way in which the atmosphere solves some of its problems. But a general theory of the general circulation, which successfully describes all the observed characteristics, is still lacking. Because of our incomplete knowledge and understanding of the workings of the atmosphere, we cannot predict its future state beyond a few days in any specific sense or beyond a month or so in more general terms.

Since the general problem of the variation and distribution of the water resource is one of prediction, I shall now discuss the objective forecast problem in meteorology. By means of a slight simplification, we can state that there are two essentially distinct methods of attacking the objective forecast problem.

The atmosphere is a fluid and, therefore, obeys the mathematical relationships embodied in the Newtonian equations of fluid motion. It is possible, in theory, to write equations for the major variables of the atmosphere (the wind components in three directions, pressure, temperature, and specific humidity) ; to measure the three-dimensional distribution of these quantities over the earth; and then to solve the equations to derive the future state of the atmosphere. In practice this approach is enormously difficult. Such an approach, however, made possible by the technology of the electronic digital computer, is now being pursued with some vigor. This method, because it concentrates on the physics of the problem, is scientifically satisfying and has great potential. It can be called the *physical approach*.

Unfortunately, its value for long-range predictions at the present time is limited, perhaps severely, by the extreme complexity of the laws that govern atmospheric motions. Present techniques of prediction, using the physical approach, for example, do not take into account the interaction between the oceans and the atmosphere, or the latent heat of condensation of water. A few studies have been made on the importance of energy transfer by latent heat, but the lack of general mathematical tractability of the equations of evaporation and condensation in a turbulent atmosphere have resulted in the omission of water vapor and its phase changes from present models of the atmosphere. Other simplifications involving other physical properties and processes are made but are not mentioned here.

The second method of forecasting is termed the *statistical method*. In its simpler forms it is probably familiar to most workers in this field. The use of multiple-regression and multivariate analysis comes to mind first. Such methods are applicable if, for example, a forecast of next spring's runoff is desired when data on snowpack, precipitation, and ground-water moisture are available. Another form is quite familiar to the engineers: the designing of equipment for a flood whose probability of occurrence is once in 100 years makes use of a statistical forecast. The extensive analysis of precipitation data in depth-duration analyses is another example. Such statistical methods result in forecasts unlike those that result from the physical method. First of all, they are in terms of probability statements; for each forecast an uncertainty and a statement about how good the forecast will be in the long run are attached. Second, no knowledge of the physics of the problem is necessary. Statistical forecasting is done by means of mathematical rules that are developed by examination of the past behavior of the quantities to be forecast.

Forecasting of usual atmospheric parameters by statistical means has been tried in various ways. Long-range forecasts—that is, for a longer period than 1 week or so—have been included in these attempts. The success of these attempts so far has been at least no more encouraging than the results of the physical method.

Where do we stand, then, with regard to increasing our knowledge of the future behavior of the atmosphere and the water substance it carries? I believe that the physical approach will result in essentially nothing better than we have now until we understand more about energy transformation and transport and how to handle these quantities in the equations, and until we know more concerning the proper boundary conditions to apply. Such statements are glibly made; but the insights and techniques will not come easy.

In a more philosophical vein, let me propose a thought that deals with the question of how soon a strictly deterministic forecast system will be able to forecast with any usable degree of accuracy the necessary parameters to enable, say, a hydrologist who is interested in a small watershed of a few hundreds of square miles to predict runoff a year or more in advance. When sober meteorologists think about this example and the scientific knowledge necessary to bring it to reality, they can, in my opinion, conclude only that such forecasting ability is yet a number of years distant.

Considerable discussion has been carried on in recent years by meteorologists regarding the degree of predictability inherent in the atmosphere. At present there seems to be a "plateau of predictability" that, in terms of the objective accuracy of the forecasts, is moderately easy to attain but so far has been impossible to surpass. Relevant to the philosophical question just raised, it behooves us to examine closely this degree of predictability. If, as Lorenz (5) has pointed out, the nonlinear interactions in atmospheric behavior are capable of producing a large degree of unpredictability after sufficient lengths of time, we may never be able to cope completely with the prediction problem.

On the other hand, the statistical approach presently seems to hold some promise in the case of hydroclimatic problems—promise, that is, to provide usable information in a form perhaps not as satisfying as that coming from a deterministic system but nevertheless usable. Perhaps the quickest way to come to the point is to refer to specific examples.

In recent years two topics in statistics have received much attention. The first of these is called the *queuing theory*—the study of the statistics of dynamic processes when a store or a queue exists. Such a study has a wide variety of applications, including hydrology, since a reservoir is a store. Much work, principally by P. A. P. Moran in Australia (6), has shown promise of contributing to our knowledge of how to design and operate dam-reservoir systems.

The second topic is a time-series analysis. Renewed interest in this field—estimation and extraction of information for a process characterized by a parameter or parameters running along in time

—has already reached the meteorological profession. An analysis of a historical series of monthly or annual atmospheric or hydrologic parameters can indicate whether any statistical predictability is present or whether the parameters are essentially random in time. Analyses like this suggest, for example, that precipitation amounts totaled by season or by year are indistinguishable from random numbers (3, 4, 10). The same analysis, when it is applied to runoff or discharge data, indicated in particular instances that such data are not random; a certain amount of statistical predictability is present. In these cases simple physical reasoning suggests that storage and evapotranspirative effects are transforming the initially random precipitation into a series that has some significant persistence and, thus, an element of predictability.

Although the discouraging shortness of our historical records and our incomplete knowledge of the homogeneity of the records that we do have make such analyses uncertain to a large degree, an increment of knowledge is there, albeit small. We have very little knowledge of the important natural changes that affect the local hydroclimate—the secular or climatic changes. The behavior of the supply of water made available to us by the atmosphere in the next few decades—until wholesale desalinization occurs, say—will be critical. Our records, unfortunately, are too short for us to be able to determine with confidence the statistics necessary to place probability statements relative to future behavior on this time-scale. We almost certainly have not seen evidence in our historical hydrometeorological records of the variability that atmospheric processes can bring about.

Statistical techniques are important because even short past records of hydrometeorological variables can indicate at least an iota of information about their variability and expected future behavior, even if we do not succeed in understanding or uncovering the physical causes for their behavior. It seems to me that statistical methods can be used immediately in making statements about our future supply of water. These statements could be of value not only in technical fields, such as systems design and operation, but also in fields where socioeconomic factors are important. The statistical fact that in the United States an inverse relationship exists between the annual long-term average of precipitation and the variability of the individual year's totals is significant in an arid or semiarid region with respect to both reservoir design and future industrial and agricultural development, for example.

## SUMMARY

What knowledge, then, can the meteorologist presently contribute to mankind concerning his future supply of water from the atmosphere? He must say that the answer lies in solving the riddle of the general circulation of the atmosphere—why it behaves as it does. He knows that water and water vapor form an important part of the energy balance of the atmosphere and that certain types of circulation seem to be preferred in performing certain necessary transfers of energy and momentum. Past records of hydroclimatic variables, precipitation, and stream runoff suggest to him that many interacting, complex, physical mechanisms are at work producing precipitation and streamflow, because these records are dominated by a large random component.

He must also admit that he does not now comprehend certain basic physical processes that he must eventually understand in order to solve the problem of how the atmosphere operates. One example of this kind of problem is turbulence. The critically important process of evaporation cannot be understood until the meteorologist has a workable theory of turbulent transfer. The problem of climatic change is another. What are the causes of the secular changes in our climate? Although the meteorologist can discuss many theories, he must confess that which one of them is valid, if any single one, remains unknown.

And perhaps most important of all, he must acknowledge that he is really not certain to what degree the atmosphere is predictable. This is, after all, the ultimate question of our science. With description and understanding comes the ability to predict, according to the popular view of science, but long-range prediction of the atmosphere may not be possible by purely mechanistic means.

But the meteorologist also can make positive statements. By using climatological data he can designate the long-term supply of water in statistical terms. Because of increased skill in short-range forecasting, he can assist in warning of natural disasters or advise of the supply of water in the immediate future. New mathematical methods are being developed to utilize the information that he has at his disposal concerning the statistical distribution and time-dependent structure of hydrometeorological variables. He may be able, before many years, to say when and where the hydroclimate can be modified. Perhaps by modifying his environment in various ways, man can compensate for his inability to forecast the future supply of his water resource.

Pertinent to this last remark, I cannot refrain from pointing out that scientific bases for action are quite frequently ignored when the water resource is involved. The geophysicist who is interested in the problems presented by the supply and variability of the supply of water quickly becomes enmeshed in economic, sociological, and political considerations. My own opinion is that the geophysicist must strive to separate, insofar as possible, the scientific from the sociopolitical problems and solutions with which he deals; and, furthermore, he should make an effort to make the same distinctions in public whenever the opportunity arises. Water and climate present an environmental reference frame to man, which, for reasons of his own or by virtue of his ability to modify that environment, he may choose to ignore. So, the ultimate questions raised here are, I believe, more polarized toward mankind than toward his environment.

### REFERENCES

1. Benton, G. S., and M. A. Estoque, "Water vapor transfer over the North American continent," *J. Meteorol.* 11, 462 (1954).
2. Jacobs, W. C., "Large-scale aspects of energy transformation over the oceans," *Compendium Meteorol.* 1951, 105 (1951).
3. Julian, P., *A Study of the Statistical Predictability of Stream Runoff in the Upper Colorado River Basin,* pt. 2 of final report on past and probably future variations in streamflow in the Upper Colorado River (Univ. of Colorado, Boulder, 1960).
4. Landsberg, H., *et al.,* "Power spectrum analysis of climatological data for Woodstock College, Maryland," *Monthly Weather Rev.* 87, 283 (1959).

5. Lorenz, E. N., *Prospects for Statistical Weather Forecasting,* final report of statistical forecasting project (MIT Dept. of Meteorology, Cambridge, Mass., 1959).
6. Moran, P. A. P., *The Theory of Storage* (Wiley, New York, 1959).
7. Starr, V. P., and J. P. Peixoto, "On the global balance of water vapor and the hydrology of deserts," *Tellus* **10**, 188 (1958).
8. Starr, V. P., and R. White, "Balance requirements of the general circulation," *Geophys. Res. Papers (U.S.)* **35** (1954).
9. Wüst, G., "Verdunstung und niederschlag auf der Erde," *Z. Erdkunde* **37**, 35 (1922).
10. Yule, G. U., "On a method of studying time-series based on their internal correlations," *J. Roy. Statistical Soc.* **108**, 208 (1945).

# Capturing Additional Water for the Increase of Supplies

JOHN W. HARSHBARGER

*Department of Geology, University of Arizona, Tucson*

In recent years considerable effort, time, and money have been devoted to a search for methods and techniques that would increase our water supplies. Much has been written proclaiming the merits or detailing the inadequacies of a large number of water-production techniques and conservation practices. In this paper, it is not possible to review all the pertinent aspects of capturing additional water. The primary message contained here is that no new water has been created, nor is it likely to be created in the foreseeable future.

Actually, considerable confusion exists about whether we have real problems in water supply. Persons who like to delve into numbers are enchanted with the idea that large amounts of water are available in the United States and that the solution to any existing water problems is merely to construct pipelines. The major shortcoming of this solution is that people are not willing to pay the high delivery costs.

The poor distribution pattern of the available water (5) is further complicated by the problem of pollution and contamination of many of our major rivers and lakes by industrial and municipal wastes. This large subject is beyond the scope of this paper; but, unless measures are taken to conserve these copious water supplies, real water shortages will occur in our heavily populated areas.

With reference to the poor distribution of water, the U.S. Senate Select Committee on National Water Resources (9) clearly has stated that a major area in the United States that should begin immediate comprehensive development comprises the southwestern states. This area lies in the arid and semiarid zone and in recent years has been discovered by many persons. The remainder of this paper is devoted to this particular area. It attempts to discuss some of the pertinent features of the hydrologic system and to describe a few ways that man can use to develop additional water for the ever-increasing demand.

## HYDROLOGIC SYSTEM ANALYSIS

The usefulness and necessity of a "hydrologic system analysis" as a means to understanding the hydrologic regimen of a region warrants some discussion. Too many research studies and water-development projects are activated without the aid of such an understanding. Much has been written describing the hydrologic characteristics of the arid and semiarid zone in the southwestern United States; however, many of these facts are ignored, and research planners and project managers often are not aware of previous studies.

What do we mean by a "hydrologic system analysis"? In our highly complex society we find that our most essential needs— air and water—are being polluted by man's activities. Because air and water are transitory resources, they are difficult to control and develop. Water in the atmosphere moves in vapor form over the land; after it condenses into liquid and falls on the earth's surface, it enters one of several other systems. A large part of the water that reaches the land surface soon evaporates and returns into the vapor system. A much smaller amount runs off the ground surface as surface water. Part of the water sinks into the soil; however, much of the soil water is converted back to vapor. Some of the water in the soil-water system moves deeper into the earth and becomes a part of the ground-water system. Much is still to be learned about the movement of water through the unsaturated zone. At present it is very difficult to ascertain the exact amount of water that moves into the ground-water system from a particular storm.

Water in the ground-water system of an area generally travels in a direction similar to that of its surface water, and eventually both return to the ocean. Along its route, however, the ground water may move in and out of several systems. Ground water moves at rates ranging from less than 1 inch to several feet per day. Surface water moves in feet per second or per minute, depending on the nature of the channelway.

So far, I have been talking about systems under natural conditions. Diversion of water by man from these several systems modifies the natural regimen. In arid zones his dominant use converts the liquid water back to the vapor system in the growth of crops. Large amounts of water are lost by evaporation from man's surface reservoirs before he can use it for beneficial purposes. In some instances man uses water several times before it escapes his control into vapor. In power generation, recreation, domestic, and industrial uses perhaps, only small amounts are actually consumed. During such use, however, the water is often polluted or contaminated so that it is not suitable for further beneficial purposes.

It should be apparent why a system-analysis technique is essential to obtain the optimum utilization of water resources. The interplay of the several hydrologic systems soon becomes quite complex, owing to man's modification, and only by making careful analyses will he be able to manage this vast resource for his optimum useful benefit. The initial key to the capture of additional water in arid zones is a complete understanding of the interrelationships of the systems. The second step is the employment of scientific know-how in managing and manipulating the water.

We might take a brief look at the gross aspects of the hydrologic systems in the state of Arizona. It has been estimated that about 80 million acre feet of liquid water falls on the ground surface. Less than 10 percent runs off as streamflow, which constitutes the perennial water source available for capture. Much of this returns to the vapor system. A little more than 2 million acre feet of surface water is diverted for beneficial use. Accurate determination of the amount that constitutes ground-water recharge has not been made, but it is estimated to be less than 2 million acre feet. Thus it would appear that about 50 percent of the runoff is lost to vapor.

Large amounts of ground water are stored in the alluvial basin reservoirs, but additional water continually is being pumped from these aquifers. In recent years the annual pumpage has been slightly less than 5 million acre feet (2). Since most of this water is used for crop irrigation, part of it does return to the alluvial aquifer, but the magnitude of this return has not been determined. Because the water table continues to decline in heavily pumped areas, the pumping of ground water is primarily a depletion process. As available surface waters are fully utilized, expansion in water development will depend on ground-water resources.

The utilization of both surface water and ground water in the Salt River Valley area has resulted in a highly complex interrelationship among the several systems. Although an analysis has not been made in detail, the significant aspects and parameters are given by Skibitzke and colleagues (7). The report provides adequate evidence of the complex interrelationship between natural water movements and the water problems that man creates when he modifies the natural system.

## METHODS OF CAPTURING WATER

Space does not permit a complete review of the many methods and tentative results of research that has investigated ways to capture additional water. Several pertinent aspects, as related to the principles and concepts of the hydrologic system analysis, are given, however.

### Water transport

Transporting surface water from mountainous areas to desert lands and centers of population has proved successful in many parts of the western states. The transport of water from an undeveloped valley to an adjacent valley or community seeking larger water supplies has become common practice, and management has hopes of providing future supplies with conduit transport. Several limiting factors are the availability of water, legal rights, installation, and transport costs. Litigation and controversy about the ownership of water rights are commonplace today and probably will continue so for many years. On the other hand, compromises and satisfactory allocations have been achieved in certain areas.

A number of undeveloped aquifers in the Southwest have not been exploited but could yield ample supplies for industrial and municipal purposes. The possibility of transporting water pumped from such aquifers has not been explored to advantage. The city of Tucson has recognized that future growth depends on adequate water supplies and is making long-range plans to transport water from the San Pedro River Basin, which is separated from Tucson by the Rincon Mountains. The city hopes to supplement its supply with about 15 million gallons of water per day by pumping water over the intervening mountain range. The water is to be pumped from the alluvial sediments of water-bearing lands that were purchased by the city in 1960. Ground-water supplies are being transported from undeveloped areas into areas where the demand is great, such as Amarillo and Lubbock, Texas, in the High Plains area. In future years, as water becomes even more valuable, more of this type of water development will be necessary to support arid-land occupation.

### Water management of interrelated hydrologic systems

A number of the alluvial valleys in the southwestern states contain a geomorphic unit commonly referred to as the *inner valley*. The width of the inner valley can range from about ½ mile to several miles. Areas of this type have been carved by the stream channels and constitute the existing flood plain. Inner-valley alluvial material commonly consists of sand, silt, and gravel, mostly unconsolidated. Consequently, it is quite permeable; and, owing to the stream action during flood periods, the floors are constantly scoured, a condition that permits rapid infiltration from streamflow. The thickness of the alluvial material ranges from a few tens of feet to more than 200 feet. The length may be up to several hundred miles. We might call these geomorphic units "shoestring" aquifers, since they are quite long and their breadth is several times their thickness (Fig. 1). Streams in the Southwest's inner valleys replenish ground water, and ground water

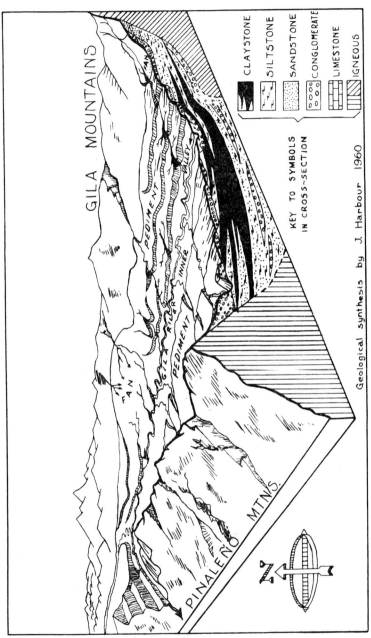

Fig. 1.  Geomorphological features and principal stratigraphic units in the Safford Basin.

feeds streams that have high rates of water loss to vapor. Proper management of these "shoestring" reservoirs offers a real opportunity to capture additional water supplies.

Inner valleys commonly occur in the tributaries near the bases of many mountain blocks. They, therefore, are in an ideal geographic position to receive maximum runoff from rugged topography and dense mountain rocks. Many inner valleys are already filled with water, much of which is lost to bank storage and eventually leaves the region as vapor. By the development of subsurface storage space and by proper manipulation of planned pumping programs and recharge techniques, much of this water could be salvaged and stored for peak demands.

C. V. Theis (8) clearly describes the interrelationship between recharge and discharge conditions of nonartesian aquifers and the optimum location of wells to obtain water that was otherwise lost to the system as rejected recharge and natural discharge. He gives an excellent description of the factors that must be taken into account for sound management and makes recommendations for maximum utilization of an aquifer. The guidelines have long been established and understood, but action to implement these tools has not been readily employed. In several places water management has taken place in an unplanned manner on a hit-or-miss basis.

Conover (1) reports the effects of pumping in the Rincon and Mesilla valleys of the Rio Grande, New Mexico. He states that "this unplanned though somewhat effective use of ground-water reservoir in conjunction with surface streams benefits those who have wells but works a hardship on those who have only surface water rights" (1, p. 5). He further states: "A fully managed ground-water and surface-water supply not only will maintain but will increase the firm supply because of (a) the savings in evaporation resulting from storing surface water underground, (b) the capture of floodwaters by surface reservoirs made vacant by storing water underground, (c) the reduction of evapotranspiration losses by phreatophytes, and (d) the recirculation of water by pumping" (1, p. 6).

## Artificial recharge

Much has been written about the use of artificial recharge procedures to replenish ground-water supplies and enhance their value for the conservation of water. Muckel (*4*), Resnick and Maddox (*6*), and many others have given excellent reviews of the many methods and applications. Artificial recharge has been employed by man in different parts of the world for more than 100 years. Meinzer (*3*) summarizes the general principles and methods, the relationship to geologic factors, and some of the problems encountered. The application of artificial recharge is equally useful in humid environments and arid zones. Usually it is combined with several ground- and surface-water management techniques.

Following is a brief review of the principles involved in the artificial recharge of water by a direct method, through wells. As is shown in Fig. 2, several pertinent factors relate to the method: (i) Water is introduced into a zone that has been dewatered by previous pumping of ground water. (ii) The aquifer

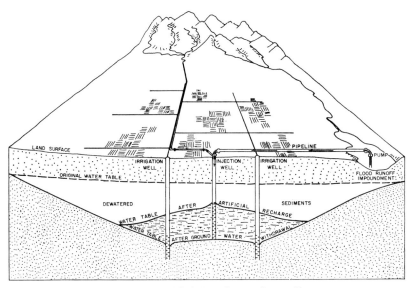

Fig. 2.   Artificial recharge by wells.

media are homogeneous mixtures of sand and gravel similar to those found in the inner-valley fill. (iii) Floodwater has been impounded in a surface reservoir for desilting purposes, and nearly clear water is pumped to the injection well, which is located near the center of the dewatered area. (iv) Water is also transported from the foothills area where it has been captured. Collecting the water in this area assures a lesser amount of silt and clay particles to clog the pore space in the aquifer. In many areas of the Southwest, winter rains and snow will yield a substantial amount of clear water runoff. There may be little or no demand for the water in the winter; however, it can be stored in a subsurface reservoir for peak demands in the spring and summer months.

Several advantages are attendant upon recharging water into dewatered zones: (i) Nearly all of the water can be recovered upon demand, because most of the wetting requirement or specific retention of the aquifer media is already satisfied. This may amount to as much as 50 percent of total volume introduced into bone-dry materials. (ii) Since water moves at very slow rates in the saturated zone (commonly less than 1 foot per day), and the recharge mound lies within the depression cone, the amount of water likely to leave the area is small. (iii) If highly saline water occurs in the lower part of the aquifer, the introduction of fresh water tends to prevent it from moving upward into the depression during the pumping season.

Many problems and disadvantages also are encountered with recharge wells. These include (i) clogging of the aquifer by silt and clay particles; (ii) base exchange of ions when recharge water comes in contact with certain clay minerals, which causes clogging conditions in the aquifer; (iii) bacterial clogging owing to bacterial growth in the aquifer; and (iv) entrapment of air and gases, which also tend to decrease the coefficient of permeability and effective porosity. In several projects where clogging has occurred, it has been necessary to remove part of the water by pumping to reestablish the original permeability of the aquifer.

Recharging through wells offers considerable promise as an integral managerial procedure for utilizing the "shoestring" aquifers to their ultimate efficiency. In many areas where dams are not feasible because of the lack of adequate space for storage of surface water, the subsurface reservoir offers considerable opportunity for storage. In several alluvial valleys, it has been estimated that as much as 50 percent of the streamflow, which is otherwise lost, could be captured by the use of artificial recharge through wells. This method has not been fully utilized for water capture in the southwestern states, yet the technique is a standard operation by many water districts and individuals in areas such as the High Plains region.

### Conversion of saline ground water

Much money and effort is being devoted to exploration of the exciting possibility of obtaining fresh water from the ocean by conversion methods. The cost of producing good quality water in this way is a major limiting factor at present. Experts inform us, however, that we can expect the cost to be as little as 25 to 30 cents per 1000 gallons within a few years, and I have no evidence to refute such an opinion. Even though the conversion cost for sea water may become as low as $100 per acre foot, however, only the areas near the seacoast will be able to receive benefit from such production of fresh water. The transport cost to interior areas, such as central Arizona, has been estimated to be possibly 3 to 4 times the conversion cost. Thus, it is not reasonable to expect ready availability of large supplies of converted sea water for use in the interior states.

On the other hand, the news of practical low-cost conversion procedures using solar energy provides hope for expecting the eventual feasibility of converting brackish waters in alluvial basin deposits. An interesting fact connected with some of these deep-seated saline waters is that they occur at temperatures of more than 100 degrees Fahrenheit, with some at more than 130 degrees Fahrenheit. These high-temperature waters favor reduced costs of conversion. Further, the total saline content of many of these waters is less than 5000 parts per million, and the disposition of accumulated salt would not present a severe problem.

The volume of brackish, high-temperature ground water that may be available is not known at present. Partial information on the total thickness of alluvial deposits and a crude knowledge of the deep-seated rock types lead me to believe that the brackish water in storage may exceed the fresh water in storage. Crude estimates of the total water in storage in Arizona's alluvial basins indicate more than 4 billion acre feet. The amount that can be feasibly withdrawn is unknown but might be in the order of 1 billion acre feet. A factor favoring the utilization of much of the saline water is that it occurs in the lower coarse-grained sediments under artesian pressure. In many areas water from hot saline aquifers, penetrated by deep wells, flows at the surface. The duration of such artesian flow may be short-lived, however, and undoubtedly pumping would have to be used for long-range future developments.

I believe that the conversion of saline ground water represents a potential source for future production in areas that have a shortage of water for industrial and municipal purposes. Resource studies will have to be coupled with economic studies to determine whether water for such purposes can be produced at a lower cost than that supplied by some of the other methods.

### Ground-water reservoir mechanics

One more possibility of increasing the amount of water that can be withdrawn from the ground-water reservoir, particularly from the fine-grained rocks, should be discussed briefly. Fine-grained rocks, such as fine sandstone and siltstone, are known to have very low coefficients of permeability, usually less than 10. Yet they have a large porosity, up to 40 percent in many cases. Under normal gravity draining conditions, only a small fraction of the water can be withdrawn through wells. The problem is one of increasing the permeability of the reservoir medium.

In many respects the petroleum industry has made considerable advances in the technology concerned with the behavior of fluid dynamics and the application of reservoir mechanics to increase yields. The application of hydrofracturing techniques certainly offers one method of increasing the rock permeability of fine-grained rock aquifers. The petroleum industry has successfully increased fluid production by using high pressures to create secondary fractures and subsequently filling the fractures with coarse sand.

It is well known that, when fine-grained rocks have been highly fractured and faulted by natural tectonic forces, the yield from water wells increases 10 to 20 times over the yield from areas that have not been disturbed. If adequate forces can be brought to bear artificially and inexpensively, the production of large quantities of ground water from the vast fine-grained aquifers offers exciting possibilities. The price that man is willing to pay for water in a specific area will largely dictate the practical application of reservoir mechanics for increasing water capture. Much remains to be done to perfect some of the methods discussed here; but, as competition for water increases, some of them certainly offer potential ways to increase water supplies.

## SUMMARY

All the possibilities and techniques for capturing additional water have not been covered here. Several views based on my experience as a ground-water hydrologist have been presented.

As is pointed out by Nace (5), because of the poor distribution of water on the earth, the ultimate development of an adequate water supply over the world will depend on the scientific management of the ground-water reservoir. Man can use the earth's natural features, coupled with a hydrologic system-analysis technique, to manipulate water for his optimum benefit.

Regional studies of major stream and "shoestring" aquifer systems are needed to unravel the complex interrelationship of water movements. It is encouraging to note the initiation of several recent river-basin projects, such as the one in the Humbolt Basin in Nevada by the state engineer and the integrated investigation program on the Lower Colorado River by the U.S. Geological Survey. Information gleaned from these and similar studies will greatly facilitate our eventual realization of the maximum water crop.

In addition to the much-needed technical information, many other factors, such as legal aspects, social conditions, and economic considerations, must be assessed. Experts in all these areas should sit down at a common table and integrate all the factors into a reasonable solution for optimum benefit to mankind. A related dilemma involves experts that stray from their fields of expertness; that is, the hydrologist tends to make decisions on economic, legal, and social conditions, and persons in these areas tend to act as hydrologic experts. If multiple-use water planning is to be achieved, each element must be kept in its proper perspective. There seems to be little question that land-management problems should include the management of the water crop. Water-bearing land may produce as its most important resource the potential for development of water.

## REFERENCES

1. Conover, C. S., "Ground-water resources—development and management," *U.S. Geol. Surv. Circ. 442* (1961).
2. Harshbarger, J. W., "Use of ground water in Arizona," in *Climate and Man in the Southwest* (Univ. of Arizona Press, Tucson, 1958), pp. 51-68.
3. Meinzer, O. E., "General principles of artificial recharge," *Bull. Econ. Geol.* 41, 191-201 (1946).
4. Muckel, D. C., "Replenishment of ground-water supplies by artificial means," *U.S. Dept. Agr. Tech. Bull. 1195* (1959).
5. Nace, R. L., "Water management, agriculture, and ground-water supplies," *U.S. Geol. Surv. Circ. 415* (1960).
6. Resnick, S., and G. M. Maddox, "Artificial ground-water recharge," *Watershed Symp., 5th* (Watershed Management Div., Arizona State Land Dept., Phoenix, 1961).
7. Skibitzke, H. E., *et al.,* "The history of development of water supply in an arid area in southwestern United States, Salt River Valley, Arizona," *Ground Water in Arid Zones, Intern. Assoc. Sci. Hydrol. (Athens)* 57, 2, 706-742 (1961).
8. Theis, C. V., "The source of water derived from wells," *Civil Eng. (N.Y.)* 10, 277-280 (1940).
9. U.S. Congress, Senate Select Committee on National Water Resources, *National Water Resources and Problems,* Comm. Print 3 (Washington, D.C., 1960).

# III   CRITERIA AND POLICIES

# Economic Priorities for Water Use in Arid Regions

NATHANIEL WOLLMAN

*Department of Economics, University of New Mexico, Albuquerque*

Projections of water use made by various federal agencies for the U.S. Senate Select Committee on National Water Resources were estimated without considering interindustry competition for scarce water supplies and without considering the effects of variations in the cost of water on amounts used. All projections took into account, however, two major sets of variables: (i) general growth of the economy and estimated indexes of production for the nation as a whole; (ii) technological changes in the use of water that could properly be anticipated on the basis of past experience and present knowledge (see Table I). Within this limited common framework, each industry projection was made by industry specialists. In making their projections, industry specialists had knowledge of horizontal competition—that is, the interregional distribution of production and sales of an industry—but had no way of anticipating prospective interindustry competition for factors, notably water. Since, for the arid West, the projected total of water use exceeds maximum available supply, it is apparent that the logic of the projections must give way to the implacable forces of reality.

This paper* starts with the projections made for 1980 and

* The author gratefully acknowledges the innumerable benefits derived from the opportunity to discuss this paper extensively with his colleague, William L. McDaniel, of the Department of Economics, University of New Mexico. He also acknowledges the critical comments on an earlier draft made by Karl Gertel, of the U.S. Department of Agriculture, Allen Kneese and John Krutilla, of Resources for the Future, and Kenneth Nobe, of the U.S. Public Health Service. Only the author, however, is responsible for any misconceived notions that still remain. Kay Camin, research associate, and Larry Seamons, research assistant, helped to prepare the data. Research for this paper has been supported by a grant from Resources for the Future, Inc., to the University of New Mexico.

explores the manner in which total demands can be reconciled with available supply. The arid region selected for study is the Upper Missouri River Basin. It was selected because, in addition to the prospective conflict between agriculture and urban uses, the region serves a major role in the propagation of waterfowl—ducks and geese—and therefore is likely to reveal conflict between agriculture and wildlife uses to a greater degree than elsewhere. I shall assume that neither (i) technological advances other than those already incorporated in the projections nor (ii) interbasin transfers of water will occur. Adjustments will therefore be limited to the reducing of projected aggregate requirements to the limits of available supply. Whether these adjustments are achieved by operation of the market as it is now constituted, by a market as it might be constituted in the future, or by administrative rule is a separate question that is not examined at this time.

## PROJECTIONS OF WATER USE

Construction of a scheme of priorities begins with study of the pattern of projected water requirements. This pattern, as has already been noted, is based on stipulated national aggregates for population, gross national product, and production of water-related products. The present regional distribution of activity, along with prospective changes based on knowledge of industrial location trends as guided by markets, raw materials, energy, water, and labor, were implicitly taken into account. Where data were available, possible product substitution, factor substitution, and interregional substitution were considered. The results, when they were converted to water requirements, are given in Table II.

Projections are for 1980 along the medium path of growth. Water "requirements" are equal to the following two items, shown separately in order to indicate their relative importance: (i) losses to the atmosphere resulting from evaporation and transpiration beyond those losses that would occur in nature undisturbed by man's activity, plus water incorporated in the product; (ii) stream-flows required to maintain "adequate" stream quality. *Adequate quality* was defined as water that has an oxygen content of 4 milligrams per liter after it has received the effluent of treated

Table I. Basic economic projections, United States and the Upper Missouri, 1980

| Item | U.S. | Upper Missouri |
|---|---|---|
| Population (millions) | 244 | 7.9 |
| Labor force (millions) | 102 | 3.3 |
| Civilian employment (millions) | 95 | 3.1 |
| GNP (billions of dollars) | 1060 | |
| *Indexes of production (1954 = 100)* | | |
| Agriculture: crops | 145 | |
| Mining—all minerals | 210 | |
| Manufacturing | | |
| Food | 194 | |
| Pulp and paper | 268 | |
| Chemicals | 510 | |
| Petroleum refining | 221 | |
| Iron and steel | 211 | |
| *Indexes of productivity (1954 = 100)* | | |
| Water per unit of agricultural output | | 150 |
| Water per unit of manufacturing output | | 66 |
| Labor per unit of agricultural output | | 220 |
| Labor per unit of manufacturing output | | 166 |

Sources: U.S. population and labor force, gross national product, and indexes of production were taken from Resources for the Future, Inc. (4). Indexes of productivity were computed from materials prepared for the U.S. Senate Select Committee on National Water Resources. See Wollman (6) for complete list of sources.

wastes. Kenneth Nobe, of the Colorado River Basin project, U.S. Public Health Service, points out that salinity is a more important and limiting quality characteristic in arid regions than is bio-chemical oxygen demand (BOD). If agriculture must offset salinity concentrations, the effect is to increase rate of water use per unit of product for agriculture beyond the figures used in this paper and, therefore, to increase further the slope of the water constraint (see later). It is seen that projected requirements exceed maximum supply by 5400 million gallons per day (MGD).

Table II indicates that major water uses are agriculture, swamp- and wetland habitat for ducks and geese, and dilution flows for municipal manufacturing wastes. Water requirements for domestic and commercial uses, thermal electric power, and mining are relatively small in physical amounts and represent a comparatively small component of money budgets. I assume that demands for these uses are inelastic. Another use of water is the land-treatment program designed to reduce erosion and conserve soil moisture. I assume that water for this program will be made available as a matter of course. Sport-fishing habitat would constitute an independent requirement were it not for the possibility of using regulatory storage for this purpose. In the Upper Missouri, projected storage capacity will cover projected sport-fishing requirements, after adjustment for depth restrictions. Navigation and hydroelectric-power requirements are treated as passive residuals. This leaves for analysis the requirements for agriculture, manufacturing, and swamps and wetlands.

### OPTIMIZING GUIDES

Since other papers in this symposium are devoted to the question of theoretical criteria, I have limited my treatment of this aspect to a statement of assumptions. (i) Within a given region, for example, the Upper Missouri, we are faced with a continuous growth in the supply of capital and labor but a fixed supply of water. (ii) The entrepreneur's desire to maximize profits will lead to marginal adjustments such that the marginal revenue product (MRP) of each factor is equated to its marginal cost (MC). Alternatively, in the face of a capital restriction, the ratio $MRP/MC$ will be the same for all factors. If a restriction applies to one factor but not to all, use of the restricted factor will take place up to the limit of the restriction, provided that

$$MRP \geq MC$$

(iii) Regional welfare is advanced when, if water is the limiting factor, a transfer of water from one use to another raises regional gross social product net of water costs. This is based on the assumption that an increase in gross regional product is a measure of increased utilization of existing regional resources, but that increased expenditure on water supply, especially since most of such expenditure is for the abatement of pollution, cannot be equated with an increase in welfare. Wherever possible, account

Table II. Water requirements indicated by projections, the Upper Missouri, 1980 medium

| Requirement | Amount (MGD) | Total (MGD) |
|---|---|---|
| Losses | | |
| Agriculture | 15,000 | |
| Mining | 135 | |
| Power | 26 | |
| Manufacturing | 93 | |
| Municipal | 107 | |
| Land treatment and structures | 660 | |
| Swamps and wetlands | 13,150 | |
| All losses (rounded) | | 29,200 |
| Waste dilution[a] | | |
| Municipal | 3,200 | |
| Manufacturing | 900 | |
| Total dilution (rounded) | | 4,100 |
| Total requirements | | 33,300 |
| Maximum regulated flow after reservoir losses | | 27,900 |

[a] To yield 4 mg/l of dissolved oxygen after 95-percent treatment.
Source: Wollman (6).

is to be taken of any disparity between private and social product that may be concealed in market prices.

Entrepreneurial marginal adjustments designed to increase profits will coincide with adjustments that raise gross regional product when certain conditions are met, namely, when the marginal cost per unit of factor is the same for all users. By implication, the marginal revenue product of the factor will also be the same for all users at the point of maximum profit.

Assume that one resource, water, can be transferred from product $A$ to product $B$, or vice versa, keeping all other factors constant. Profit is maximized (or costs minimized) with respect to use of water in production of $A$ when water is used in such quantity that

$$MRP^A = MC^A$$

Similarly for products $B$, $C$, and so forth. If the supply of $W$ is limited but its price does not rise, or if the supply of capital is limited so that the firm's use of $W$ is restricted and the price of $W$ does not fall, or if some form of nonmarket rationing is applied, an alternative profit maximizing condition is

$$\frac{MRP^A}{MC^A} = \frac{MRP^B}{MC^B} \text{, and so forth} \qquad (1)$$

Maximum value added (that is, regional gross product) under given conditions of resource availability requires that

$$MRP^A = MRP^B \text{, and so forth} \qquad (2)$$

Maximum value added net of water costs, where water costs result from a dedication of resources that could be used for other things, is equal to

$$MRP^A - MC^A = MRP^B - MC^B \qquad (3)$$

Where capital is available in unlimited quantities at a given interest rate $i$, the condition for maximum net profit, net of water cost would be given by

$$\frac{MRP^A - MC^A}{MC^A} = i \qquad (4)$$

If a single interest rate prevails in the market, then

$$\frac{MRP^A - MC^A}{MC^A} = \frac{MRP^B - MC^B}{MC^B} \qquad (5)$$

Or if capital is limited, maximum profit requires that

$$\frac{\dfrac{MRP^A - MC^A}{MC^A}}{i} = \frac{\dfrac{MRP^B - MC^B}{MC^B}}{i} \qquad (5a)$$

Thus the two conditions that must be met simultaneously if maximum profits and maximum value added are to be realized are given by Eqs. 3 and 5. These conditions are met when

$$MC^A = MC^B$$

which implies that

$$MRP^A = MRP^B$$

If, therefore, the marginal costs of water are the same for all users, any movement designed to increase profits via marginal adjustments will also increase regional gross product. If marginal costs of water are different for different users, no simple relationship between behavior that maximizes profits and behavior that maximizes regional gross product can be formulated.

As the region's economy grows, the supply of labor and capital will grow but the supply of water will remain unchanged. The remainder of this paper deals with the constraints on output imposed by labor and water supplies, based on the technical coefficients and prices implicit in projections made for 1980. Data are not yet available to make it possible to incorporate capital constraints into the analysis.

## A SIMPLE PROGRAMMING ANALYSIS

Studies for the Senate Select Committee yield data that make possible a simple programming analysis designed to show the feasible limits of production as fixed by two constraints, labor and water (2).* Information about water requirements (losses plus waste dilution) per dollar's worth of value added, based on the 1980 productivity relationships, when coupled with estimated supplies of water available to manufacturing and agriculture taken together, make it possible to show how much manufacturing activity the available supply of water could support if it were all allocated to manufacturing, or how much farm production could be supported if the allocation were wholly to agriculture. This information can be plotted on a coordinate diagram in which one axis represents manufacturing and the other agriculture. Output is measured as "value added"—that is, as the market value of production less purchases from other businesses. If it is assumed that prices are kept constant, the measure of value added is tantamount to a measure of output in physical terms, provided that the product mix is kept unchanged over the entire range of allocation.

On the basis of the estimated labor supply available to manufacturing and agriculture, coupled with information on the value added as produced per laborer, the maximum outputs of manu-

---

* Data for a capital constraint are not yet available.

facturing and agriculture allowed by the available labor supply can be shown on the same diagram. In Figs. 1–4, the labor points (and water points) on each axis are connected by a straight line that indicates the combination of values added produced in agriculture and manufacturing for all conceivable allocations of labor (and water) between the two activities. The lines so drawn, referred to as *constraints,* indicate the boundaries of production as determined by each input taken separately as well as together. For example, in Fig. 1 the line marked "Labor" shows all conceivable combinations of output between manufacturing and agriculture based on the allocation of labor. If all labor were allocated to manufacturing, value added in manufacturing would be $12,750 million, and value added in agriculture would be zero. If all labor were allocated to agriculture, value added in agriculture would be about $5000 million, and value added in manufacturing would be zero. If half of the available labor supply were allocated to manufacturing and half to agriculture, values added would be $6375 million and $2500 million in manufacturing and agriculture, respectively.

Any point to the right of $B$ on the labor constraint in Fig. 1 indicates an output incapable of being produced because of lack of water. Any point above $B$ on the water constraint indicates an output incapable of being produced because of lack of labor. At point $A$ all labor is being utilized in manufacturing but only a part of the water is being used. At point $C,$ all water is being utilized but only a part of the labor supply. Any point on the line segments $AB$ and $BC$ indicates a combination of values added that is capable of being produced; but only at point $B$ are the water supply and labor supply both being fully utilized. The kinked line $ABC$ indicates the boundary of feasible production expressed in units of value added. Any point within the region $OABC$ is feasible; any point outside is not feasible. If data were available for a capital constraint, such a line might show a reduction in the feasible boundary by intersecting either line segment $AB$ or line segment $BC$. It is probable that such a constraint does intersect the $BC$ segment and, thereby, reduces the maximum gross product that can be produced by manufacturing and agriculture when all three constraints are taken into consideration.

## PROJECTIONS FOR 1980 FOR THE UPPER MISSOURI

Table III shows how the labor and water constraints were derived from estimates of value added in manufacturing, value of irrigated farm production, labor requirements, and water requirements drawn from data prepared for the Senate Select Committee.*

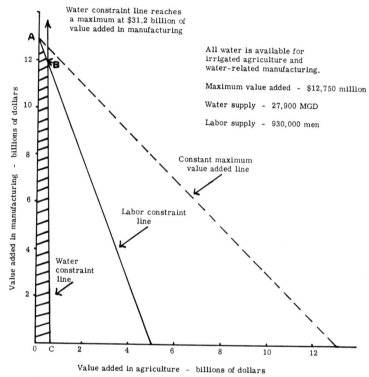

Fig. 1. Upper Missouri, 1980 medium projection. Labor and water constraints: irrigated agriculture and water-related manufacturing.

The labor force was estimated as 41.6 percent of the 1980 population; civilian employment was estimated as 38.8 percent of population. Both of these figures were estimated percentages for the nation as a whole in 1980 and were assumed to be applicable to the western regions (4). Although the 1960 percentages for

---

* See especially Committee Prints 8, 12, and 32.

Table III. Computations of water and labor constraints on the basis of data derived from projections for the Upper Missouri, 1980

| | |
|---|---|
| Estimated civilian employment (number employed) | 3,100,000 |
| Maximum labor supply available to water-related manufacturing and irrigated agriculture (equal to 30 percent of civilian employment) (number of people) | 930,000 |
| Projected market value of irrigated agricultural product, 1980 | $442,000,000 |
| Estimated value added by irrigated agricultural product, at 0.67 of market value, 1980 | $295,000,000 |
| Estimated value added of water-related manufacturing, 1980 | $1,100,000,000 |
| Estimated agricultural employment for projected value added (number) | 55,000 |
| Estimated manufacturing employment for projected value added (number) | 80,000 |
| Estimated water losses for projected agricultural value added (MGD) | 15,000 |
| Estimated water losses plus waste dilution for projected manufacturing value added (MGD) | 1,000 |
| Number of times projected agricultural value added would be increased: | |
| If all labor were allocated to agriculture | 16.9 |
| If all water were allocated to agriculture | 1.9 |
| Number of times projected manufacturing value added would be increased: | |
| If all labor were allocated to manufacturing | 11.6 |
| If all water were allocated to manufacturing | 28.7 |

western water-resource regions have not yet been computed, it is likely that they are below the national level.

Total labor supply available to manufacturing and agriculture taken together in the Upper Missouri was estimated to be 30 percent of civilian employment. This compares with a 1980 estimate for the nation as a whole of about 28 percent. In 1950, agricultural and manufacturing employment in the Upper Missouri accounted for 36 percent of total employment; in the United States, 37 percent. The relative reduction in this percentage for the Upper Missouri is, therefore, assumed to be less than is to be experienced in the nation as a whole.

Total water supply available to manufacturing and agriculture was taken to be the average annual runoff after adjustment for reservoir losses, both with and without an allocation to other uses.

In computing water requirements for waste dilution, it was assumed that treatment removed 95 percent of the biochemical oxygen demand contained in the waste. Higher levels of treatment are theoretically possible but would not reduce the required waste dilution flows.*

The position of the intercepts on the vertical and horizontal axes (Figs. 1–4) assumes retention of the 1980 price ratios, technology, and industrial structure. As McDaniel† shows in the next few paragraphs, the points on the axes can be connected by straight lines, showing the feasible boundaries of production, if the production function is of a Cobb-Douglas form and if it is assumed that the prices for water and land remain unchanged, regardless of the allocation between manufacturing and agriculture or between agriculture and wetland habitat.

"Assume that both manufacturing and agricultural outputs are determined by the following Cobb-Douglas production functions involving two factors, labor and water:

---

* As the level of treatment rises, organic matter is converted into inorganic nitrogen and phosphorus. These fertilize the water and induce algal blooms which require dilution water. The higher the level of BOD treatment is, the more are algal blooms stimulated. Accordingly, 100-percent treatment to remove BOD would not reduce dilution requirements to zero (3).

† William L. Daniel, Department of Economics, University of New Mexico, for the benefit of the author.

$$\text{Agricultural output} = O_A = aL^\alpha W^{1-\alpha}$$

$$\text{Manufacturing output} = O_M = bL^\beta W^{1-\beta}$$

If the prices of labor and water are fixed, the expansion path in each industry is a straight line through the origin.† As a consequence, labor and water will be combined in fixed proportions in both industries. The ratio of labor to water is denoted by $R_A$ for agriculture and $R_M$ for manufacturing; the maximum amount of water available is denoted by $W^*$.

"Let all of the water $W^*$ be assigned to agriculture, then $R_A W^*$ of agricultural labor is required. The corresponding production $O_A^*$ is found by substituting these values in the production function; that is

$$O_A^* = a(R_A W^*)^\alpha (W^*)^{1-\alpha} = a(R_A)^\alpha W^*$$

The horizontal intercept of the water constraint line, therefore, is $a(R_A)^\alpha W^*$, since no water is available for manufacturing. Similarly, when $W^*$ is assigned to manufacturing, the resulting output is $O_M^* = b(R_M)^\beta W^*$. The vertical intercept of the water constraint becomes $b(R_M)^\beta W^*$.

"The water constraint line connecting these two intercepts has a slope of

$$-\frac{O_M^*}{O_A^*} \qquad \text{or} \qquad -\frac{b(R_M)^\beta}{a(R_A)^\alpha}$$

By the slope-intercept formula, the equation of the water constraint line becomes

$$O_M = b(R_M)^\beta W^* - \frac{b(R_M)^\beta}{a(R_A)^\alpha} O_A$$

"We now show that any other allocation of water results in values of $O_A$ and $O_M$ that also lie on the water constraint line; that is, they satisfy the foregoing equation. Let some fraction $k$ of the available water $kW^*$ go to agriculture and $(1-k)W^*$ go to manufacturing. The labor required is $R_A kW^*$ for agriculture and $R_B(1-k)W^*$ for manufacturing. The corresponding values of production are

$$O_A^{k*} = a(R_{AkW*})^\alpha (kW^*)^{1-\alpha} = a(R_A)^\alpha kW^*$$

$$O_M^{(1-k)W^*} = b[R_M(1-k)W^*]^\beta [(1-k)W^*]^{1-\beta} = b(R_M)^\beta (1-k)W^*$$

---

† See J. M. Henderson and R. E. Quandt, *Microeconomic Theory: A Mathematical Approach* (McGraw-Hill, New York, 1958), pp. 63-64.

The following substitution shows that these values satisfy the equation of the water constraint line.

$$O_M = b(R_M)^\beta W^* - \frac{b(R_M)^\beta}{a(R_A)^\alpha} O_A$$

$$b(R_M)^\beta(1 - k)W^* = b(R_M)^\beta W^* - \frac{b(R_M)^\beta}{a(R_A)^\alpha} a(R_A)^\alpha k W^* =$$

$$b(R_M)^\beta W^* - b(R_M)^\beta k W^* = b(R_M)^\beta(1 - k)W^*$$

Every allocation of water, therefore, results in values of output which lie on the water constraint line if changes in production take place along the indicated expansion paths and factor prices are fixed."

The "optimum use" of water demands a criterion of optimality. For the moment I shall assume that resource use is at its optimum when aggregate regional product, measured in dollars, is maximized within the limits of available resources. The combination of water and labor use that yields the largest total value added in manufacturing and agriculture is, then, the optimum pattern. This combination is quickly revealed by constructing a "constant value-added line" tangent to the boundary of production. If the scales of the horizontal and vertical axes are equal, such a line slopes at 45 degrees downward to the right. Any point on this line represents a combination of manufacturing and agriculture that will yield a given gross regional product. The line tangent to the boundary, *ABC,* or the line that touches a corner point, represents the most value added that can be generated. Figure 1 shows that maximum value added is produced at point *A*. At this point all of the labor and 41 percent of the water would go to manufacturing. The remainder of the water would automatically go to activities that were excluded from the analysis, for example, swamps and wetlands.

Figure 2 shows what happens when water requirements for projected nonagricultural uses other than manufacturing, as well as water requirements for soil and moisture conservation programs, are met. The only use of water not accounted for in this figure is that for swamps and wetlands. In Fig. 2 the water requirements given in Table II for mining, power, and municipal losses, municipal waste dilution, and losses resulting from land treatment and structures have been subtracted from the total supply of water available to the region. What remains is the supply of water available to manufacturing and agriculture. As is shown in Fig. 2, water supply for manufacturing and agriculture is reduced from 27,900 million gallons per day (Fig. 1) to 23,800

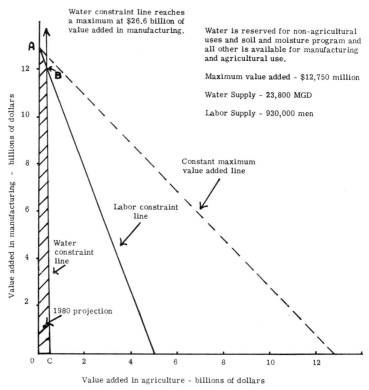

Fig. 2. Upper Missouri, 1980 medium projection. Water reserved for nonagricultural uses other than manufacturing and soil and moisture programs. Labor and water constraints: irrigated agriculture and water-related manufacturing.

million gallons per day. The intercepts of the water constraint are moved inward to indicate a proportional reduction in the region's output of agriculture and manufacturing value added. No change is made in the labor constraint, since it was initially drawn to show only the labor supply available to agriculture and manufacturing.

It is possible to compare projections made for the Senate Select Committee with boundary conditions as they are given in Fig. 2. As long as projected requirements for swamps and wetlands are ignored, there is no difficulty in meeting agricultural and manufacturing water needs along with all other projected requirements. This is indicated by the position of the 1980 projection within the boundary marked by *OABC*. In Fig. 3, however, when water is reserved for swamps and wetlands, the 1980 projection for agriculture and manufacturing cannot be met.

The *potential* loss in regional gross product that would result from meeting projected water requirements for wildlife habitat is indicated by a comparison of the maximum value-added lines in Figs. 2 and 3 and adjustment for the additional gross product yielded by hunting. The net result is no loss at all, but rather a gain equal to the addition of the full value yielded by hunting. This results because the labor supply is fully absorbed by manufacturing, and therefore there is no irrigated agriculture.

Movement along either constraint line implies a proportional transfer of all other complementary resources. In other words, movement along a boundary represents movement along a scale line. Movement along the water constraint line is considered to be movement accompanied by proportional changes in capital and labor force. This means that there is no way in which to "bend" the constraints in order to indicate diminishing marginal rates of substitution between agriculture and manufacturing, unless changes in relative prices are introduced. At any given moment, however, diminishing marginal rates of transformation might be encountered if a product transformation curve included all relevant circumstances. The phenomenon of a diminishing marginal rate of transformation is not a "constraint" attached to water. Rather, it arises from other characteristics of the region—for example, sparsity of population, distances from markets, and any other characteristic that constitutes a departure from the condition that prices (net to the region) are independent of the region's output.

It should also be noted that behavior patterns of the water and labor constraints are likely to vary over time with respect to each other. With increasing population, power production, and municipal water and waste-dilution requirements, the amount of water available for manufacturing, agriculture, and wildlife will diminish. Thus the water constraint will gradually move toward the origin as the labor constraint moves away from the origin. However, one can expect that movement of the water constraint will be slower than movement of the labor constraint.

The position of the 1980 projection in relation to the water and labor constraints implies that one or more other limiting factors are unaccounted for in Figs. 1, 2, and 3. If capital is the only limitation omitted, then it can be assumed that the capital constraint runs through the position marked by the 1980 projection. It is possible, however, that institutional factors, such as the acquisition and exercise of water rights, will fix the distribution of water and, hence, of production without reference to a region's maximum economic potential. Should this be the case at present and be perpetuated in extrapolations made for the future, one can expect a result such as is indicated in Fig. 2. The possibility of this occurring for a basin in California is indicated by Gaffney (1).

By converting the 1980 projections shown in Fig. 2 to equivalent water requirements, it is seen that an unused water balance of 7800 million gallons per day exists if 1980 projected manufacturing and agricultural outputs are realized. This water can be allocated to swamps and wetlands or can be applied to manufacturing and agriculture by moving out to the feasible boundary or to some intermediate position within the feasible area. Gross product is maximized, of course, by moving to $A$. Even at point $A$, however, there will be unused water.

Figure 4 shows the effect on regional gross product of a shift of water between agriculture and wildlife habitat (swamps and wetlands) on the basis of 1960 prices, after provision has been made for the water requirements of all other projected uses, as is shown in Table II. In the measurement of value added from swamps and wetlands, data on expenditures of hunters* were converted to value added by using ratios developed for sport fishing, camping, and picnicking in the Rio Grande Basin. Essentially this involved

---

* U.S. Senate Select Committee on National Water Resources, Committee Print 18.

measurement of value added as a fraction of gross expenditures in appropriate trade and service sales plus license fees.

Using the relationships shown in Fig. 4, if the unused water in Fig. 2 were allocated to wildlife habitat, value added would increase by about $18 million, compared with an increase of $11 billion if it were allocated to agriculture and manufacturing at point *B*. An allocation to swamps and wetlands in excess of 7800 million gallons per day would result in unused labor, if assumed labor force conditions prevailed. (A labor shortage, on the other hand, might result in an automatic residual quantity of water available for swamps and wetlands.) The effect on value added of

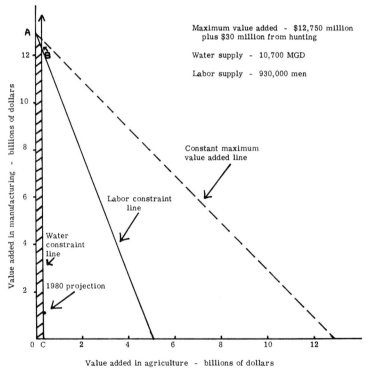

Fig. 3. Upper Missouri, 1980 medium projection. Water reserved for nonagricultural uses, soil and moisture programs, and swamps and wetlands; all other water available for manufacturing and agriculture. Labor and water constraints: irrigated agriculture and water-related manufacturing.

various allocations of water between agriculture and swamps and wetlands is shown in Fig. 4. Since value added by hunting originates primarily in service industries, labor is not likely to be a constraint. Even if a labor constraint became effective, an allocation of water to swamps and wetlands would not be warranted at the assumed ratios of labor productivity in the two activities. A slight change in labor productivity, however, would induce a shift in the use of water. (See the line marked $L\,(3)$ in Fig. 4. Line $L\,(2)$ is a reference line of the same slope as the labor constraint.)

A number of possible circumstances might inhibit an allocation of water corresponding to the corner points at $A$ or $B$ in Fig. 2: (i) Marginal costs of water rise to prohibitive heights because of the pattern of water use that is adopted; (ii) price and productivity relationships assumed to prevail in the future are not realized; (iii) market prices are rejected, at least in part, as a guide for public policy; (iv) another constraint—for example, capital—is operative. Any one or all of these circumstances would produce an unused balance of water, which is almost the same as inducing an allocation to wildlife habitat. (Whether the two effects are identical would depend on where the unused balance materialized.)

Effect of water costs on the allocation of water can be inferred from Ruttan (5). Based on present practices regarding the charges imposed on irrigators, marginal revenue product and marginal cost of water would be brought into equality with 3 times as much irrigated acreage as is shown in the 1980 projection. At prevailing prices and technology, the water supply would prohibit such expansion, even if no allocation were made to wildlife habitat. If irrigators were to pay full marginal costs, however, acreage and water use would be about 20 percent less than was projected.

If costs of storage and treatment are deducted from the feasible boundary, leaving value added net of storage costs, the relative slopes of the constraints are not affected enough to indicate any departure from the pattern of water use given in Fig. 2. This is true even though treatment costs of about $500 million are deducted wholly from the productivity of labor in manufacturing. Some 90 percent of projected costs of water will be for pollution abatement. Since such costs will be incurred in other regions as well, it is likely that water costs per se will have a relatively small effect on the location of manufacturing activities and on the pattern of water use.

Regarding the possible change in price ratios, as well as the possibility that prices are rejected as guides to policies, several points can be noted. First, recreational uses of water are probably inadequately "valued" in relation to other uses by virtue of the poorly articulated market for outdoor recreation. Many have pointed out with perfect justification that the "value" of a national park can never be adequately represented by sales of food and shelter to park visitors. Even if park visit fees and capital,

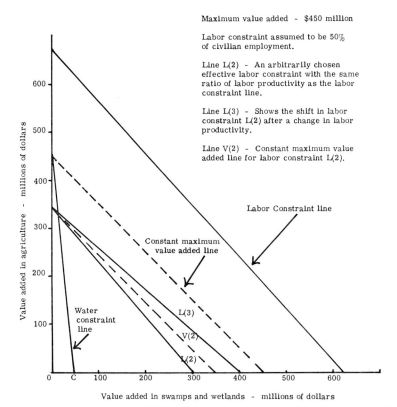

Fig. 4.  Upper Missouri, 1980 medium projection. Water reserved for all uses except irrigated agriculture and swamps and wetlands. Labor and water constraints: irrigated agriculture and swamps and wetlands.

operation, and maintenance costs were designed to maximize park net revenues, the money value of the fee would not necessarily reflect marginal social benefit if some of the benefits were external to the individual visitor—as may well be the case. A change in relative market valuations could easily be anticipated if pricing policies were adopted that were designed to accord more closely with intuitively perceived "social valuations." For example, fishing and hunting licenses might be priced differently or be given imputed valuations that differ from the actual license fees. It would require, however, a large relative change in value added per unit of water to induce transfer of water from agriculture to duck hunting (see Fig. 4). We might, on the other hand, explicitly reject market pricing as a guide for allocating water to recreational uses and adopt a national policy affirming that the Upper Missouri flyway is a unique asset not to be found elsewhere and, therefore, to be protected as a national monument, whereas manufacturing and agriculture can readily be carried on in other regions. On these grounds, water could be allocated to ducks and geese in spite of the fact that the regional gross product would then have a lower value than would be yielded by a different pattern of water use.

Apart from what might be revealed when a capital constraint is computed, the ratios of productivity that are implicit in the 1980 projections indicate that the region's gross product is maximized when irrigated agriculture is reduced to zero. This occurs, not because of the relative productivity of *water* in agriculture vis-a-vis manufacturing, but because of the relative productivity of *labor* in agriculture vis-a-vis manufacturing. The position and shape of the constraints lead to the conclusion that the way in which water is likely to be used will be primarily a function of the productivity of labor in alternative occupations within the region, rather than a function of the productivity of water. If value added per unit of labor in agriculture would rise by a factor of 3, in relation to manufacturing, the allocation of water that would maximize regional gross product would move from the manufacturing axis to the intersection of the water and labor constraints. In the case of agriculture versus swamps and wetlands, however, the shift has to occur in the relative productivity

of water in order to support an allocation to swamps and wetlands without reducing regional gross product. The relative shift
in productivity of water for wildlife habitat has to be quite large—
in the neighborhood of 10 times its present productivity in relation to agriculture.

A final word on water-pricing policy. As long as a capital limitation or the relative productivities of labor determine the pattern
of water use, pricing policies with respect to water are not important determinants of the pattern of its use, except as between
recreation (wildlife habitat) and agriculture. With respect to
competition between these two uses, markets are imperfect in
several senses. Water-pricing policies, therefore, may well add
to "distortions" of allocation, if any, that may already exist in
relation to maximum regional or national social net product.

When water is clearly a limiting factor, entrepreneurial profit-
maximizing decisions will have to coincide with regional net-
product-maximizing decisions in order to eliminate (or at least
minimize) underemployment of other regional resources (assuming that product measures derived from the marketplace are
adjusted for discrepancies between private and social benefits).
This coincidence is automatically assured when the marginal
cost of water to all users is the same. Such a policy would not
prohibit price discrimination among users with respect to infra-
marginal units of water under certain conditions—for example,
where there is a single large class of water users whose inactivity
as a result of high water costs would result in unused water.

## SUMMARY

Within the arid regions of the West projected economic activities, based on the assumption that the West's share of the nation's
population and production continues to follow the trend of the
past few decades, will require more water than is available, even
after accounting for anticipated economies in water use. As a consequence, some revision in the pattern of water use in relation
to the projected pattern may be desirable. A purely economic
criterion is limited in its applicability, because some goods and
services are not "adequately" measured by market prices. The in-

adequacy of market valuations is especially significant for esthetic, psychological, cultural, conservational, and recreational elements of the economy. Nonetheless, economic guidelines do exist. One criterion is allocation of resources among alternative uses in order to maximize the value of regional product. (Problems created by interdependency between prices and output are, in this paper, recognized but ignored.) The question, "How should water be used?" cannot, however, be answered wholly in terms of the relative "productivity" of water. If this were the case, all water would go to urban, manufacturing uses. Two other considerations will affect the pattern of water use: (i) the supply of other factors of production, notably labor and capital; (ii) the relative productivity of these other factors in the activities that use water. Although water is a limiting factor, it is not the only limiting factor at any given moment, even in a desert. Depending on the supply of complementary factors and their respective marginal productivities, certain low-valued "wild" uses—for example, swamp and wetland habitat—may be satisfied, even if value added per unit of water is relatively low.

## REFERENCES

1.  Gaffney, M., "Diseconomies inherent in western water laws: a California case study," paper for Western Agricultural Economics Research Council, Tucson, Ariz., 23 Jan. 1961.
2.  Isard, W., *Methods of Regional Analysis* (Wiley, New York, 1960), chap. 10 especially.
3.  Reid, G., *Water Requirements for Pollution Abatement,* Comm. Print 29 (U.S. Congress, Senate Select Committee on National Water Resources, Washington, D.C., 1960).
4.  Resources for the Future, *Resources in America's Future,* in preparation.
5.  Ruttan, V. W., "Projections of irrigated acreage and water requirements for western water resource regions," in *Western Resources Papers 1960,* H. L. Amoss, Ed. (Univ. of Colorado Press, Boulder, 1961).
6.  Wollman, N., *Water Supply and Demand,* Comm. Print 32 (U.S. Congress, Senate Select Committee on National Water Resources, Washington, D.C., 1961).

# Management Associated with
# Complex Use of Wildlands

A. L. McComb

*Department of Watershed Management, University of Arizona, Tucson*

Nontillable wildlands in the West are valuable for the water, wood, livestock, recreation, and wildlife that they produce. When several of these products come simultaneously from a given piece of land and the products compete for the basic elements that control their individual yields, a form of multiple use that can be termed *complex use* prevails. Successful complex-use management, in contrast to single-use, requires a higher level of knowledge of soil, water, plants, animals, and all their various interactions.

It is pertinent to ask why there is presently so much interest in complex-use management. Several reasons, economic and political, can be cited. In a society with a high ratio of natural resources to population, complex-use management is given little consideration, because the supply of land and its associated resources is adequate, and each parcel of land can be devoted to a single use. If multiple use is practiced under such conditions, it is done so primarily because the wildland plant and animal communities represent a natural complex best suited for the low-input management that is economically feasible. However, when resources become scarce and take on value, intensive complex-use management becomes important (7). This is because the total returns from such management are probably greater than from single use. From a political viewpoint, multiple-product management may be a good way to satisfy the competing desires of diverse groups of people.

The objective of complex-use management is largely to maximize, over the long run, the values inherent in the products and services associated with the land. Man, consciously or unconsciously, is humanistically oriented and thinks of his environment in terms of how it affects himself. His evaluation of these basic products of the land changes with time as his economic and social environment changes. Thus, wildland management for multiple products is best viewed against a background that reflects (i) the rapidly increasing human populations, (ii) the decreasing percapita land and natural resource base (Table I), and (iii) changes in the pattern of living precipitated by a rapidly developing technology and an increase in living standards.

In the United States, complex use has been thought of mainly in connection with forested and other wildlands. In southern Europe it occurs on agricultural lands. In Italy, for example, hybrid poplars and trees such as olive and citrus are often grown in intimate association with grapes, cereals, legumes, and other annual crops.

## CONCEPTS USEFUL IN MANAGEMENT FOR
## MULTIPLE PRODUCTS

In considering complex-use management of wildlands, it is useful to think of the land—that is, the soil and water—and the plant and animal communities as a complex organism producing a number of products and services. This organism may be referred to as the *ecosystem* (3). The energy that drives it comes chiefly from the sun, which heats the earth, modifies and drives the atmosphere, and supplies the energy for photosynthesis. This captured energy is used or dissipated in a number of ways that involve the lives of whole pyramids of interdependent plants and animals.

In the functioning of such an ecosystem, the total energy available to the system remains more or less constant. Man cannot increase the total incoming energy, and it varies but little with time. What he can do is to change, within limits, the amount of energy that is captured and converted to organic forms (4), or is used in vaporization of water or in the heating of soil and atmosphere. He also can alter the paths through which energy is dissipated in order to obtain larger yields of "useful" products. Plant and animal scientists increase yields (i) by selecting, breeding, and increasing populations of organisms that make more efficient use of the sun's and other environmental energy, and (ii) by applying knowledge about the attendant physiological processes and the factors that determine their efficiency in energy conversion. The longer the intervening chain of interdependent organisms that need photosynthetically bound energy, the smaller the percentage of the original bound energy available to man.

Table I. Total and per-capita land areas in continental United States exclusive of Alaska, 1960. Population and per-capita areas projected to 1980 and 2000

| Land use and population | Land area (millions of acres) 1960 | Acres per capita | | |
|---|---|---|---|---|
| | | 1960 | 1980 | 2000 |
| Population, median estimates[a] (millions) | | 180 | 240 | 320 |
| Total land area[a] | 1904 | 10.6 | 8.0 | 6.0 |
| Arable land[a] | 400 | 2.2 | 1.7 | 1.2 |
| Commercial forest land[b] | 489 | 2.7 | 2.0 | 1.5 |
| Noncommercial forest land[b] | 163 | 0.9 | 0.7 | 0.5 |
| Rangeland[a] | 633 | 3.5 | 2.6 | 2.0 |

[a] M. Clawson, R. B. Held, and C. H. Stoddard, *Land for the Future* (Johns Hopkins Univ. Press, Baltimore, Md., 1960).
[b] U.S. Dept. of Agriculture, Forest Service, *Timber Resources for America's Future* (U.S. Govt. Printing Office, Washington, D.C., 1958).

Management for multiple products and services is based on ecological relationships and is given direction through a knowledge of human value systems, needs, and desires. It is usually directed at fulfilling human needs by increasing the total useful production of the ecosystem or changing the yield ratios among the different products, or both. Complex-use management requires detailed knowledge of the competitive and complementary actions that occur within the system. In this connection the implications for management that are inherent in the zoological concept of homeostasis should be considered.

Zoologists use the concept called *homeostasis* to indicate the maintenance of balance and steady state in an organism through regulation and coordination of the different physiological processes. In contributing to the functioning of the whole organism, each tissue system or gland may function at a level below its maximum potential. The appearance and the nature of the organism are determined by the interactions among the various glands and tissues and by the levels at which they individually function. In nature, undisturbed by man, the functioning of each tissue usually is regulated so that the organism as a whole behaves in a way that has high survival value—a way that we call "normal." Through interference by man, tissue-functioning levels can be changed with concomitant changes in the nature of the whole organism. These changes may or may not be of value to man.

The ecologically complex wildlands resemble in many ways the single organism, and the concept of homeostasis is useful. The wildlands are mosaics of plant and animal life with their climatic and soil controls. Constant competition and many complementary interactions occur among the individual components. Complex-use management may favor one or more of the product-producing complexes, and multiple products can be combined at many different relative yield levels. For each tract of wildland, the manager must choose the level at which each plant-environmental or animal-environmental complex will be allowed to function. For example, should the forage-livestock producing complex be favored over the forage-browse-wildlife complex; the water-yielding complex over the wood or tree-product complex? What combinations of yield levels are possible, and which will give the highest return? These are basic economic questions, and their answers rest, in the last analysis, on the value judgments of people and the factors affecting these judgments.

In complex-use management two points are especially important. First, those treatments of the resource complex should be avoided that seriously affect the long-run functioning of the whole and result in lower total product-value yields. Management must work toward the "healthy," balanced landscape, one that retains unimpaired its capacity to yield many different products and permits present and future flexibility. Second, management that favors a single product-producing complex usually decreases the yields from some other complex within the whole. The laws of conservation of energy apply, and management is involved largely in redirecting energy flow and in trying to make efficient use of energy in terms of stated human needs and desires.

## MANAGEMENT FOR COMPLEX USE

The development of a complex-use management plan requires a great deal more information about the plants and animals of the wildlands and the environment in which they live than is required for single-product management. This information is obtained through surveys and inventories of wildland resources and through research designed to explain the processes that are occurring on these lands and the factors that control them. Expanded research is essential to a more intensive complex use.

Resource inventories have long supplied the base for management of public forest and rangelands by the U.S. Forest Service and the Bureau of Land Management, and for management of both private and other public lands. These inventories, from which detailed maps are developed, attempt to show and describe each parcel of land that differs in its production capabilities and uses from every other parcel. The conservation needs inventory of the Soil Conservation Service and the California soil-vegetation survey are excellent examples. Many of the surveys, however, are not detailed enough. A finer degree of classification and a more accurate description of the capabilities of the land in terms of each of the products it can produce are needed.

We do not now have satisfactory information on existing capabilities of much of the western wildland for each possible product. We do not know how much yields could be increased by intensive management. Nor do we know what effect increasing the yield of one product would have on the yields of other products that are, or could be, produced on the same land at the same time. Detailed studies of product yields in terms of all important limiting factors are needed. The degree of compatibility among multiple products on the same land also requires study. With such research-developed information, an intensive resource inventory, and knowledge of the costs of different levels and combinations of management, it should be possible to make sound complex-use management decisions based on present demands.

The development of long-range, complex-use management plans, however, requires an estimate of the effect of the changing demands for each of the multiple products. Demands are extremely difficult, if not impossible, to forecast. They fall into two generally recognized categories: (i) those that can be measured by prices in a relatively free market, and (ii) those that find expression primarily through organized political activity. Economists have long struggled with the problem of estimating the value of, and future demand for, wildland products, especially water, recreation, and wildlife. Until satisfactory estimates can be made, stable long-range plans will be unattainable, and the manager should aim at maintaining the resource in such a condition that future shifts in use can be made and will cause a minimum disturbance.

### Interactions with water in complex-use management

Multiple-use management occurs in two forms. In one, a given tract of land is divided into subunits. Each subunit is managed primarily for a single product, although multiple use prevails over the entire tract. In the other form, which represents complex use, each subunit is managed for two or more products simultaneously. Some of the problems of complex-use management are illustrated by a consideration of the interactions of water with other wildland products.

Water is an element common to all wildland products and services. It is at once a separate product of the land and an important ingredient of the other products. A wildland manager can manage for water alone or some combination of yields of water, forage, wood, recreation, and wildlife. As an example, consider the interrelationships of water, forage, and livestock.

On an area occupied by range plants, water is lost to the atmosphere through interception by leaves and stems and subsequent evaporation, by evaporation from the soil, and by absorption and transpiration. A relatively insignificant part is fixed in organic compounds. If the only objective of management were to maximize water yields, all vegetation would be removed. Such a procedure could reduce evapotranspiration losses by as much as 50 percent but could be accompanied by increased surface run-off, irregular streamflow, floods, and greatly accelerated erosion. To reduce evapotranspiration to an absolute minimum, evaporation of soil moisture would have to be stopped by "tin-roofing," paving, or sealing the watershed. If it is decided that denuding and paving a grassland watershed are not economically feasible or socially desirable, then the question of the level of product integration in multiple-product complex-use management becomes real.

In arid climates water is usually the most important factor that limits forage growth and livestock production, and yields are directly related to water consumption and use. Plant size and density increase with the increasing availability of water, the soil is better protected, and fertility is usually maintained or improved. Denser vegetation also generally increases infiltration of water into the soil and lessens surface runoff and erosion, but it also results in increased absorption and transpiration by plants and decreased streamflow.

Thus, the real problem in complex-use management involving water, forage, and livestock is the weighing of values. What is the value of a unit of water for downstream use by agriculture or industry as compared with its value for forage and livestock production on the watershed? What is the value of a unit of water used to increase plant density, maintain soil fertility, decrease floods, control erosion, and provide recreation? These are not simple questions to answer, and the answers will vary with each tract of land.

In the first place, increased water yields from the upper watershed may be largely nullified through evaporation and transpiration losses from stream bottoms lower down, and the cost of preventing downstream losses may be prohibitive. Second, the efficiency of a unit of water for forage production follows Mitscherlich's law of diminishing returns, being greater for the first unit than for subsequent units. Efficiency of water use also varies with soil fertility and macro- and microclimate. Considerable research must be done before the value of an extra unit of water that is yielded as streamflow can be compared with the value of the same water for increased forage and livestock production and other complex-use products. Yet this information must be available before defensible management choices can be made.

The water-forage-livestock complex has been used as an example. The kinds of relationships illustrated apply equally well to the water-wood complex and to most other types of complex land use. Such relationships are very important in determining the levels of integration of the several wildland products under complex-use management.

### Livestock-wildlife interactions in complex-use management

The use of wildlands for wildlife usually complements recreational use, because wildlife is a part of the primeval landscape that many recreationists enjoy. In contrast, conflicts often arise when the same area is used simultaneously for wildlife and livestock (5). The degree and nature of this competition vary with each tract of land. They depend on the kinds of wildlife and livestock in question; their food habits and living requirements; the composition and productivity of the wildland vegetation; soil, climatic, and topographic factors related to animal and plant needs; the degree to which water availability limits animal distribution; and the level of management economically possible on different parts of the range. Little conflict occurs when game occupies the more inaccessible parts of the range or utilizes plants not eaten by livestock. The forage resources are more completely used and the economic return is probably greatest when both livestock and wildlife feed on different plants within the same area (2). Competition is the most intense when game and livestock use the same plants and the same areas. Increasing human populations with their growing demands for both livestock and game will intensify competition and require greater consideration of complex-use management.

The future trends in complex-use management for wildlife and livestock are difficult to forecast. Forage production throughout much of the mountainous West below the forest zones is limited by water availability. In areas of this type a number of considerations suggest that future livestock production will be concentrated on the better-watered and more fertile soils, while wildlife is maintained on the steeper, drier, less accessible areas. The capture and use of more runoff water, the control of weeds, and the application of fertilizers to the better soils could bring about large increases in forage production. The attainment of such increases in forage production, when added to the use of improved breeds of livestock requiring higher animal investments and the increased costs of operating on less accessible rougher land, may tend to concentrate a larger amount of the livestock production on limited land areas. The degree to which this occurs will be determined by relative demands for livestock, wildlife, and recreation, and on the extent to which the economy is free to reflect the natural advantages of different parts of the country for livestock production.

In the Southwest, where water is the most limiting, the livestock-wildlife balance and the nature of complex-use management may depend on future demands for water by municipalities, agriculture, industry, and recreation, and on the possibilities of supplying these increasing demands through vegetation manipulation and watershed modification.

### Recreation in complex-use management

Wildland recreation has increased greatly since World War II, a phenomenon usually attributed to increasing population, higher family incomes, more leisure time, greater mobility, and intensified individual need for outdoor recreation. With growth in population and income has come a great diversity in types of recreation. Because large-scale wildland recreation is relatively new, information and experience on which to base management are deficient, and it is very difficult to assess the place of recreation in complex use.

Recreation is both competitive and complementary with other uses. When it is associated with wildlife, through hunting with gun, camera, or fieldglasses, it complements good forestry practices, because forest management produces more edge effect and more wildlife than does the unmanaged virgin forest. Wilderness use, however, is definitely competitive with wood production on commercial forest land. Judging from European experience, hiking, skiing, and, to a lesser extent, camping fit well with tree forestry. There is general agreement, however, that unique areas or those that have particular scenic value, as well as areas adjacent to streams and lakes, will be reserved for recreational use, and noncomplementary uses will be eliminated from these sites.

Recreation has been important in forested areas of the West because they have pleasant summer weather, many lakes, miles of perennial streams, and good fishing and hunting, and because of the beauty of their vistas. In the Southwest, however, recreation is also important on the rangelands, particularly during seasons other than summer. One can expect marked increases in range and brushland recreation, especially where water is sufficient to permit development. To the extent that it is limited by the availability of water, recreation involving wildlife and fish will be competitive with livestock. In other areas it may be complementary with, and enhanced by, livestock operations.

The difficulty in assessing the place of recreation in complex-use management stems from certain deficiencies in knowledge. The most important are (i) knowledge of the psychological, social, and economic values inherent in recreation and how these are related to certain landscape qualities, and (ii) knowledge of future population increases and the shifts in demands for certain types of recreation that occur as social pressures and standards of living change.

Recent studies in the Lake States show that a large number of recreationists come from large centers of population. Bultena et al. (1) cite a number of studies that show a positive relationship between social class, or occupational level, and the nature of leisure pursuits. Social and occupational status designations are in flux. Before long-range plans involving recreation can be developed, it is important to know how the social environment may change and affect the demand for different types of outdoor recreation.

The importance of information related to the psychological

and social values in recreation is suggested by events that surrounded the recent (1958) celebration held in Zurich, Switzerland, in honor of Eugen Wyler. Wyler has been concerned with the future of Europe, and in his book *Grünes Europa—Wohin?* he sharply and favorably contrasts the life of the hunter and the farmer with the members of what he calls modern mass society (6). Wyler states that hunter and farmer possess a higher degree of stability and self-reliability, and that freedom, hardiness, loyalty, trustworthiness, fellowship, and readiness to help are qualities that are bound close to the land and nature. I do not know the degree to which modern psychologists would agree with Wyler's judgment, but a number of recent articles have dealt with the therapeutic values to be realized through camping experiences, especially with reference to delinquent youths (1). The relative importance of these values and the kind of landscape required to produce them will have a marked effect on wildland management. Since some of the factors that affect recreation and its place in complex-use management are so difficult to evaluate, the thought persists that a diversified and balanced landscape should be maintained while, at the same time, management keeps a high degree of flexibility.

## SUMMARY

Considerable attention is currently focused on complex-use management, primarily because of the increasingly unfavorable ratio of natural resources to population. Complex use is a form of multiple use that occurs when there is competition among the multiple products for the elements that control yields. When two or more products compete for the same factors of production, an increase in the yield of one is usually accompanied by a decrease in the yield of another. This poses the principal problem of complex use: how to determine for each parcel of land, the desirable level of integration of its several products.

The development of complex-use, multiple-product management plans requires more information about plant and animal ecosystems, economics, and human needs than does single use. Good planning requires more detailed resource inventories;

knowledge of the production capabilities of each parcel of land for each possible product; recognition of the degree to which different land uses are competitive, supplementary, or complementary; and accurately estimated production rates of each product in terms of the important controlling environmental factors. A great need exists for expanded research to provide this information.

Some problems of complex use are illustrated by a consideration of the interactions involved in the simultaneous use of land for water, forage, wildlife, and recreation.

Since complex-use management plans generally must be long-range, forecasts of future demands and studies of potential human needs are required. Because the level of accuracy of demand forecasts is not high, the wildland resources should be maintained in a condition that will permit future changes in management objectives and flexibility in resource use.

### REFERENCES

1. Bultena, G., R. Lucas, and W. Hathaway, "Recreation in the upper Great Lakes area: a summary of social research," *U.S. Dept. Agr. Forest Serv., Lake States Forest Expt. Sta., Sta. Paper 89* (1961).
2. Julander, O., "Deer and cattle range relations," *Forest Sci.* 1, 130-139 (1955).
3. Odum, H. T., "Ecological potential and analogue circuits for the ecosystem," *Am. Scientist* 48, 1-8 (1960).
4. Ovington, J. D., "Some aspects of energy flow in plantations of *Pinus sylvestris* L.," *Ann. Botany (London)* 25, 12-20 (1961).
5. Smith, J. G., and O. Julander, "Deer and sheep competition in Utah," *J. Wildlife Management* 17, 101-112 (1953).
6. Wyler, E., *Grünes Europa—Wohin?* (Bubenberg-Verlag, Bern; Verlag George Fromme, Wien-München (1958).
7. Zivnuska, J. A., "The multiple problems of multiple use," *J. Forestry* 59, 555-560 (1961).

# Scientific Management of
# Renewable Resources on Wildlands

J. Whitney Floyd and L. A. Stoddart

*College of Forest, Range, and Wildlife Management, Utah State University, Logan*

In this paper the term *wildland* is used to refer to land that is supporting natural, although not necessarily undisturbed, vegetation. Its products may include water, forage, timber, animals, and intangibles, such as esthetic satisfactions. Its management will be influenced by the land's capability to produce certain products, by consumer demand for the potential products, whether the land is publicly or privately owned, and by other factors that may vary with individual situations. In any given instance, over-all management objectives may be keyed to either a multiple- or a single-use basis and may change over time as demands change.

Single-use management is more likely to occur on privately owned than on publicly owned land and may be implemented for a variety of reasons. When private capital is invested, there is a tendency to maximize output, and no use will be included if it does not return a net profit to the private owner. Some land is inherently restricted in its capability to produce a variety of products. In many cases desert land is virtually valueless for anything but livestock grazing, because of its limited precipitation and flora and rugged topography. On city watersheds water as a product will generally receive primary consideration over other values or uses. Land that will support the growth of redwood forests is likely to be managed solely on the basis of lumber production, because of the high economic value of that commodity.

By contrast, management of wildlands for multiple use to meet the needs and desires of the public is more complex. It must necessarily allow for integrated activities within the ecological whole.

It does not imply activation of all possible uses, although it does try to realize the fullest practicable use of all resources within an area according to a planned program. It does not mean that no conflicts exist among uses, or that each use is maximized. It does mean that no one use is necessarily sacrificed merely to accommodate other uses. In general, it tries to achieve a total benefit to the public greater than that which might be realized through single-use management.

The benefits derived from multiple-use management of public wildlands obviously cannot always be assessed adequately in terms of dollar returns. A permit to graze or to cut trees benefits an individual, and society benefits by using the ultimate products; but what of the effects on the land? Value may be measured by a stockman in terms of dollars' worth of forage produced; but who can place a monetary value on a mountain view? The right to enjoy a picnic concerns more people directly than does a permit to log a public forest. It is impossible to compare a rancher's need for rangeland to support his family with the value realized by use of the forage for game that supplies sport and relaxation for hunters.

Land managers are constantly making decisions and compromises, often with inadequate foreknowledge of the full consequences of the programs they initiate. A crucial problem facing those currently concerned with public land-use patterns is how to assess accurately present and future public interest in relation to the natural resources of the country. In assigning priorities to land uses on public wildlands, a manager makes decisions that often are not readily reversible and have social, as well as scientific, implications. Research has supplied some greatly needed answers to past production problems and is currently laying the basis for increasingly intelligent decision-making in the future, but the social aspects of managing wildland are proving nonamenable to ready solution.

## COMPATIBILITY OF USES

Research-developed criteria have helped resource managers to predetermine with reasonable accuracy what degrees of supplementarity, complementarity, and competition are likely to exist among the various potential uses for wildlands.

## Water

In arid parts of the United States water often is recognized as the primary product of wildland. Domestic, agricultural, and industrial demands for water, already great, are increasing. Future development of the West will depend to no small extent on the availability of water and the efficiency of its use. Expanded research is necessary to provide the background information essential to planning this development.

We lack adequate knowledge of how upstream land use affects water yields and water quality. For example, domestic stock reduce herbage volume and, thus, decrease transpiration of water. Simultaneously, however, livestock may trample soil, decrease soil permeability, and increase erosion, thereby adversely modifying the seasonal streamflow pattern and lowering water quality. Kind of vegetation, topography, soil type, and intensity of grazing are important factors in determining whether livestock and water can effectively be produced on a given parcel of land.

Trees transpire large quantities of water and also intercept precipitation, thus reducing the quantity of water that reaches the soil. Some studies show large waterflow increases from deforestation, but soil stability may be reduced concomitantly.

In determining proper land use, land managers should recognize that livestock or lumber may successfully compete with water on an economic basis as the preferable land product. In other words, depending on relative prices and land productivity, water may be as advantageously used on the watershed to produce meat or wood as off the watershed to produce some other value.

Recreation and water generally are compatible products from wildlands, except on certain watersheds that supply culinary water. On such watersheds the pollution that results from a concentration of human population may be an almost insurmountable problem. Increasing numbers of outdoor enthusiasts have forced complete closure of many watersheds to human entry because of pollution dangers. Also, increased fire hazards accompany recreation development. Devegetation or alteration of vegetation to increase the waterflow from a watershed might result in conditions less satisfying to sight-seers and picnickers; but an assured flow of high-quality water from a well-managed watershed is a boon to fishermen and picnickers.

### Grazing

Scientific investigations have greatly clarified the effects that domestic stock and wild game have on wildlands, and the extent of competition that actually exists among different animal species with reference to foraging habits.

Domestic livestock can graze land that is also used for sightseeing and picnicking if the livestock are properly managed. Cattle naturally tend to congregate in bottom lands around water in the same areas that are most accessible to, and preferred by, the recreationist. Judicious fencing or persistent herding, together with the development of alternate sources of stock water, can materially reduce this conflict.

Mere presence of domestic stock on the land is not undesirable from the tourist's viewpoint. Indeed, the "Wild West," fabled by novel and television, would lack much of its glamor without these animals.

Both big game and domestic livestock depend on vegetation for food, and a certain amount of competition is inevitable. Game can utilize more rugged topography than can domestic stock, and certain plants favored in the game diet are unimportant to domestic animals. Most game animals, especially deer and antelope, are not primarily grass-eaters. It is false to assume that game and livestock can be interchanged on an equal basis, and it is equally false to assume that ranges can tolerate large populations of both big game and domestic stock simultaneously. Generally, meat yield per unit area is maximized through a combination of animal species that is maintained in balance with the topography and flora.

Many operations that are initiated to improve livestock range, such as spraying broadleaf herbs, plowing, planting to grass, and brush removal, are detrimental to big-game production, because they discourage game forage and cover plants. Considerable conflict between sportsman and livestock operator has resulted from such operations. Normal movement and migration of antelope are hindered by woven-wire fences. This is another source of controversy between ranchers and sportsmen, making range sharing difficult.

## Timber

Research has shown that grazing and timber production are more compatible in coniferous than in hardwood forests. Domestic animals forage but little on western forest species if livestock numbers are correctly balanced with a supply of more desirable herbage. Sheep occasionally eat terminal buds of certain tree species, but rarely does this curtail tree reproduction. Big-game animals are somewhat more likely to damage tree seedlings, especially during periods of heavy snowfall.

Grazing has been shown to favor reproduction of seedlings of some coniferous species by providing a more favorable mineral-soil seedbed, because of trampling and breaking up of litter. In areas of mixed forest growth, competition from deciduous trees is reduced by grazing, and this results in an increased coniferous growth and higher-quality lumber production. The reduced forest-fire hazard that accompanies grass removal can probably be cited as another important adjunct to grazing.

Conversely, a dense growth of trees reduces the surface herbage growth and grazing capacity. Despite some benefits to the animals themselves such as protection against severe weather, commercial tree production generally cannot be regarded as beneficial to livestock production.

If they are properly integrated, silvicultural practices and timber cutting seem to interfere but little with recreation on wildlands. Logging operations are of interest to the sight-seer. If buffer strips are preserved along highways and if highway use by logging trucks is minimized, intelligent harvesting of forests can be made compatible with recreation. Modern methods of logging and reforestation need not result in the land scars that gave early-day lumbering its bad reputation.

## IMPACT OF SCIENTIFIC MANAGEMENT ON
## PRODUCTIVITY OF RANGE AND FOREST LAND

Scientific management has already brought about increased productivity on both rangelands and forest lands. Further increases can be expected as more research is undertaken and scientific management is applied to additional areas.

### Ranges

Public ranges, which exist primarily in the 11 western states, generally are supporting decreasing numbers of range livestock over the years. This has resulted largely because the management objective has been shifting in emphasis from livestock production to water production, game production, or recreation, in response to public demand. Too, in some instances range users "borrowed from the future" in past years by overusing the range resource and depleting soil and vegetation. The decline of livestock numbers on these public ranges is likely to continue, even though it has been estimated that by 1975 beef, veal, mutton, and lamb consumption in the 11 western states alone will be from 70 to 75 percent higher than it is now. More people, greater demands for livestock products, and shrinking ranges are irreconcilable, unless scientific developments can facilitate more efficient use of available range resources.

On public, as well as private, ranges, however, sharply increased production can be achieved in the immediate future through scientific management based on currently available information. If we were to implement all the economically feasible range-management knowledge now at hand, the production capacities of most ranges in the West could be increased by at least 35 percent.

Chemical and mechanical control of undesirable shrubs on rangelands has been demonstrated to increase forage yields as much as 10 times, and to constitute an economic means for ranchers to increase range forage. Fire as a management tool in brushlands has played a similar role. Introduced grasses now provide more forage and forage of higher nutritive value than did the original species in many regions. The seeding of deteriorated ranges in the West has increased grazing capacity by more than 8 to 10 times and, in addition, has increased efficiency of livestock production through larger lamb and calf crops and greater gains. Lambing percentages on such reseeded ranges may be 17 to 20 percent higher than before, and lamb and calf gains may be as much as 6 to 8 pounds and 30 to 40 pounds greater, respectively.

Reseeding and improved management can greatly increase feed production on many western grazing lands. (Courtesy U.S. Department of Agriculture, Soil Conservation Service)

An application of only 40 to 80 pounds of nitrogen on a mountain meadow has been shown repeatedly to increase forage production 7 to 8 times. Further research trials have demonstrated that such fertilization also substantially increases the forage palatability and its nutrient content. The response of old and previously abused grasslands to fertilization can be spectacular, and the improved vigor and production of the plants is reflected in better animal performance.

Numerous experiments have indicated that range operators can materially improve meat and wool yields by modifying their management techniques. Correct animal numbers and proper season of grazing have been shown to result in one-fifth higher gains for both steers and sheep. Better reproduction rates, increased quantity and quality of wool, and higher marketing values for meat and wool can be achieved by use of what is known about correct intensity of grazing rates for different types of ranges.

Investigations have also proved that supplemental feeding when range forage is deficient in quantity, or nutrients, or both can provide wool yields that are up by as much as 1 pound per head and can increase lamb and calf crops by 10 to 15 percent. Supplemental feeding that is tailored to meet the needs of a specific situation can also result in better rates of gain.

Research also has provided information that allows the livestock grower to better assess the condition and response of his range. By being able to detect at early stages what effect his management is having on the range, he can avoid the detrimental vegetation changes and soil erosion that can take a great toll of productivity.

Much of what research has established regarding potential improvement of rangeland in arid regions is not yet economically feasible on a large scale—but some of it is. By applying such information as it becomes available, whenever and wherever it is practicable, managers of wildlands used as ranges can offset some cuts in acreage and grazing permits.

### Forests

Wildlands on which forest products grow have had their production rates materially augmented by scientific developments in recent years. The use of aerial-photo interpretation now makes it possible to measure rapidly and efficiently area, volume, kind, and to a certain extent quality of timber on a given site. Information of this nature gives a precise basis for the development of utilization and management plans.

Aerial equipment, such as helicopters, used to scout fires and to deliver men and supplies to the scene of action, and fixed-wing aircraft, used to drop chemical retardants and equipment, has practically revolutionized fire-suppression methods. Many new chemicals have been developed for forest insect and disease control. Of particular significance is the actidione BR now used for the treatment of white-pine blister rust. Such new chemicals reduce control costs and, thus, should find wide use in cutting losses of timber.

The development and use of synthetic resin glues have revolutionized forest utilization. Boards, beams, and composition materials synthesized from small-timber species formerly thought to be inferior are now common construction materials. These are stronger, more adaptable, and in many respects more attractive than the earlier types. Such advances have made a greater quantity of harvestable material economically usable and have contributed to a more complete use of the growing capacity of each forest acre.

## MULTIPLE-USE MANAGEMENT: A DYNAMIC PROCESS

Obviously multiple-use management of wildland must be dynamic—a process in which the technician or land manager, armed with the best knowledge available, makes his "never final" land-use decisions. These decisions and any adjustments they entail often will have immediate effects on the resources and, quite probably, will also affect the nature of the resources in the future. Because the kind and quantity of wildland resources cannot be considered static entities, these resources cannot logically be assigned permanent values in an inflexible use pattern.

Restrictions placed on full use of land by agency policy or custom may result in decreased efficiency of land use. Perhaps the best example of this is the extensive reservation of park or wilderness lands to preserve natural conditions or to provide very limited recreation use. Vast areas of Yellowstone National Park literally are never seen by man, and they contribute little to the economics of society, except possibly water. This park of almost 2¼ million acres was visited by an estimated 1,524,088 people during 1961, some being at best "casual" visitors. This means that almost 1.5 acres of land is being reserved for each person. With rare exceptions, these people actually see only a narrow strip of the land that borders the highway. Although the comparison is admittedly tenuous, this contrasts sharply with the recreation derived per acre from, say, a Florida beach or a Los Angeles golf course during the year.

Rapidly changing economic demands and population increases make it unwise to commit ourselves to unalterable, long-time land uses. Economists cannot forecast future demand patterns with any degree of preciseness. A policy of flexibility in resource planning that will permit future shifts in objectives seems mandatory. Recent advances in scientific knowledge have done much to facilitate adoption of such a policy, but in too many instances the acquired knowledge is not being fully used.

Certainly a day is approaching when we can no longer afford the luxury of inefficient land use. Current and future land management must go beyond mere conservation or preservation. We cannot afford to abuse our natural resource base any further, but neither can we afford not to use it.

Needs, desires, and value systems of society tend to change as times and modes of living change. Natural resources themselves change over time as they are used and as they respond to the environmental changes wrought by man.

Plant associations are continually changing, particularly where nature's processes have been altered by use. As a result, current-day range vegetation may be better or worse as forage for domestic livestock. Forest vegetation may be more or less suitable for modern-day needs, which, in turn, may not be lumber and fuel so much as pulpwood and scenery. Watershed vegetation in some localities has been modified to achieve a more efficient water yield and possibly at the same time a more effective erosion control.

Animal associations also have changed. Predator control and rodent control have had far-reaching effects. Hunting and fishing have created new pressures. Introductions of new species and the building of wildlife preserves have modified kinds and numbers. Even more important, human beings have profoundly modified natural habitat, food supply, and cover for animals by introducing domestic animal competitors, plowing, cutting forests, burning grasslands, and building cities, fences, and roads.

Change, then, is the byword of the day—sometimes intentional, but just as often accidental. Science sometimes precipitates changes, sometimes eases changes brought about by other circumstances. Its place in the natural resource picture is being more deeply etched every day. It is helping the land manager to make more efficient use of the available resources and is struggling to help him to project intelligently his decisions into the future, both as they affect the natural resources directly and as they have implications for future generations.

To be effective, present-day scientific management of wildlands should take cognizance of at least three general areas of information: (i) the current resource needs of society and the estimated future needs; (ii) an inventory of the nation's resources that probably will function in filling current and anticipated needs; (iii) the role of social and technological developments in understanding multiple-use relationships and in formulating a scientific plan for integrated land-use management. Scientific management of renewable resources will have to become a more widespread reality than it is today, or we are likely to shortchange seriously future generations.

## SUMMARY

Only lands of limited capability or those inherently well adapted to some important special purpose have to be restricted to a single use. But the increased efficiency usually achieved by multiple use is attained only through complicated management procedures. The manager must understand and weight social needs and demands, including economic relationships. Merely considering the biological capability of the land is not enough.

A dynamic management of public land means that the manager must anticipate future demands and economic changes. Land resources cannot be assigned immutable uses in a changing society. Laws and policies pertaining to land use should be as nonrestrictive to intelligent management adjustments as possible. At best, decisions related to public land management, such as deforestation or irrigation development, are not readily reversible. All the potential ramifications of a decision should be considered and projected into the future before action is taken.

Livestock numbers are not expected to increase on public lands; indeed, further reductions are likely, because of urgent diverse pressures on these land resources. Through modern techniques of seeding, fertilizing, spraying, and supplemental feeding, together with improved livestock management and a better understanding of range ecology, however, ranchers can maintain impressive meat- and wool-production rates. Increased livestock production to meet increasing demands may have to come mostly on private ranges, although access to public ranges will continue to be essential to livestock ranchers.

Forest-land acreage probably will not be increased in the United States, yet our forest lands will undoubtedly have to meet ever-growing demands for wood and wood products in the foreseeable future. The conversion of relatively stagnant stands of old growth into young, growing forests by systematic harvesting will increase the per-acre growth. New developments in protection techniques will reduce losses from fire, insects, and disease. Change in utilization standards—for example, the development of more effective glues—will continue to promote the use of small trees and species that were formerly considered unusable.

Scientific advances in the field of natural resources can provide a more substantial basis for future management decisions. Managers of wildlands should thus be able to maintain the degree of flexibility that is essential if they are to meet the continually widening range of demands.

# Providing for Multiple Use in the Management of Land and Water

John A. Hopkin

*Bank of America N. T. & S. A., San Francisco, California*

In the literature on land and water management, multiple use has been controversial ever since it was first formalized by Pinchot and his followers in their opposition to the narrow use that was implicit in the act that established the Forest Reserve (5). On the one hand, multiple use became the battle cry of the "spokesman for the multitude" when he denounced the *special-interest* evils of the "primary-use" advocates. On the other hand, those who favored the primary-use concept held that multiple use presented each administrator with an unmanageable set of criteria and was merely a shibboleth under which mediocrity and mismanagement could hide. This situation could be corrected, they argued, only when the administration was charged with the responsibility of administering the land under its jurisdiction in a manner that would maximize the returns from the use for which the resource was best suited. The battle lines were rather fluid, but the Department of Agriculture generally was on the multiple-use side opposing the Department of the Interior. Ranchers shifted back and forth from one camp to another.

## POLITICAL ACCEPTANCE OF MULTIPLE USE

The weight of political pressure has been on the side of multiple use for obvious reasons, and the Department of the Interior, the Department of Agriculture, and most of the groups of users are now in harmony with its broad objectives (3). It is interesting to note that the "recreation" interests, who were among the advocates of multiple use in the early days when timber production was considered to be the primary product of national forests, are today among the most vocal advocates of "single use" for an increasing number of areas that they want set aside as wilderness areas. Times change, and with it our tastes and technology. Nevertheless, the concept of multiple use as a general policy objective in administering our public land and water resources has become an accepted—and I might add, a useful—*concept* on the political front.

## MULTIPLE USE VERSUS OPTIMUM USE

The economic problem of multiple use is not unique to public land and water. It has existed since man first discovered that the same resources could be used for two or more products; and a neat body of economic theory has been developed that centers on the problem of allocating scarce resources among competing products so that the total net returns will be maximized. Clearly, this sounds like exactly what we want out of our public resources. However, as any good student in economics can point out, this is a problem of *optimum* resource allocation among uses *(2)*, and whether it should be multiple use or single use is an intricate and critical problem to be resolved for each set of resources and for each given set of values. In the words of S. V. Ciriacy-Wantrup, "To regard multiple use as a general objective or criterion for policy is not warranted logically—it puts, if you permit, the cart before the horse . . . . To analyze whether or not multiple use replaces or is replaced by single use is one of the most important tasks of resource economics" *(1)*.

## CRITERIA FOR OPTIMUM USE

On the theoretical front, then, multiple use has had to yield to optimum use. But the usefulness of the concept of optimum use in determining the objectives and guiding the decisions of public policy hinges on the practical applicability of these criteria.

Just to review: The maximizing decision, according to the theoretical construct of optimum use, is determined by the interaction of two sets of relationships: (i) the physical relationships, that is, the marginal rates of physical substitution among alternative products (forage, timber, water, and so on); and (ii) the relative preferences of society for the products in question. Everyone concerned with the management and use of public land and water should remember that, if and when these two sets of data can be estimated with sufficient accuracy to warrant confidence, the theorems of economics can lead to a "best" decision.

### Physical relationships among products

In the real world, unfortunately, these sets of data can be estimated only for limited situations. Research is expanding in this area, and the opportunity is great for joint research efforts between economists and representatives of the several physical sciences involved in this problem (4, 6). The design and initiation of physical experiments that should provide us with improved estimates of the effect of successive intensities of one particular use (timber harvest, for example) on other uses (grazing, flood control and water yield, and recreation) are taking too much time. Such information at best is accumulated slowly, and the results often vary tremendously among sites, owing to location factors, and among years, owing to varying weather patterns. Nevertheless, decisions continue to confront our land and water administrators concerning the allocation of their limited resources among the several products in question. Better estimates of the functional relationships among these products are necessary to improved decisions concerning the use of these resources. Familiarity with the logic of diminishing marginal rates of substitution—a basic concept in economics—plus a working knowledge of the postulates of the physical sciences in question, whether range management, forestry, or engineering, can be a starting point for improved decisions.

### Relative preferences for products

The other side of the theoretical maximizing equation—the relative preferences of society for the products—often is as diffi-

cult to obtain as are the physical relationships, and it is subject
to fully as many limitations. Where the products in question are
sold on the open market in sizable quantities, preferences can be
derived from market prices. For products like beef and lamb, market prices are useful (6). Similarly, timber and its derived products are sold in the market. Thus, society can express its current
relative preference for beef or timber through the market. However, the preferences that are *expected* to be in effect when present
allocation decisions will yield their respective products are the
ones that are relevant. This involves the uncertain future. Furthermore, we are much further into the future with one product
(timber) than with the other (beef), so appropriate discount
rates also must be considered.

If the products in question include some form of recreation—
deer hunting, for example—the pricing problem becomes even
more complex. Since few marketplaces exist where one can buy
the unrestricted pleasure of hunting, there is no established
market price and, hence, no readily available expression of people's
preferences for hunting deer. As long as free individuals are
assumed to be the best judges of their own needs and wishes,
however, the relative importance of various goods and services to
society can best be approximated by relating them to the amounts
of other goods and services that members of society are willing to
give up in exchange. Thus, it seems to me, expenditures that
people make in pursuit of wildlife compared with expenditures
made for other goods and services represent our soundest basis
for comparing the contribution of each to society's welfare, provided that the total number of issued hunting permits is reasonably sufficient to meet the demand at the cost.

Important definitional and accounting problems have to be
resolved in deciding, in each specific case, just what the individual
"gave up"—that is, what his expenditures were—in pursuit of the
specific hunting trip in question (8). However, more formidable
problems have been undertaken. In this case, we can easily define
and identify the "universe" involved, since all legal hunters
are registered, and they usually are checked when they enter or
leave an area that is open to hunting. But economists have been
reluctant to undertake research designed to help put price tags

on some of these goods—such as recreation—that are not acquired in the usual market channels.

## PROBLEMS IN APPLYING OPTIMUM-USE CRITERIA

Only part of this reluctance stems from the magnitude and complexity of the problem of valuation. There are other important obstacles, as well. First, a number of the products in question are so severely rationed under administered (and highly subsidized) prices that a quantitative expression of total demand is not feasible. This tends to complicate the problem and makes it difficult to maintain objectivity among interested researchers.

A second problem arises because a private firm will tend to use only one of the several potential products from multiple-use resources. If problems of multiple use of public lands and water existed within the ambit of single firms, the problem would be essentially a matter of joint costs and joint products (9). Although the reduction of grazing by 100 units on a given public range, for example, might increase both timber and hunting by 200 units each, the fact remains that the rancher would lose by this shift. And who can say whether the 200 units of timber to a lumber company plus 200 units of game hunting to the local sportsmen more than compensate for the rancher's loss of 100 units of grazing?

The body of theory called *welfare economics* is concerned with the limits to which economists can go *as economists* in making policy recommendations. To date, this body of theory seems to have been more successful in defining these limits for economists than in helping to identify what economists might recommend at the limits.

Other important problems arise because of uncertainty. Of special concern are the uncertainties of changes over time in technology, preferences, and institutions. The probabilities of these are not amenable to quantitative measurement.

If optimum resource allocation is to be achieved over time, two sets of conditions must be met. First, the efficiency or maximizing conditions must be met on the particular set of projects and economic activity that prevail at each given time period. Second, the longer-run changes in tastes, technology, and institutions must be anticipated, and sufficient flexibility must be built into our research and management programs to permit adjustment to these changing conditions.

In practice, a meticulous clinging to the first set of conditions would tend to remove the flexibility required for the second. This could be a damaging solution. It would be carrying rationality to an irrational point, so to speak.

Thus far I have tried to show that, on theoretical grounds, multiple use has to give way to optimum use. Quantitative maximizing, however, is seriously limited in the real world by its restrictive assumptions, a paucity of meaningful data, and the high degree of uncertainty inherent in projecting the results into the future.

On the political front, *multiple use* has become a popular and seemingly workable term around which to marshal sufficient political and economic support to bring some order out of chaos in the administration of our public lands and water during the past half-century. Its banner sufficiently united the opposing economic and political forces to permit action and research programs that have been, without question, beneficial. To my knowledge, however, no one claims that numerous mistakes were not made over the years.

I would like to pose the question: Do we really *want* to provide for multiple use? As a concept for guiding management—both in its short-run and long-run decisions—multiple use leaves much to be desired, because it provides no criteria for choosing among competing objectives. At best, it does little more than state very broad objectives in terms of "the greatest good for the greatest number." We simply cannot be content with such lack of clear-cut criteria and must, therefore, continue to refine our tools, extend and expand our information, and even develop new tools.

## TOWARD ECONOMIZING THROUGH POLITICAL DECISIONS

In the policy issues of western range and water resources we have some real problems of political economy. Most of these decisions are made by delegated representatives of the people.

Although the process of decision delegation was at first envisioned as one in which the delegators (the voters) had direct contact with, and control over, the decision-makers (since they would be their elected representatives), a vast and growing (and, for the most part, a highly competent) bureaucracy now dominates the decision-making process. Not only do the administrative bureaus formulate the details of policy as it is carried out; frequently they write the legislation, subject to the approval or disapproval of the Congress and the President. The Congress does control the purse, however, and this is its most effective control of the bureaus—as the Forest Service, the Bureau of Land Management, and the Bureau of Reclamation have come to know.

Thus, important decisions are being made by people who are not choosing for themselves. Because of the complexity of the decisions, it is necessary that we delegate them. But at the same time it is important that those who make such decisions for us have the clearest possible expression of our collective preferences among alternative products.

At the present time, the managing bureaus appear to rely on three primary sources for expressions of the people's preferences —pressure groups, advisory boards, and national elections—each of which has definite limitations (7).

Although pressure groups make their relative preferences known at several stages of the delegated decision-making process, many people are not politically activated. Are their preferences to be ignored in these decisions? Similarly, advisory boards often do not represent all the groups of users of the resources in question. Furthermore, they frequently have limited means for knowing the preferences of their constituents.

Voting can be used to reflect the first preferences between or among alternatives if (i) the people affected by the decision are able to vote, (ii) the appropriate alternatives are defined and communicated to the people, and (iii) the alternative courses of action are specifically identified with the alternatives of voting. Only rarely are the alternatives in multiple resources use clearly defined when they are associated with the voting alternatives in our two-party system. Consequently, voters seldom can express their preferences among alternatives by voting.

Although there are the limitations to which I referred earlier, the preferences of the people frequently can be expressed through the price system or can be estimated in monetary terms. This procedure will be reasonably accurate (i) when the products to be allocated, even when rationed, are in sufficient supply to meet the bulk of demand at the specified price; (ii) when the important costs and returns to individuals and firms can be evaluated in monetary terms; and (iii) when the contemplated change is relatively small. This latter point is based on the supposition that radical allocation changes probably will affect the distribution of income enough that the decision must be considered from that standpoint, also.

## A preference survey

But there are vast numbers of situations for which neither voting nor market prices are adequate or applicable. A recommended supplement for estimating the preferences of a community or society would be a *preference survey*, in which the alternatives would be explained in detail to a selected sample of individuals, and their relative preferences would be recorded. From the relative preferences of the sample, inferences could be made concerning the preferences of the population. The nature of the questions to be asked, the individuals or groups, or both, that should comprise the universe, and the method of aggregating the preferences would depend on the nature of the allocation problem in question.

The services of professional statisticians, psychologists, and trained enumerators would be required to insure that the individuals being sampled could think and respond in the terms of the questions being asked. I believe that it would be possible to obtain a statistical sampling service that could achieve the same high degree of competence and objectivity that has characterized research institutions generally. Logistically, it would be a part of the Bureau of the Census—which, by the way, is now using the sampling techniques to evaluate the accuracy of its enumeration. The information obtained through the preference-sampling service would be used alongside information obtained from other scientists (from the various social and physical disciplines) in making decisions regarding resource allocation.

## Implications of a preference survey

The extensive use of preference sampling would have some interesting implications, so far as public resource administration is concerned. For instance, the present practice, followed by public land agencies, of using rancher advisory boards might be materially affected. On the one hand, the need for the advisory boards as a means of obtaining "grassroots" opinions of the various segments of the economy would be diminished. On the other hand, the advisory boards could become better informed concerning the preferences of the group they represent and could speak with greater certainty. It would seem advisable, under these circumstances, to revise the advisory boards to include representatives of all important users of the resources in question.

Direct sampling of community preference would no doubt also have some interesting effects on the activities of pressure groups. The administration's need for the "services" of the pressure groups would be eliminated. Should a preference-sampling procedure become effective, the efforts of the pressure groups likely would be redirected toward influencing the desires of the citizens. Actually, the activities of pressure groups directed toward the citizenry would then be a form of advertising—that is, describing to the public the alternatives of the public resource allocation problem in terms that would make one alternative seem more desirable than another. It seems to me that the extent and direction of the influence of pressure groups could be more nearly assessed and controlled under such a system than they are at present.

### SUMMARY

On economic grounds, multiple use falls short of supplying public land- and water-resource management with economic criteria by which to formulate policy and programs. On theoretical grounds, it must give way to optimum use. The assumptions explicit in the maximizing conditions of optimum use are so limiting, however, that they make its direct application in the real world very limited indeed.

This limitation should not deter us in undertaking cooperative research designed to improve our knowledge of the variables needed to estimate optimum use. The pricing system should be used wherever it is applicable to reflect the preferences of society. Furthermore, in some important situations, preferences for extra-market products probably can be estimated in monetary terms.

But research on these problems yields results slowly. In the meantime, decisions have to be made. Under these circumstances, the logic of optimum use combined with the theoretical postulates of the applicable physical sciences can provide our soundest basis for decisions and action. Even so, improved communication between all resource users and resource managers in relation to the preferences of users is important. Among the suggestions made for improving these communications are (i) a more extensive and imaginative use of our pricing system, even for extra-market goods, and (ii) a preference survey.

The real question considered here is, How can we move in the direction of optimum use of our public land and water resources? We will never move all the way; there may even be danger in moving too far. Under conditions of uncertainty, a too-close adherence to the maximizing conditions for particular locations and points of time tends to remove the flexibility that is required to meet the important long-run changes. But we must recognize that multiple use provides no criterion to guide resource managers, nor does it even point them broadly in the direction they should go.

## REFERENCES

1. Ciriacy-Wantrup, S. V., "Multiple use as a concept for water and range policy," in *Water and Range Resources and Economic Development of the West,* Rept. 9 (Western Range Resources Comm. and Western Water Resources Comm., Western Agricultural Economics Research Council, Tucson, Ariz., 23-24 Jan. 1961).
2. ———, *Resource Conservation Economics and Policies* (Univ. of California Press, Berkeley, 1952).
3. Clawson, M., *Uncle Sam's Acres* (Dodd Mead, New York, 1951).
4. Cook, W., "Common use of summer range by sheep and cattle," *J. Range Management* 7, 10-13 (1954).

5. Hibbard, B. H., *A History of Public Land Policies* (Macmillan, New York, 1924).
6. Hopkin, J. A., "Economic criteria for determining optimum use of summer range by sheep and cattle," *J. Range Management* **7**, 172-175 (1954).
7. ———, "The use of economics in making decisions relating to range use," *J. Farm Economics* **38**, 1595-1603 (1956).
8. Kelso, M. M., "Multiple land use objectives for public resource allocation," in *Economic Research in the Use and Development of Range Resources,* Rept. 2 (Comm. on the Economics of Range Use and Development, Western Agricultural Economics Research Council, Tucson, Ariz., 1959), pp. 117-129.
9. Upchurch, M. L., "Resource allocation under conditions of multiple use of land," in *Economic Research in the Use and Development of Range Resources,* Rept. 2 (Comm. on the Economics of Range Use and Development, Western Agricultural Economics Research Council, Tucson, Ariz., 1959), pp. 135-145.

# Criteria and Planning for Optimum Use

Emery N. Castle

*Department of Agricultural Economics, Oregon State University, Corvallis*

It has been said that "Science might almost be defined as the process of substituting unimportant questions which can be answered for important questions that cannot."* Both professional and lay people concerned with natural resource use frequently speak of an "optimum use of resources." Upon examination, it becomes obvious that the term *optimum* means different things to different people. Mischief is done when professional people use the term in a limited professional sense, but their statements are interpreted to mean something different.

## NATURE OF AN OPTIMUM

An optimum may be defined as a state of affairs that results in the most favorable degree, condition, or amount of some desirable magnitude, property, or attribute. The definition, as such, says nothing about what the desirable "magnitude, property, or attribute" might be. Nor does it suggest how these are to be specified or achieved.

Obviously, recourse must be made to criteria outside the formal definition if we are to specify, or proceed toward, an "optimum." A logical step would be to examine the disciplines that are generally recognized as having relevance to natural resources management for criteria that might be used in managing the natural resources that man has at his disposal. We shall consider two such disciplines—ecology and economics—to see if they contain concepts that might help to define optimum resource use.

---

* K. Boulding, *The Image* (Univ. of Michigan Press, Ann Arbor, 1956), p. 164.

**Ecological concepts**

The ecological approach envisions an equilibrium among physical and biological phenomena that permits the survival of certain climax species. *Climax* is defined in the words of Odum (*14*, p. 266) as "The final or stable community in a successional series is the climax community; it is self-perpetuating and in equilibrium with the physical habitat."

The concept of a climax has been extended to include the notion of a disclimax, which describes a stabilization of plant and animal associations that provides for prolonged use by man (*14*, p. 269). The basic functional unit of ecology is the ecosystem, which is any area of nature that includes living organisms and nonliving substances interacting to produce an exchange of materials between the living and nonliving parts (*14*, p. 10). Knowledge gained from such a field has considerable relevance to the management of natural resources by man. The various specialized fields of ecology can help to predict the consequences of man's changing of the natural habitat in any way. They also permit the identification of stable systems before and after such interference has occurred.

Equating such stable systems with a "social optimum," however, leads to difficulty. There is value in defining an optimum within the limits of a particular intellectual discipline and using it to identify tendencies or deviations. It is quite another matter to use it as a normative concept to guide the affairs of man as he manages his natural resources. Two definitions of conservation proposed by ecologists can serve as examples.

"The aim of good conservation is to insure a continuous yield of useful plants, animals, and materials, by establishing a balanced cycle of harvest and removal" (*14*, p. 421).

"For the nonrenewable resources, good management is chiefly wise use with the avoidance of waste. It is possible to string out the supply for a long period and to use the resource only for worthwhile purposes, but if it is to be used at all it will eventually disappear. For the renewable resources, management involves, as a minimum, practices which will result in a sustained yield" (*6*).

It would serve little purpose to present a lecture on the non-operational nature of such words as *good, useful, wise use,* and *waste.* The words *good, useful, wise use,* and *waste* are necessary to statements like the foregoing quotations, because, to use the biological concept, one must relate it to the goals of man. It is assumed that defining and identifying man's objectives is a simple matter, and that it is possible to establish classifications such as "useful" on the one hand, and "wasteful" on the other, even though the definitions supply no criteria for these judgments. If man is held to be of consequence, then a concept that either assumes or ignores his objectives in resource management will not be an appropriate guide for him to follow, however useful it may be in specifying information about the resource he is managing.

## Economic concepts

The same line of argument can be applied to economics as an aid to resource management. Just as the ecosystem is crucial to the study of ecology, the firm is fundamental to the study of economics. From the assumption that individuals in a society wish to enhance some economic magnitude, it has been possible to deduce a set of rules that must be followed if certain results are to be obtained. The equation of marginal costs and returns over time can be used to define an "optimum state of conservation" (*4,* p. 76). Again, such an "optimum state of conservation" may be useful in the study of the economics of conservation. But if it is equated with a social optimum, the assumption is that man ought to behave in a particular way. The concept of an economic optimum rests on an implicit value judgment that cannot be verified by examining the evidence; the evidence indicates that the value judgment is incomplete and does not encompass all of the relevant values on which men base their actions. Furthermore, "the economic state of conservation" will depend on the institutional framework in which an individual is operating. Just as ecologists found it necessary to specify the role of man and to develop the idea of a disclimax, economists frequently assume institutions as given. If institutions are viewed as definitions of one man's relationship to another, they represent the means that man has developed to regulate the affairs between men while permitting man to satisfy both his individual and his collective wants. Consequently, any analysis that assumes them to be constant is a partial analysis.

Both ecology and economics are relevant and helpful to the natural resource planner if they are used as positive sciences—that is, to predict the biological and economic consequences of particular lines of action. They may be misleading if they are used in a normative manner to specify what "ought to be"—an optimum use of natural resources.

## ROLE OF VALUES

What then can be used to guide natural resource policy decisions if the intellectual disciplines that are commonly drawn upon are inadequate for specifying the ends or goals of resource management? In his book, *Mind, Man and Land,* Firey (7, p. 26) identifies the ethnological approach to resource phenomena. It has its roots in anthropology and sociology and rests on the observation that different peoples, when confronted with the same or similar natural resource situations, may make different use of those natural resources. From this observable fact, it is deduced that the reason rests with the cultural differences among people. The optimum pattern of resource use, according to this approach, is the pattern that is most consistent with important themes of peoples' culture, such as their attitude toward progress, the way decisions are made, and the distribution of the fruits of their economic order. Its limitations as a definition of an optimum use of resources can be expressed in two ways: (i) The main themes or values of a people's culture may be inconsistent at any point in time, regardless of whether they may have been consistent at some other point in time. Changes in technology, the natural resource base, populations, the income level, or other variables can throw existing value patterns into conflict. (ii) The acceptance of any given set of values represents an assumption with respect to the desirability of those values. It may well be that if the consequences of a given set of values were clearly understood, they would no longer be accepted by the society. Certainly, many problems of economic growth and development can be traced to inconsistent values or to someone's dissatisfaction with the pattern of values that exists in those societies where a lack of growth is judged to be a problem (*10*) .*

As with the ecological and economic approaches to optimum natural resource use, we must conclude, with Firey, that although the ethnological approach may be helpful to the natural resource planner, it does not supply a blueprint that will guide him to an optimum use of resources. The information of sociology and anthropology can be ignored only at the expense of realism and relevance, but such information does not constitute the whole picture of man's desires and the means of satisfying those desires.

## Origins of principal values

In analyzing the role of values in agricultural policy, Brewster has traced the origin of the principal values in America (*1–3*). Brewster shows how such concepts as (i) the work ethic, (ii) the enterprise creed, (iii) the creed of self-integrity, and (iv) the democratic creed were once in harmony. (Concepts i, ii, and iii are relevant.) Early conditions on this continent were such that these values could be held with deep conviction without inconsistency. The family type of farm and business enterprise combined with a virgin continent and a political system of a democratic nature to make compatibility possible. The work ethic resulted in the judgment that, if people worked proficiently and well, they could close the gap between their "present circumstances and their aspirations." The democratic creed involves the value judgments that all men are of equal worth and dignity, and that no man is wise enough or good enough to have dictatorial power over any other. The enterprise creed implies that proprietors have the right to prescribe the working rules for their

---

* Hirschman argues that the problem of development can be traced to the concept that people have of their relationship to the groups of which they are a part. Either an extreme group focus or an extremely individualistic focus is inimical to growth. He argues that both are necessary for development. If we accept this line of argument, the formal definitions of these relationships—institutions—become important in effectuating change, as well as in identifying obstacles to change.

production units; the individual family is responsible for its own economic security; and the role of government is to prevent interference with proprietors to run their businesses as they see fit. The creed of self-integrity provides for the right and obligation of the individual to dissent from generally held opinions, customs, and traditions.

Brewster argues that the coming of machine technology threw these values into conflict. He believes that the enterprise creed suffered with the formation of labor unions and social security. Labor unions and social security were necessary, however, in order to preserve the concept of justice implicit in the value of the work ethic. We have been reluctant to choose among these values as they apply to agriculture and cannot agree on any one of several policies and resulting programs that might resolve the difficulty.

Many of our government programs, with respect to both agriculture and natural resources, may possibly be traced to the pattern of value judgments identified by Brewster. One consequence of the work ethic was the emphasized importance of economic opportunity, so that the "common man" could, by effective work and self-denial, close the gap between his "present circumstances and his aspirations." Our early land policy was characterized by the conveyance of parcels of land to private individuals with safeguards to prevent an undue amount going to any one person. The establishment of land-grant universities was an effort to provide opportunity for the "common people." In more recent times, government credit has been made available to the farmer who was unable to obtain credit from any other source. One long-standing justification of the reclamation program has been that it created opportunity in agriculture.

### Resources: final or intermediate consumption good

The philosophy that underlies agricultural input programs is also apparent in our natural resource policy. We have attempted to use our natural resources to create economic opportunity and to stimulate economic growth. This is consistent with the basic value system advanced by Brewster. Unless the small proprietor, including the farmer, could accumulate wealth, it was impossible to hold to the work ethic and all that it implied *and* to the enterprise creed. Viewed in this light, natural resources become intermediate goods—factors of production to be transformed into consumption goods. Farmers, lumbermen, cattlemen, miners, and power producers tend to view natural resources as intermediate goods. In a developing economy, which emphasized production and possessed abundant natural resources, the use of natural resources as a final consumption good (for recreation) was automatically assigned an incidental role.

With the growth of national and per-capita income, and an increase in leisure time, a different view of natural resources has developed on the part of many. This group, which may be called *mass recreationists,* views natural resources as a final consumption good. In large numbers they use natural resources for fishing, hunting, camping, water sports, and observation of scenery.

Around the turn of the century only a Roosevelt, a Pinchot, or a Rockefeller could spend considerable time in the beauties of the West unless a person happened to live there. Anyone living in the area at that time was probably there for the purpose of earning his livelihood by treating natural resources as an intermediate good. He made multiple use of these resources. He hunted, fished, swam, and hiked, but these uses were a by-product or incidental to his treatment of natural resources as an intermediate good.

Today, a large number of our population can spend a week or more enjoying some type of outdoor recreation in the West, even though they do not live there. They have the leisure time and they have the money. A strong feeling seems to exist that such resources belong to "all of the people." Consequently, many believe that access to all public land should be guaranteed to all citizens. Further, in this context the interests that use these resources as intermediate goods are viewed as special-interest groups; such uses do not benefit "all of the people." Perhaps equality in consumption becomes a dominant goal in an affluent society, which also believes in the democratic creed. We have here a conflict in basic values: Do we use the resources to create economic opportunity or to provide recreation for those who have achieved a sufficient level of income to enjoy such resources?

Furthermore, when recreational resources are in private hands
there is an obvious conflict between private property rights and
the belief that "all of the people" have a right to enjoy such
resources.

Still another group also must be identified at this point. This
group favors the establishment of wilderness areas (or what certain other groups have labeled limited multiple-use areas). One
argument in favor of wilderness areas is based on scientific
grounds. It holds that only by leaving certain areas undisturbed
can principles of ecology be discovered; the wilderness becomes a
laboratory. Others apparently derive esthetic satisfaction from
contemplating or observing the forces of nature at work without
interference by man. The term *wilderness* obviously does not
mean the same thing to all people. The type of use just indicated
is an extreme case; if such areas were visited by a significant number of people they would cease to be wilderness in this extreme
sense. The motivation of this group may stem partially from the
stern structures of the work ethic. In an affluent society, when
what were once called the necessities of life are provided for, additional consumption may be considered "bad" when it is at the
expense of natural resources *(8)*.* But regardless of the basic
motivation, this group also views natural resources as a final consumption good, rather than as an intermediate good to be used
in the production of another commodity.

The conflict generated by these three groups over the use of
our natural resources has been caused by the rapid and considerable economic development of our nation. The conflict has
actually been with us for some time, as John Ise's *Our National
Park Policy* makes quite clear *(11)*. However, the growth of income in relation to our resource base has made the problem much
more acute. If rather fundamental value judgments did not

---

* Galbraith says, "In an opulent society the marginal utility of all kinds of goods
is low. It is easy to bring our doubts and questions to bear on automobiles. But
the case is not different for (say) that part of our food production which contributes not to nutrition but to obesity, that part of our tobacco that contributes
not to comfort but to carcinoma, and that part of our clothing which is designed
not to cover nakedness but to suggest it. We cannot single out waste in a single
product without questioning the product."

underlie the motivation of each group, a resolution of the conflict would be much easier to achieve.

When value conflicts occur in relation to the use of natural resources, a finite number of alternative solutions usually are possible. As long as unknown relationships, whether of a biological, social, or physical nature, are associated with any of these alternatives, the opportunity for positive scientific work exists. Such work arises from a need in social problem-solving, but this does not necessarily detract from its scientific nature. Whether the work is fundamental or superficial from a scientific point of view is independent of the immediate need for application of the results. The worth will depend on the research organization and the caliber of the investigator.

## ILLUSTRATIONS FROM ECONOMICS

The foregoing notions may be illustrated by reference to economic studies. Parallels undoubtedly exist in other disciplines, but I leave their development to others.

### Of what use are analyses?

In recent years computational techniques have been developed that permit selection of an "optimal solution" from many possible "feasible solutions" according to some predetermined objective criterion.* These developments, coupled with the availability of increasingly larger electronic computers, have opened up the possibility of making the concepts of welfare economics operational on a wide scale. The close correspondence between the maximizing or minimizing process of the computational technique and the maximization concept in economics has permitted experimentation in empirically estimating theoretical economic concepts. For example, a linear programming study might be made of the optimal development and distribution of water for an area or a region,

---

* The reference is to linear programming or activity analysis.

given (i) the costs and returns from alternative uses in the sub-areas or subregions and (ii) some objective criterion, such as net economic benefits to be maximized. Many other examples might be given from the growing number of similar studies that are being made.

My purpose here is not to single out particular studies for criticism. Rather it is to make some general observations that may be helpful to the users, doers, and critics of such studies. Such studies may be of either a normative or a positive nature, depending on their interpretation and the use made of the results. The formulation of a criterion, or "choice indicator," clearly involves a value judgment. With the present state of our knowledge, the criterion can be only a partial and incomplete statement of the objectives of society. Under such circumstances, a resulting "optimum" plan is an optimum only in a limited technical sense and should not be equated with a social optimum.

It must also be pointed out, however, that the misuse described here does not mean that the techniques have no value. They may be used to discover and make explicit both economic and physical relationships. As a consequence, they may be used to predict part of the consequences of alternative use of resources.

It is also possible to use the concepts of economics in analyzing the results of past programs and policies. For example, a standard of economic efficiency might be postulated and the results of a particular program be measured against such a yardstick. Investigations of this kind should be encouraged on the grounds of improving the predictive power of economics, and on the more practical grounds of improving the programs and policies themselves. However, deviation of the actual results from the economic efficiency ideal does not necessarily mean that the program was "bad," "irresponsible," or "ineffective." Such a conclusion clearly rests on the implicit value judgment that economic efficiency is *the* objective of such programs. Failure to recognize economic efficiency aspects, however, may result in either (i) payment of too high a price to attain these other objectives, or (ii) failure to attain other objectives because economic forces were not taken into account.

In his analysis of conditions on a Bureau of Reclamation project in central Oregon, N. D. Kimball examined the consistency of the objectives stated by the bureau and the planning techniques used to achieve those objectives (12). He also compared subsequent project experience with anticipated developments at the time the project was planned. It was concluded that, in their desire to create maximum settlement opportunity on the project, the farms established by the bureau were too small to survive the economic climate that prevailed. More attention to the concept of economic efficiency probably would have resulted in a greater number of survivals on the project. An appropriate research activity is to examine the compatibility of public and private resource-use programs with underlying biological and economic conditions. Predictions about the outcomes of such programs are to be encouraged. Subsequent experience provides the scientist an opportunity to test his predictions, regardless of whether the findings of his field are recognized or ignored in the planning process.

## Choosing among alternatives

If the economist wishes to do positive research that may yield results useful in the social decision-making process, reference to value conflicts will help to identify needed information. This can be illustrated by reference to the three-way conflict in natural resource use that was mentioned earlier (intermediate good, mass recreation, and wilderness use).

We have here the familiar economic problem of alternative uses of a limited resource. The applicable tool or principle is that of opportunity cost, and the fundamental relationship is that of the transformation function. In its simplest form, the transformation function specifies the combinations of two or more uses that may be possible for a given resource. For an example, the quantities of mass recreation that could be produced from a particular site could be related to the amount of lumber that could be realized at the same time. Such a relationship commonly takes one of three forms: competition, where an increase in one use results in a decrease in another; supplementarity, where an increase in one use has no effect on the other; and complementarity, where an increase in one use makes possible an increase in another use. Empirical estimation of these relationships would be an appropriate joint activity of ecologists and economists. It is difficult to conceive of any kind of rational decision-making where economic progress is assigned so low a value that such information would not be of value. In fact, we now know enough about the nature of our resources and the characteristics of the alternative uses to speculate about these relationships. By doing this, it is possible to illustrate the use and misuse that may be made of such information.

We first select timber production and mass recreation as alternative uses for a particular site. If a site is managed primarily for timber production, it seems likely that some mass recreational activity would be possible without interfering significantly with timber production. At the other extreme, some timber production would be possible on most sites if they were managed to provide a maximum amount of recreation. In the intermediate range, the two uses would become competitive; there would probably be a range over which one use could be expanded only at the expense of the other.

If the wilderness use, rather than mass recreation, is considered, a somewhat different relationship probably prevails. In this case wilderness use and forestry appear to be competitive from the outset, although much depends on the definition of *wilderness* used. Apparently there are "degrees" of wilderness. Some advocates of wilderness would permit management for fire and insect protection. If such protection is permitted, wilderness use may be competitive with timber production in present use, although present use in wilderness would not necessarily preclude future timber production.

Even though such information is basic to the decision-making process, numerous reasons can explain why it may be inappropriate to use the concept involved to define a "socially optimum" combination of the three uses. Presumably this combination would result if the relative price ratios of the uses were equated to the transformation function or the opportunity cost line. Reasoning like this would lead to the conclusion that as long as the value of any of the uses is positive, some combination would be the most economic. This tends to preclude single-use classification of resources, except under unusual price circumstances, or, more specifically, when the value of one use is zero, or negative.

Such a simple solution to the problem is quite appealing. It is worthwhile, therefore, to enumerate the difficulties associated with applying the concept.

1) A transformation curve for a particular natural resource is not an iso-resource curve for society. Other inputs of labor and capital are required to transform the natural resource into the respective uses. Simply because timber exists on a particular site does not necessarily mean that it has economic value. In other words, classifying a site for multiple or single use does not necessarily mean that it will be used in that way. Furthermore, a site may have economic value in terms of its anticipated future yield of timber but may not be used for that purpose today. Therefore, wilderness use of that site today, when coupled with certain preventive measures, will not preclude forestry use in the future.

2) Until some method of valuing recreation is developed, prices cannot be assigned to two of the three alternative uses postulated. This suggests another area for economic research. It may be possible to estimate the prices that would exist for recreation if it were sold in the marketplace. Knowing such values, of course, would not necessarily mean that they constitute the appropriate social value to give to recreation.

3) Because of the multiplicity of existing interest groups, items treated as costs from the viewpoint of one group become benefits to another, and vice versa. For this reason, the benefit-cost type of analysis suggested by the aforedescribed economic model will interest few who influence decisions on natural resource use. Until the same data are viewed from the standpoint of the various interest groups, we will fail to understand or to anticipate the objectives and the influence of all parties to the process.

4) Failure to appreciate the alternatives available to us from our total natural resource base may lead to the wrong conclusions,

if reasoning is from the physical relationships on a particular site. For example, single use on a particular site is not inconsistent with multiple use when the total resource is considered.

### Role of the analyst

This is not an argument to abandon the tools of analysis that are the hallmark of the economist. It is a plea to resist the temptation to apply them before making a careful examination of what it is we hope to accomplish from their application.

These suggestions for making positive economic analysis and research useful in political decision-making are based on the assumption that our political decision-making process is similar to Lindblom's description of that process (13). Lindblom argues that we have a heritage of successive incremental policy moves that give interested parties a commonly shared background of experience. Furthermore, people agree more readily on what they are against than on what they are for. He argues that disagreements on abstract values are often disagreements on utopias from which actual policy choices are far removed. Since political policy-making is fragmented, it is not necessary that analysts agree on values. At first glance, this may appear to be inconsistent with the writings of Brewster (1–3), but reflection will show that this is not necessarily the case. The resolution of value conflicts will result from the "hammering out" of policies that will differ only incrementally from those we now have. In this process empirical information will be of use; by their nature it is possible to achieve agreement on empirical propositions. Scientists should be sufficiently knowledgeable about political problems to be able to anticipate the kinds of information that will be useful and can be developed from positive analyses in economics, ecology, engineering, and other relevant disciplines.

The purpose of this section of the paper has been to demonstrate that naive application of the tools of economics with unquestioning acceptance of the implicit value judgments of economics may yield results that are largely irrelevant, given the political process that we have. Positive economic research, however, can be quite relevant, if we are able to identify the parties to the conflict and to appreciate what they are attempting to achieve.

## Influence of institutions

There is another dimension to the social scene that is helpful in identifying relevant information. We may refer to this as the institutional framework that influences natural resource use. Institutions are the formal and informal means by which relationships among men are specified. They create the framework within which individuals and groups are permitted to satisfy their ends. Consequently, they reflect the social values that have persisted over time. For this reason, it is often inappropriate either to assume that they are out of the picture or to assume that they are constant and treat them as constraints. They are, in the final and ultimate sense, means, but in an intermediate sense they often constitute ends.

When a particular institution appears to be an obstacle to, say, the enhancement of national income, certain information is suggested as being of value. The change in institutional arrangement needed to accomplish the enhancement may be developed, but this may involve a sacrifice in another value that the institution was created to preserve. Some appreciation of other values of this kind is necessary to the development of alternative institutional arrangements that will permit the realization of multiple values. The Pelton Dam decision in Oregon illustrates this type of conflict. The granting of the permit to build the dam constituted redefinition of relationships among men. The potential economic gain that may come from this type of institutional precedent must be judged against what it does to the relationships that exist among men and groups of men.

The analysis of possible institutional arrangements that would permit these kinds of considerations to be brought into the open is an appropriate activity of the scientist. For example, the classification and treatment of certain areas as "wilderness" at the present time does not necessarily preclude their future use as forestry. An institutional arrangement is needed that would permit a limited use at the present time for those areas that have low value in the production of intermediate goods but, at the same time, would protect those resources for an alternative use in the future if this becomes necessary. To be of maximum value, the institutional arrangement should permit the alternative use to be considered periodically, rather than encourage the present classification to harden into a permanent-use category.

## ROLE OF THE PLANNER

Thus far only positive research has been described, and planning has not been treated. Some planning is normative in nature, and on this basis the work of the planner is to be distinguished from the activity of the scientist. As it is used here, *research* refers to the activity of searching for, and establishing, relationships relevant to the way things are. *Planning* refers to the activity of organizing information relevant to a particular policy decision. It may be normative in being oriented in the direction of bringing about changes in what is, so that it will conform with what "ought to be" (9).

The preceding analysis permits the formulation of some suggestions that may be helpful to planners. These suggestions are based on two assumptions. (i) Although planners are an integral part of the decision-making process, their activity should not be substituted for this process. (ii) No prejudgment should be made by the planners regarding the relative importance of the objectives of the numerous groups interested in natural resource decisions. The suggestions are as follows.

1) When the group for whom the planner is working specifies the objective to be achieved, relevant disciplines should be able to supply appropriate information for the development of a "plan" that will achieve the objective. When the objective is not specified, the planner may have to assume alternative objectives and shape his plans accordingly. When multiple goals exist, weights will have to be assigned if plans are to be developed. Numerous plans can be formulated if multiple goals exist.

2) It may be possible to eliminate the things that all groups are trying to avoid. Among the values that remain, areas of complementarity can be identified.

3) When value conflicts prevail, the alternative plans that are developed should bring these conflicts into sharp focus; conflicts should not be submerged in plans.

4) The planner should attempt to develop plans that will facilitate the "incremental decision-making" process described earlier. Sweeping and revolutionary changes in resource use or in the way relevant decisions are made are not likely in our environment (5).

5) Rather than search for "a social optimum," the planner will do well to search for a range of possible solutions that will encompass varying combinations of different objectives. Because we have no means for weighting these objectives, we are well advised to admit this frankly, rather than to develop objective-appearing formulas based on value judgments, which, if made explicit, would not be acceptable.

## SUMMARY

Various disciplines are available to the researcher and planner as they make their contribution to society while society struggles to determine how best to use the nation's natural resources. However, these disciplines are best used to discover "what is" or to predict "what will be," rather than to specify "what ought to be."

Conflicts currently exist concerning the combination of intermediate and final consumption goods that will result from our use of natural resources. It is currently beyond the ability of economics to specify what combination of uses will result in a social optimum. Economics can be used, however, to predict the economic consequences of alternative-use plans. The final resolution of conflicts properly rests with the political system, rather than with technicians, whether they be economists, ecologists, sociologists, or engineers.

## REFERENCES

1. Brewster, J. M., "Society values and goals in respect to agriculture," in *Goals and Values in Agricultural Policy* (Iowa State Univ. Press, Ames, 1961), chap. 6.

2. ———, "The impact of technical advance and migration on agricultural society and policy," *J. Farm Economics* **41**, 1169-1184 (1959).

3. ———, "Value judgments as principles of social organization with special reference to the rural scene," paper for Southwestern Social Science Assoc., Galveston, Tex., Mar. 1958.

4. Ciriacy-Wantrup, S. V., *Resource Conservation* (Univ. of California Press, Berkeley, 1952). Ciriacy-Wantrup recognizes the limitations of his definition as a policy norm.

5. ———, "Concepts used as economic criteria for a system of water rights," *Land Economics* **32**, 295-312 (1956).

6. Dasmann, R. F., *Environment Conservation* (Wiley, New York, 1959), p. 7.

7. Firey, W., *Mind, Man and Land* (Free Press, Glencoe, Ill., 1960).

8. Galbraith, J. K., "How much should a country consume?" in *Perspectives on Conservation; Essays on America's Natural Resources*, H. Jarrett, Ed. (Johns Hopkins Press, Baltimore, Md., 1958), pp. 94-95.

9. Halter, A. N., "The identification of problems in agricultural economics research," *J. Farm Economics* **42**, 1459 (1960). Halter's technologist corresponds to my planner.

10. Hirschman, A. O., *The Strategy of Economic Development* (Yale Univ. Press, New Haven, Conn., 1959).

11. Ise, J., *Our National Park Policy: A Critical History* (Johns Hopkins Press, Baltimore, Md., 1961).

12. Kimball, N. D., "The impact of economic and institutional forces on farmer adjustments in the north unit Deschutes project," a thesis submitted to Oregon State University in partial fulfillment of the requirements for the Ph.D. degree, 1961.

13. Lindblom, C. E., "Handling of norms in policy analysis," in *Allocation of Economic Resources*, essays in honor of Bernard Francis Haley (Stanford Univ. Press, Stanford, Calif., 1959).

14. Odum, E. P., *Fundamentals of Ecology* (Saunders, Philadelphia, ed. 2, 1959).

# IV  ROLE OF GOVERNMENT

# Problems Associated with Wilderness and Other Reserves of Public Lands

C. R. Gutermuth

*Wildlife Management Institute, Washington, D.C.*

National land and water resources have acquired a new significance in the last few years, and at no previous time have the policies and programs of the federal management agencies been under such close and continuing scrutiny. Great challenges and opportunities in the proper administration of public land resources lie in the years immediately ahead.

Public interest in natural resources management—conservation, as it generally is called—seldom has been more vocal than it is today. This is evident in the attention being given to legislative matters and agency programs, and in the respect that it commands from both resources administrators and political parties.

The 1960 national political campaign, for example, marked the first time that conservation groups ever were invited to appear before the platform committees of both major parties. Most of them accepted, and their advice and suggestions helped to shape the natural resources planks of the two platforms.

President Kennedy's natural resources message to the Congress, dated 23 February 1961, is striking proof of this new-found public interest. Never before in the early days of a new administration, or at any time in the life of most, has a President handed the Congress such a compelling and comprehensive assessment of natural resources problems and opportunities.

Experienced analysts and astute observers have no doubt that the federal government will continue to exercise control over the millions of acres of land that make up the public domain, national forests, parks, monuments, and wildlife refuges. Public ownership of these large areas is sure to continue for a long time, and no appreciable change in their over-all total acreage is expected.

## BUREAU OF LAND MANAGEMENT

Developments in the Bureau of Land Management of the Department of the Interior during the last few months of 1961 strengthen this opinion. Formed in a merger of the General Land Office and the Grazing Service in 1946, the BLM has had a rather rugged and unheralded existence. Few persons, either within or without government, realize that the BLM has returned more than $7 to the United States Treasury for every $1 appropriated for its resources program. On the other hand, efforts to obtain much-needed legislative and financial support have been defeated at nearly every turn. The morale of its professional staff has suffered greatly. Many people have regarded the BLM as a mere holding agency for parts of the public lands pending their eventual disposition to private interests.

All this started to change, however, about the time that the BLM released Project Twenty-Twelve, the first long-range program ever issued by that agency. The bureau then disclosed that, during the next half-century, it intends to dispose of only about 10 million of its 477 million acres, exclusive of Alaska entitlements under the Statehood Act.

This, to many of us, was a significant declaration. It was voiced in 1960 at a time when the prevailing political philosophy was inclined toward public land disposal. This reversal in attitude, as was documented by the release of Project Twenty-Twelve, has been followed by a number of separate actions designed to give the BLM the authority it needs to manage the lands for which it is responsible. All these actions move in the direction of correcting the serious imbalance that exists between the resources programs of the various federal agencies.

## CENTRAL REVIEW NEEDED

A principal cause of federal natural resources management problems is the lack of a centralized review of agency programs and objectives. Failure to provide such review has led to program imbalance, duplication, and contradiction. It has spurred agency competition for financial and legislative support and influenced decisions that more properly should have been made on the basis of merit and need. The agencies that have been most favored under this system have risen to positions of dominance and are able to enlist considerable political and public support. Such support is not entirely unwelcome, since much good has been accomplished. The success of these agencies, however, sometimes has worked to the detriment of other resources and public interests.

How soon the government will get around to correcting this situation is questionable. Special commissions have been appointed from time to time to study major problems, and nothing much has resulted. A number of excellent reports have been published, but the Congress rarely has implemented commission recommendations.

The efforts that are being made in Washington right now to elevate the BLM from a position of obscurity and subservience to a place befitting the administrator of more land than any other federal agency would overcome most of the shortcomings in public land policy. Examination of some of the factors that are catalyzing this interest in the BLM should arouse even more support.

The fact that the BLM had a secondary role and was operating at a level far below its recognized potential for public benefit has been realized for a long time. Well-organized resource-user groups have suppressed most of the efforts for program expansion. No appreciable gains were possible until 1959, when the late Senator James E. Murray, chairman of the Interior and Insular Affairs Committee, wrote then-Secretary of the Interior Fred A. Seaton: "There is totally lacking any program comparable to that for forests and parks from another great resources agency. It is my desire that your department prepare and submit to Congress at the earliest practicable date a program for the Bureau of Land Management."

Although it was a notable first attempt to chart the BLM's program needs, Project Twenty-Twelve fell far short. It surprised and shocked both the public and the politicians. The landlord of the public's largest real estate holdings had little accurate information about the resources it was supposed to be administering. The report prompted Senator Murray to request further information about program needs in terms of resources, projected activities, staff requirements, costs, benefits, legal authorizations, and other pertinent matters.

## ANCIENT LAWS AND PRINCIPLES

Then and now, the most formidable obstacle confronting the efforts to turn the BLM from the past toward the future is that its program stems from antiquated laws and outmoded philosophies. One applicable act is the Mining Act of 1872. Another, the Taylor Grazing Act of 1934, provides for forage use on 59 grazing districts, involving 142 million acres in 10 states. Its preamble starts with the shortsighted phrase: "That in order to promote the highest use of the public lands pending *its final disposal* . . . ." This indicates one thing: the Congress in 1934 obviously assumed that the public lands ultimately would be liquidated; and, when you read further, it becomes clear that grazing was regarded as the highest use. Repeated reference to these concepts by a few leading livestockmen in the West has been a deterrent to the proper administration of the public lands.

Another turning point for the BLM, and for the expression of a new national attitude toward natural resources, was the report of the Senate Appropriations Committee on the 1961 fiscal year budget requests for the Department of the Interior and related agencies. Commenting on its increase of several items, the committee declared that it "has taken into consideration the need to provide more intensified management of our public lands and national forests. These lands represent a major national asset that produce over $500 million in federal revenues annually . . . . While the increases recommended are large in comparison to some of the individual requests, attention is called to the fact that the total increase . . . is only about seven percent of the estimated revenue . . . that will be derived from public lands administered by the agencies involved."

## NATIONAL LAND RESERVE

Further impetus was given to the national asset concept by President Kennedy in his natural resources message of February

1961: "The federal government owns nearly 770 million acres of public land, much of it devoted to a variety of essential uses. But equally important are the vacant, unappropriated, and unreserved public domain lands, amounting to some 477 million acres—a vital national reserve that should be devoted to productive use now and maintained for future generations. Much of this public domain suffers from uncontrolled use and lack of proper management."

Elk are one form of wildlife that compete for natural resources.

The President directed the Secretary of the Interior to inventory and evaluate the public domain holdings, to develop a program of balanced usage, and to accelerate the installation of devices and practices to improve moisture conservation and reduce soil erosion.

Several related administrative actions subsequently have been taken and others are pending. Applications for public domain lands—the national land reserve as it now is designated—have been put off until the tremendous backlog has been cleared. The Interior Department is moving to overhaul its National Grazing Advisory Board Council to give representation to water, timber, mining, wildlife, recreation, and others who have an interest in the national land reserve. Proposals also have been sent to the Congress that would mandate the Secretary of the Interior to administer the national land reserve for multiple-use purposes. The Congress issued a similar directive to the U.S. Forest Service in 1960.

These developments do not mean that the BLM's era of short funds and political slighting suddenly is about to end. They do mean, however, that the bureau is moving into a position where it can compete more favorably with other agencies for available funds, congressional attention, and more widespread public endorsement.

## PRESSURES ON NATURAL RESOURCE AGENCIES

All natural resource agencies are subject to almost perennial attempts by various user groups to gain, maintain, or improve their positions in the use of the resources, and the BLM is no exception. For example, pending proposals before the Congress would grant to local district courts the power to review administrative decisions of BLM field officers on the number of livestock that grazing permittees may run on the public lands. Courtroom decisions would be substituted for skilled determinations of relative degrees of range use, forage production, carrying capacity, and other factors that should be decided by trained persons out on the land. Such a shift to judges and juries is sought in the hope that they would be more sympathetic to arguments involving the local economy and friends and neighbors.

Conservationists also are disturbed by a recent departmental ruling that tends to give permanence to the number of livestock a permittee may graze on the national land reserve. Although it did not change the Interior Department's authority to require a permit-holder to put fewer livestock on his allotment whenever a reduction is held necessary to protect the range, the reduction now is regarded as only temporary and the permit is left at the original number of animals. The justification for this change certainly is subject to question.

Permits to graze livestock on the public lands attach considerable value to the base property and bring a neat sum each time the property changes hands. This so-called "incentive" for range rehabilitation might pacify the rancher about the stock reduction, but the objectionable part is that the department is letting him keep an inflated permit to sell, if he chooses. However, it is unlikely that this will be a real selling point to the average livestockman who has been forced to take a cut.

Range conditions change slowly. Studies and evaluations take time. Overgrazed ranges may require soil and moisture work, reseeding, and years of careful handling before they are ready to withstand additional grazing. Livestock quotas on public lands should be based on sound management practices and scientific facts. If grazing should be reduced, it should be reduced, and the permit cut. Permittees that deliberately overuse and abuse public land do not merit special privileges.

## SQUATTERS TAKE OVER

Turning to another problem, thousands of people in all parts of the West are squatting on hundreds of thousands of acres of public land. They have moved in and taken over valuable federal lands along streams and lakes, in national forests, and throughout the public domain. They have built residences and summer homes, developed large agricultural tracts, and started all kinds of commercial enterprises.

The Interior Department's inventory of public land resources is forcing a well-fleshed skeleton out of that agency's closet. Fieldmen have found at least 10,000 cases of trespass on the national land reserve. Quick-saw pilferers are believed to be cutting federal timber illegally in several hundred areas. This practice has grown because successive administrations, down through the years, have not had the desire to take on the political forces that will muster against remedial action. Land locators, taking advantage of the squatter aspects of the mining laws, are staking claims and selling worthless titles to eager, uninformed citizens. This must be corrected to achieve proper control of the public lands.

Some of the other, more flagrant cases are along the Lower Colorado River, where the government has permitted and even encouraged land usurpation to go on for more than 25 years. Down there, in both Arizona and California, one sees pretentious residences, farms, stores, gasoline filling stations, motels, boat marinas—developments worth up to $200,000 or more, all on federal land. The government is producing electric energy and has run lines to those people at federal expense. Squatters pump allocated water from the river unlawfully, and the government, in some cases, has paid subsidies to illegal farmers for taking federal land out of crop production.

A bill before the Congress in 1961 would give all those people priority rights to the land they have grabbed. With such a congressional safeguard, they would be able to dictate the basis of property evaluation and terms of purchase. There is no provision in the bill for public recreation.

I have devoted attention to the Bureau of Land Management because it is an agency in change, an agency that illustrates problems and policies associated with the public lands. Before turning to other proposals for minimizing public land problems and clarifying policies, I wish to touch on a situation that may become serious —serious to the point of becoming highly detrimental.

## FORESTS VERSUS PARKS

An unfortunate tug of war has developed between the U.S. Forest Service and the National Park Service. The latter has considerable congressional and public support for an ambitious program to expand the national park system. The new proposal includes the acquisition and development of recreation areas along seacoasts and shorelines, and the creation of new national parks carved out of lands administered by the Forest Service. In 1962, administration bills were introduced and congressional hearings were held, but the measures were not enacted.

It is true that we have reached the place where expert attention must be given to the setting aside of the few remaining places of outstanding scenic and natural beauty that qualify for traditional national park status. Areas of this unique character should be incorporated in the national park system where they can be preserved for coming generations.

On the other hand, park proponents must have the will to resist indiscriminate attempts to claim all kinds of land for new parks and monuments. A few park advocates would lower long-established national park standards by taking inferior lands that do not qualify. This zeal should not be permitted. It would degrade the high standards of the major parks and mislead the public into supporting new areas that do not measure up as national parks. It also would place existing parks in jeopardy as demands mount for our limited land resources.

Another disturbing philosophy of some is that certain national forest lands should be included in the national park system simply because of their recreational importance. This philosophy overlooks the fact that recreation never has been a responsibility of the National Park Service. National parks and monuments were not intended as playgrounds. Their purpose is to preserve for all time truly unique natural areas and bits of outstanding Americana for the cultural benefit and inspiration of the people.

The Secretaries of Agriculture and the Interior keep stressing repeatedly that the long-time dispute between the National Park Service and the Forest Service no longer exists. This may be true on the Cabinet level, but those who are in close contact with the two agencies know otherwise. The Interior Department has more than 500 million acres of land now, much of which is good for forestry. It would seem that some fair and equitable land exchanges might be worked out with the Forest Service.

## PROGRAMS NEED INTERPRETATION

Still another difficulty that daily becomes more acute is how to translate agency policies and programs for public understanding. The rapid and abrupt move of the agencies into implementing multiple-use concepts will require fieldmen with broader training, background, and outlook. This age of multiple use must have men that can visualize and explain programs from the standpoint of all resources and uses. They must have the ability to view the public lands in terms of water production, forage, timber, parks, recreation, mining, wildlife, and all the other legitimate and necessary public uses. Dollar interpretations no longer suffice.

## WILDERNESS BILL

An example of the present failing in vision is illustrated by the bill that would designate a national system of wilderness from qualified lands in national forests, parks, and wildlife refuges. The proposal, S. 174, which has passed the Senate and is in the hearing stage in the House, is supported widely because of the cultural, recreational, and scientific opportunities it offers.* When it was first proposed 5 or more years ago, it contained provisions that invoked criticism. These have been corrected, and the federal agencies that originally voiced doubts and reservations now are officially recorded as favoring its enactment.

Despite this support, the field employees of one of the principal agencies have continued to make speeches to local groups in opposition to S. 174 long after their organization had expressed its approval in Washington. Whether this contradiction resulted from a lack of communication between the central and field offices, or from a lack of control, is not known. In any event, official policy has been flouted.

All wilderness opponents seem to sit at the same campfire. They speak primarily for those commercial interests that want to get the last dollar from the timber, forage, minerals, and other resources in the pitifully few acres of irreplaceable wilderness. It is impossible to reconcile differences with them, because of their ambitions. They are against wilderness, and all forms of land reserves. In fact, they are against public lands of almost any kind.

The fury of the existing opposition is centered on S. 174, because it is the principal public lands legislation now before the Congress. Their distortions echo time-worn cliches: destruction of community growth, loss of revenues and taxes, damage to timber interests, interference with livestock operations, discrimination

---

* The wilderness bill was not enacted by the 87th Congress. The House Interior and Insular Affairs Committee drastically altered the measure that was approved by the Senate and tried to force it through the House of Representatives without opportunity for floor debate. This stratagem was rejected by the House leadership.

against miners. All these contentions have been disproved before and will be disproved again.

The bill S. 174 would not create a new federal agency. It would not interfere with the purposes for which the wilderness areas in the national forests, parks, and wildlife refuges already may be used. It would not surrender congressional prerogatives in public land matters. In no way would it disrupt established, legitimate activities of any commercial interest on the public lands.

The bill merely provides a procedure whereby federal lands already in wilderness status would continue to serve their present national forest, park, and wildlife-refuge purposes, but in a way that would preserve their wilderness character. The wilderness system would provide the richest nation in the history of the world with a means of preserving about 2 percent of its natural and scenic beauty for the inspirational, cultural, recreational, and scientific benefit of all the people.

## CAPITAL BUDGET

One of the most serious deterrents to over-all progress in the management and development of public land resources is the existing federal budgeting procedure. The current process categorizes expenditures for the purchase or improvement of such physical assets as forest lands, dams, parks, recreation centers, water developments, to name only a few, as operating expenses of government. It measures outlay on the cost side but fails to relate it to income. This, of course, is contrary to conventional business practice.

Expenditures for natural resources operating programs that bring in a cash return are real investments. They can be measured both in public benefits and cash returns. To budget all such appropriations as current expenditures chargeable against current taxes is to lose sight of their capital-investment value and of the future returns in cash and services.

This matter of a so-called "capital" budget was recognized by Walter Lippman, the distinguished American commentator, in his column of 28 February 1961, following the President's natural resources message to the Congress. He observed that there will have to be "... a certain re-education of American public opinion. More exactly, the re-education will mean the clearing away of the confusion which clusters about the highly charged words 'spending' and 'investment.'

"There is, for example, the notion that the public authorities at any government level never invest. They only spend. On the other hand, private corporations and private individuals not only spend but also invest. This leads to the blind prejudice that since governments can only spend, whatever money they use tends to be wasted. On the other hand, whenever private corporations or individuals invest, that is a good thing and a public benefit.

"This prejudicial use of words confuses public opinion: (1) the money spent privately to make automobiles is prudent investment; but the money spent publicly to build the roads for the automobiles is spending; (2) the money to build a public hospital is spending; but the money to build plants to make the drugs that are dispensed is investment; (3) if a public park is made, that is spending. If a new movie house is built, that is investment.

"This semantic muddle inhibits clear thinking about public questions. The truth is that there is private spending and private investment and that some of it is good and some is not so good and some of it is bad. There is also public spending and public investment, and some of it is good and some of it is not so good and some of it is bad.

"It takes good judgment to spend and invest wisely, be it publicly or privately."*

## SUMMARY

Public interest in natural resources management seldom has been more expressive than it is today. At no previous time have the policies and programs of the federal resources agencies been under such close scrutiny. This interest reflects the great challenges and opportunities in the proper administration of public land resources that lie in the years ahead.

The lack of a centralized review of agency programs and ob-

---

* W. Lippman, 28 Feb. 1961, *New York Herald Tribune* Syndicate.

jectives is the principal cause of present federal natural resources management problems. Program imbalance, duplication, and contradiction are the result.

The federal government will continue to exercise public trust over the millions of acres of lands that make up the national land reserve, national forests, parks, monuments, and wildlife refuges. Some of the agency programs and administrative and legislative activities that are discussed briefly here point to rather troublesome program and policy conflicts among agencies.

A very serious deterrent to improved management of public land resources is the current federal budgeting procedure, which characterizes investments in public land developments as operating expenses of government. This practice, which measures outlay on the cost side and ignores the income, is contrary to conventional business practice.

# Public and Private Investment in Resources Development

WILLIAM E. FOLZ

*Department of Agricultural Economics, University of Idaho, Moscow*

The legal and constitutional justification for public investment in resources development is long established. From Colonial times public funds were used to clear hostile Indians from lands that were sought for settlement. State and federal investments in roads and canals, subsidies to railroads, improvements of river and harbor channels, all have found constitutional sanction and were among the earliest federal government activities under the Constitution. Federally owned resources have also been used to attain governmental social objectives. The public domain has been used to support public education, to build railroads, to provide bounties to war veterans, to maintain the family farm, and to encourage development of the West. Precedent, as well as legality, is thus established in this field of government activity.

The economic justification for public investment in resources, however, is not so easily resolved. An equally long precedent exists for leaving all investment as much as possible to private enterprise. Orthodox economic thinking recognized exceptions to this rule under the following conditions: (i) if the required investment is too large for private enterprise to handle; (ii) if financial benefits will accrue only after a time period that is too long to interest private investors; (iii) if the private investor, in attempting to maximize profits, uses the resource in a manner detrimental to others; (iv) if the financial benefits will accrue to others than the investors; and (v) if potential nonpecuniary benefits will accrue to the public but not the private investor.

The modern corporation, with access to almost unlimited capital and with its unlimited life, has to a large extent removed the first two bases for public investment. Recent cost-benefit studies have made further inroads into its economic defense and, by placing heavy emphasis on static equilibrium models, have cut deeply into the fourth justification. This leaves as the proper scope of public investment only projects heavily laden with nonpecuniary benefits. Before consigning public investment in resources development to the uncertain category of nonmarket values, let us look again at the models themselves to ascertain the extent to which they encompass all the appropriate economic objectives and benefits.

## TWO CONCEPTS OF NATIONAL ECONOMIC BENEFITS

If public investment is to be justified, it is apparent that some benefits must accrue to the public that do not arise out of private investment. The first questions to be answered, therefore, are: What are national economic benefits? How can they be measured? Two general approaches to the identification of national economic benefits arising out of economic activity have been made in the past. The first and older approach may be termed the *gains-from-trade-consumer-surplus* approach, and the second the *equilibrium-opportunity-cost* approach.

The President's Water Resources Policy Commission seems to use the first approach. The benefits that are considered valid by the commission relate to the provision for more abundant productive resources. "On the positive side the realizable potentials over and above mere avoidance of losses through better use of our water resources are enormous. Economically, these gains would find expression in higher national productivity; higher national income; improved standards of living; increased economic stability; and more ample supplies of basic food, fibers, forest products, and many other goods whose production is dependent on water either directly or indirectly. They would also be reflected in reduction of costs for water, power, transport, forest products, and other essential goods and services, as well as new industries and better balanced economies in regions now suffering from various imbalances" (22).

The attempt of the President's Water Resources Policy Commission to assess the benefits of river-basin developments in terms of greater abundance of goods and services is reminiscent of the gains-from-trade-consumer-surplus approach to the benefits of international trade expounded by the classical and neoclassical economists. The criticism of this approach, so ably presented by McKean in his representation of the equilibrium-opportunity-cost approach, also finds a precedent in the same controversy. McKean (18, p. 147) states that the commission's reference to private values based on scarcity and public values based on plenty is either meaningless or wrong. "If values of goods and services are meant, the statement is clearly incorrect; such values, public and private alike, grow out of the fact that there are not enough goods and services to satisfy wants." McKean's position is that incremental costs and returns alone should be considered, so that as long as incremental returns exceed incremental costs, there is no need to speculate about the effect of the project on relative abundance or scarcity of the commodities produced (18).

Here we have a statement of the essence of the differences in the approaches to national economic benefits. The gains-from-trade approach seeks to find some measure of welfare expressed in terms of abundance. It recognizes that large increases of goods and services may decrease the monetary value of these goods and services, rather than increase them, but that at the same time the public may benefit greatly from such abundance. The gains of trade are to be found, therefore, in making scarce commodities plentiful, so that one day's labor can command more goods and commodities after trade than it could before trade. The monetary value of such goods and services may actually decline as a result of increased abundance, but the public benefits in terms of real wages or consumers' surplus have in fact increased (28).

The equilibrium economists, on the other hand, measure benefits in terms of marginal or incremental returns over costs. Each producer strives to allocate the factors of production in such a manner that the marginal returns to each factor are equal to the marginal returns of the other factors. All factors in each productive process are expanded to the point where marginal costs equal marginal returns. At this point, also, the marginal returns to each factor are equal to its opportunity costs, or the returns that would accrue to it if it were employed in its next most productive use. On the demand side, each individual is assumed to be restrained by the limitations of his budget. Consumer utility will be maximized when consumer outlays are so allocated that each consumer gets as much utility from each unit of purchasing power spent as he would if he had spent it otherwise. The marginal utility of each purchasing unit is equal to the marginal utility of every other unit.

This equilibrium model thus becomes a unique mathematical expression of national welfare maximization. On the demand side, each consumer is spending his income in a manner to maximize his satisfactions from it. On the production side, these goods and services are supplied by employing scarce production factors in their most efficient uses. By summing up all such individual marginal utilities, one arrives at the maximum total social utility. Similarly, on the production side, if each production factor is allocated to its most productive use in each production process, the summation of all marginal productivities will also equal the maximum social utility.

The usual procedure for project planning in water-resources projects represents attempts to formulate the equilibrium analysis into cost-benefit analysis. It attempts to determine the least-cost alternative in project planning, then to estimate the direct benefits in terms of the value with and without the project. The excess of value of goods and services stemming from the project over all costs, production as well as project, divided by project costs, provides the cost-benefit ratio. This analytical procedure is the one recommended by the Interagency Committee and with minor exceptions by Eckstein (5), Krutilla (16), McKean (18), and Renshaw (23). As long as projects are small, only incremental amounts of commodities and services are added to the already existing market, and their value over costs can be estimated and treated as net additions to income. Their competitive effect, their income-redistribution effect, and their adjustment effect can be ignored. This is the essence of the equilibrium model, and the authors cited seem to believe that the aforedescribed situation is typical enough to justify its application to investments in resources development.

## LIMITATIONS OF THE TWO CONCEPTS OF
## NATIONAL ECONOMIC BENEFITS

Both approaches to the measurement of national economic benefits described here have their limitations. The attempt of the neoclassical school and the President's commission to measure benefits in terms of abundance of consumers' goods presents three serious difficulties. First, it must assume that the total utility of all goods and services is constant, so that if a larger quantity of goods and services becomes available, greater consumer surplus will be enjoyed. This denies the possibility that consumers may prefer fewer of the goods and services that are increased and more of the goods and services that are given up to secure them (29).

Second, it must assume on the cost side that all goods and services are produced under constant costs, so that if expansion of production in one direction is foregone to expand production in another direction, we are adding or subtracting equal costs. For example, assume that consumers are taxed to develop a river-basin project that will make more agricultural products available, but to pay the taxes they give up investments that would expand manufactured goods. If the manufactured products that are not expanded are produced under decreasing costs, the increased quantities of agricultural products may decrease consumers' surplus, even if their marginal utilities are the same as those of manufactured products (29).

The third and most severe limitation arises out of the existence of noncompeting groups and the consequent immobility of resources (29). When large increases of goods and services become available within a short period of time, they have a price effect and an income-redistribution effect on producers who are already supplying such goods and services. If factors of production in the industries that are already producing the goods and services now in increased supply become redundant, they must move into other, more productive employments. If they encounter noncompeting groups, their ease of movement is lessened and the cost of adjustment is increased. The classical economists ignored these costs. They assumed perfect mobility of factors and counted the gains from trade and the increased consumer surplus only after all adjustments were made. Our present agricultural adjustment problems testify to the fact that such adjustments cannot be so readily ignored.

The equilibrium approach avoids some of the difficulties that are inherent in the older form of analysis. Their success in doing so, however, depends to a large extent on their assumption that such investments result only in incremental increases in goods and services, and that there are no other national economic benefits except those encompassed in the model.

First, let us consider the assumption of incremental increases of goods and services that result from investments in resources development. The President's commission had in mind large developmental projects, such as river-basin development projects. Such investments by their nature involve large increases in the quantities of goods and services produced. All the authors listed in foregoing paragraphs as adhering to the equilibrium model in evaluating costs and benefits recognize that the assumptions of the model do not hold when we deal with large river-basin developments. Nor are they valid for smaller projects in which some resource having a local market will be produced in such quantities, as a result of the project, that the price of the commodities will decline. Their treatment of these situations, which are termed *indivisibilities,* is vague.

On this point, Krutilla and Eckstein state: "Implicit in the discussion of the productive function and marginal adjustments in the competitive [equilibrium] model was an assumption that factors could be varied by small amounts. In some instances, however, there are technical reasons why factors can be employed only in large, indivisible doses" (*16,* p. 45). They do not explain, however, how the benefits of such a public investment should be evaluated. If the new production decreases the total value of the product, is the decreased cost of goods to be treated as a gain to the rest of the economy, or is the lower income of the older producers to be considered a diseconomy? No resolution of this difficulty is offered. We are back to the same problems faced by the classicists in their measurement of the gains from trade and consumers' surplus. One solution is to consider only projects in which technical indivisibilities do not arise, or to ignore the price and income redistributive effect. If the first solution is chosen, large river-basin projects must be foregone in favor of smaller projects, since the equilibrium models provide no means of measuring national economic values that arise from large increases in production (18). The classical problems have not been eliminated or explained; they have merely been avoided by the use of a method of analysis that does not permit them to arise.

This same difficulty occurs in the treatment of public investments during periods of depression. During such periods all resources are not fully employed, as is assumed in the equilibrium model. If cost-benefit analysis is consistent with this model, it must recognize that the cost of resources during periods of unemployment cannot be measured adequately by the cost of their alternative uses. Since they have no alternative uses, their costs must approximate either zero or very low values. None of the equilibrium theorists seem willing to pursue the analysis to this degree of consistency; they prefer, rather, to depend on changes in prices of resources used (5, 14), or on lower interest rates being applied to lower costs during depressions (3), while estimating a long-run value for the prices of the commodities produced, thus making more projects economically feasible. McKean suggests that the government should independently decide on the volume of public investment needed to stabilize the economy and then choose from among the alternative projects the ones with the highest cost-benefit ratios until the desired volume is reached. In each selection, care should be taken to vary the number of projects and the expansion of each project only to the point where marginal costs equal marginal returns (18).

Thus, while grudging concessions are made to the logic of employing resources-development projects as a factor in fiscal policy, these economists like to imply that such uses are either unnecessary or unimportant when they are viewed from the standpoint of the entire fiscal policy problem. Consistency with good theory, however, does not permit such a cavalier disposition. Whether we consider investments in resources development, or in defense, or in any other economic activity by the government, the same difficulties present themselves in working them into the equilibrium economic model. If the investments are large enough to have any significant effect on the volume of employment and use of resources during depressions, the volume of commodities produced from them will have a price effect and an income-redistribution effect (3, 6). It becomes necessary in such cases to go outside the model and make value judgments concerning the welfare or social benefits derived. Have the price effects and the income-redistribution effects increased social welfare? If so, how can these benefits be measured? We find ourselves again in the same position as the classical theorists trying to explain gains from trade on the basis of increased volume of trade or increased consumer surplus; both of these concepts, as we have seen, get us into logical difficulties.

From the foregoing analysis, it becomes apparent that the equilibrium model has been no more successful than the older classical models expressed in real terms in measuring national benefits or welfare as derived either from government investment or from trade policy. Once the assumption of incremental returns over cost either is dropped or becomes inapplicable, we are thrown back upon either subjective value judgments or inadequate objective measures of benefit. To avoid these difficulties, we must accept one of two alternative premises if the equilibrium model is to be made valid: (i) Investments or policy decisions that cause sufficient changes in quantities of commodities and services to bring about significant price changes and income redistributions occur too infrequently to concern us. (ii) If they do occur, they are not of any consequence economically.

The first alternative is clearly not true in the light of history. The second alternative implies that only the situations that fit nicely into the model are the proper subjects for economic analysis. This hardly rises to the dignity of an argument. The question at issue is whether or not government investments in resources development are justified and under what conditions. The equilibrium model tells us that national benefits can be secured only where marginal returns are greater than marginal costs. This occurs only when the increased production resulting from the project is so small that its price effect and its income-redistribution effect can be ignored. Such conditions generally prevail when government investment simulates private investment. A strict adherence to this theory would provide a strong presumption that government investments in resources development, except under rare circumstances, cannot be justified economically. We have thus drawn a very important conclusion—a conclusion, however, that we have assumed in the construct of the model itself.

## EQUILIBRIUM MODEL AS AN ANALYTICAL DEVICE FOR ECONOMIC GROWTH

The basic difficulty with both comparative advantage and equilibrium refinements is that they are essentially static models and do not lend themselves freely to dynamic analysis. Problems that arise out of changes in trade relations, fiscal policy, and economic growth and development are dynamic. Whereas small changes in trade, technology, and investment can readily be introduced into the equilibrium assumptions, large changes cannot be so easily handled. This difficulty is particularly manifested in attempts to incorporate economic growth in the models. It is recognized that coefficients encompassing growth can be introduced into these models, and consistency with equilibrium will be maintained, as the works of Von Neumann as pointed out by Hicks (*11*) and the studies of Chenery (*2*) and others testify. The models with which we are dealing, however, are of the Walras-Cassel variety. No effort is made by the authors under review to introduce such dynamic factors.

In the resources field, this limitation of the equilibrium model manifests itself in the reluctance of equilibrium theorists to treat of anything smacking of economic growth. The *Green Book* (*14*) states: "The public policies governing the development of the nation's water and related land resources are not necessarily determined solely on the basis of economic consideration .... . regional development and national defense have been objectives of various resource development programs." The implication here that regional development is not an economic objective is expressed also by Margolis: "Most of the intangible benefits are concerned with social evaluation of such matters as conservation, the family-sized farm, mobility of resources, effect upon the degree and type of competition, implications for public health, income redistribution, or balanced regional development . . . . A danger in this procedure is evident in all three volumes; the intangibles are recognized but barely analyzed. Therefore, the significance of the tangible benefits will be weighted at the expense of the intangibles" (19). McKean, while recognizing the economic nature of regional expansion, recommends against placing a value on it for evaluation purposes (18).

A more complete statement of the economic nature of regional expansion is made by Krutilla and Eckstein: "While the ultimate effect of a federally developed hydroelectric site in the Northwest results in some income transfer to the region, a host of additional redistribution consequences among members of society also attends the federal development of hydroelectric projects" (16, pp. 156–157). This statement is prefaced by one, however, which implies that such an expansion has economic importance but that it cannot be "worked into the framework of analysis" (16).

If growth and development have significant economic implications, their manifestation would be reflected in the growth of industries whose location is oriented to the resources expanded by the project. Such growth patterns are usually referred to as secondary or indirect benefits. In treating secondary benefits, however, all the authors who adhere to the equilibrium approach are agreed that they have no place in project evaluation. The *Green Book* states: "Although secondary benefits may be signified in the economic justification of projects from a local or regional point of view or in reimbursement and assessment considerations . . . from a national public point of view such benefits usually have little significance in project formulation, economic justification, and array" (14). Eckstein also is inclined to minimize the economic benefits from the secondary expansion, which he terms *stemming benefits* (5). McKean maintains that secondary benefits do not arise during periods of full employment. All that occurs is a transfer of purchasing power from one group to another. During periods of unemployed resources, secondary benefits do arise, but they are difficult to compute, and fiscal policies other than such projects may be more efficient in creating additional income (18).

We thus find that whenever dynamic elements arise, such as

economic growth or stimulation of employment during periods of underemployment, the cost-benefit analysts are reluctant to treat them as economic benefits. The reason becomes quite clear. To induce economic growth or to create significant employment opportunities, large blocks of investments are required. We must think in terms of large river-basin development projects, vast resources-development programs, multibillion-dollar investments. The equilibrium model functions best when only incremental inputs and outputs are treated.

In the foregoing analysis, it has been shown that using either the quantity of products to measure benefits, as did the classical school, or the opportunity cost of the equilibrium theorists provides an inadequate criterion for measuring benefits in a dynamic growing economy.

## NATURE OF ECONOMIC BENEFITS
## DERIVED FROM ECONOMIC GROWTH

It is apparent that if economic growth has any national significance, it must provide identifiable economic benefits, benefits that represent something more than a mere rearrangement of productive factors and a redistribution of income. Which benefits of growth are not included in the equilibrium models, and which inducements to growth are not encompassed by them?

We cannot improve on the traditional economic theories of consumers' choices in assessing benefits of production. Satisfactions cannot be measured directly. Therefore, an element of uncertainty will always exist in measurements of consumers' surplus. We assume, therefore, that a growing economy increases social welfare over time, if it provides ever-increasing quantities of the same stock of consumers' goods or if it produces a wider variety of desired goods and services, including leisure, when they are measured on a per-capita basis. We make no value judgment about the satisfactions or happiness that people derive from such an increase in economic goods (17). Obviously, if the economic well-being of a nation is to be improved, an increase in goods and services will have to provide a product mix that will coincide in some broad way with the desires of the people (12). A mere increase in the quantity of redundant or surplus agricultural commodities would not in itself qualify as a measure of the increase in economic well-being. On the other hand, we cannot deny that even an increase in surplus products may be a first step in the direction of achieving a product mix that will provide greater consumer satisfaction. In the absence of any really valid test of consumers' utilities, we must fall back on other measures.

A measure of welfare that will avoid some of the difficulties involved in estimating utility is labor productivity. We can define the measure of economic growth as a trend in the marginal productivity of labor. If the real marginal productivity of labor is increasing as a result of the combination of larger quantities of capital and resources with labor, we can say that economic growth is occurring. As long as investments increase the real marginal productivity of labor, we can assume that the adjustments in the economy will be in the direction of producing the product mix that is most conducive to consumer welfare and utility (15).

This is not to suggest that the equilibrium economists are unmindful of the welfare implications of increasing the marginal productivity of labor. Their interest in efficient allocation of resources stems from their concern over this matter. The difficulty encountered in applying their analysis to a welfare measure of labor productivity arises out of the peculiar assumptions inherent in this model. The equilibrium model assumes that all factors of production are scarce and that they are known. If all resources are scarce, the only way to increase labor productivity in a growing economy is to increase the capital employed in the productive process. In this model, therefore, labor productivity increases can be measured by the increase in the ratio of capital to labor. A principal limitation of this approach is that it "ignores the existence of other factors of production, such as natural resources" (1). The increase in labor productivity, however, can be maximized as much by increasing the natural resource base as it can by increasing capital. The fact that the one factor is easily adaptable to the equilibrium approach and the other is not provides no sound basis for its omission in an economic analysis.

In the equilibrium model as it is usually presented, we also encounter a difficulty in the handling of intermediate goods. In the assessment of the benefits of resources-development projects, as well as in the expansion of international trade, equilibrium models deal with increased production of commodities as they minister to final consumer demand. The consumption function, complex as it is, is relatively simple compared with the possibilities of substitutions, complementarities, and external pecuniary economies that exist in the production process.

The effect of the abundance of natural resources on the economic development of the United States has not been adequately treated by economists (8). Since only scarce factors could be treated effectively in traditional economic analysis, the orthodox rent doctrine was a stumbling block to Ricardian thinking in this country. Marginal productivity analysis also had difficulty with this point. The very abundance of resources reflected a low marginal productivity to natural resources but a high productivity to capital and labor. This led to an overemphasis on technology and capital as the scarce factors whose abundance would, by itself, assure ever higher standards of living (8). Little attention was given to the fact that the high productivity of capital and, consequently, of labor was related to the richness of the resources to which capital was applied in the production process. The historians, not the economists, expressed concern at the passing of the frontier.

Reflection will reveal the great importance of abundance of resources in the production process. This is not a matter of indifference in economic analysis; it involves a wide classification of activities that have profound economic significance. The more abundant and the less expensive a resource is, the more possibilities exist to substitute it for scarce resources. Thus, if lumber becomes so inexpensive that stumpage has very low value, lumber in its various forms will be used in a variety of production processes in preference to lumber substitutes. If lumber becomes scarce and expensive, however, other products will readily be substituted for it. Inexpensive lumber thus becomes not only a useful resource but a regulator of the prices and qualities of its substitutes. To become an effective substitute for lumber, another product, say, aluminum, must be as inexpensive and as effective in performing the services of lumber as lumber itself. If lumber becomes scarce and relatively costly, inferior substitutes with relatively high prices will be used. The marginal productivity of capital invested in the substitutes will rise, and the capital intensity ratio will also increase. Welfare gains will be reflected in the equilibrium model. From an economic welfare point of view, however, a plentiful timber supply would be preferable.

This illustration is akin to the concept of pecuniary external economies that result from investment described by Rosenstein-Rodan (24) and by Scitowsky (27). These authors point out situations in which profits of a firm depend not only on "its own output and factor inputs, but also on the factor inputs of other firms" (27). Rosenstein-Rodan maintains that it "might easily happen that any one enterprise would not be profitable enough to guarantee payment of sufficient interest or dividends out of its own profits. But the creation of such an enterprise, e.g., production of electric power, may create new investment opportunities and profits elsewhere, e.g., in an electrical industry. If we create a sufficiently large investment unit by including all the new industries of the region, external economies will become internal profits out of which dividends may be paid easily" (24).

There are four situations in which external economies can arise: (i) when another industry has a factor produced in a given industry; (ii) when the product of a given industry is complementary to another industry; (iii) when an industry produces a product that is consumed by people whose income is raised by the expansion in the given industry; and (iv) when an industry produces a commodity that is a substitute for a factor used in another industry (24).

Situations in which direct benefits do not measure total welfare secured from investments represent a broad category of public investment opportunities. Investments in public education present a case in point (26). The direct benefits of training in engineering, business, law, and research (10) may be small or even negative, if we count the opportunity costs of the student and the government investment in education plus opportunity costs of interest on such investments. We justify these investments in education on the basis of increased national productivity derived from better technical training, better business organization, better services, and better scientific knowledge generally. We evade the economic issue by calling such benefits nonpecuniary benefits and by leaving them outside the realm of economic analysis.

## SUMMARY

The foregoing analysis has indicated that public investment in resources development is justified only if public investment can provide national benefits that are unattainable through private investment. Neither of the two traditional methods of appraising national economic benefits, however, is a satisfactory guide to policy in this matter. The President's Water Resources Commission's measurement of benefits based on abundance overemphasizes quantities of goods and services but slights utility and costs of adjustment. Recent cost-benefit analyses emphasize marginal utility and marginal value productivity but ignore all indirect benefits that arise from greater abundance of resources.

Both approaches are static and provide no analysis of economic growth, economic stability, or increased labor productivity resulting from expansion of resources. The failure of traditional comparative-advantage and equilibrium analysis to accommodate these benefits led economists who were interested in economic growth to reject these theories through the years. From the time of Hamilton, Clay, Matthew Carey, and Frederick List (4) to Myrdal (20), Nurkse (21), Rostow (25), and Hirschman (13), growth theory found the traditional models lacking. While the traditional analysts were dealing with alternative costs and movements toward equilibrium under assumptions of market conditions and private investments, these growth theorists were concerned with government investment in internal improvements to open new lands, tariffs to provide home markets for balanced economic growth, government subsidies for canals and railroads, and water-resources projects. They were also concerned with public education and research as means to induce movements, not toward static equilibrium, but toward the greater productivity of a growing economy (*1, 11*).

The measure of growth and of the benefits derived from growth must provide some evaluation, not of direct benefits alone, but of all growth and development based on the increased resources. A strong presumption exists that if an investment, public or private, induces regional growth, there will be larger benefits from the investment than if such regional growth does not take place. The reason is that the greater the regional growth that occurs, the greater the opportunities for complementary and external economies to manifest themselves (*7*).

Although methods of measuring the economic growth and national benefits that accrue from investment in resources development are not easy to formulate, this task can be accomplished at least in some rough form (*9*). Despite the inherent difficulties, we shall not make progress toward measuring these important economic values if we confine ourselves to the use of analytical tools that deny their existence.

## REFERENCES

1. Chenery, H. B., "Comparative advantage and development policy," *Am. Econ. Rev.* **51**, 18-51 (1961).
2. ———, "Patterns of industrial growth," *ibid.* **50**, 624-654 (1960).
3. Ciriacy-Wantrup, S. V., "The role of benefit-cost analysis in public resource development," in *Water Resources and Economic Development of the West*, Rept. 3 (Water Resources Comm., Western Agricultural Economics Research Council, Washington State Univ., Pullman, 1954).
4. Dorfman, J., *The Economic Mind in American Civilization* (Viking, New York, 1946), vol. 2.
5. Eckstein, O., *Water-Resource Development; the Economics of Project Evaluation* (Harvard Univ. Press, Cambridge, Mass., 1958).
6. Folz, W. E., discussion of paper by S. V. Ciriacy-Wantrup in reference 3.
7. ———, "The economics of water resources development: a theoretical analysis," in *Water Resources and Economic Development of the West*, Rept. 0 (Water Resources Comm., Western Agricultural Economics Research Council, Washington State Univ., Pullman, 1951).

8. ———, "The theory of the relationship of resource development to economic development," in *Water Resources and Economic Development of the West,* Rept. 1 (Water Resources Comm., Western Agricultural Economics Research Council, Washington State Univ., Pullman, 1953).

9. Garnsey, M. E., "Welfare economics and water resources development," paper for the Water Resources Comm. Panel, Fort Collins, Colo., Aug. 1961.

10. Griliches, Z., "Research costs and social returns: hybrid corn and rented innovations," *J. Political Economy* **66**, 419-431 (1958).

11. Hicks, J. R., "Linear theory," *Economic J.* **70**, 671-709 (1960).

12. Higgins, B., *Economic Development: Principles, Problems, and Policies* (Norton, New York, 1959).

13. Hirschman, A. O., *The Strategy of Economic Development* (Yale Univ. Press, New Haven, Conn., 1958).

14. Interagency Committee on Water Resources, Subcommittee on Evaluation Standards, *Report: Proposed Practices for Economic Analysis of River Basin Projects* (U.S. Govt. Printing Office, Washington, D.C., 1958). Commonly referred to as the *Green Book.*

15. Kahn, A. E., "Investment criteria in development programs," *Quart. J. Economics* **65**, 38-61 (1951).

16. Krutilla, J., and O. Eckstein, *Multiple-Purpose River Development* (Johns Hopkins Press, Baltimore, Md., 1958).

17. Lewis, W. A., *The Theory of Economic Growth* (Allen and Unwin, London, 1955).

18. McKean, R. N., *Efficiency in Government through Systems Analysis, with Emphasis on Water Resources Development,* a Rand Corp. research study (Wiley, New York, 1958).

19. Margolis, J., "The economic evaluation of federal water resources development," *Am. Econ. Rev.* **49**, 96-111 (1959).

20. Myrdal, G., *Rich Trends and Poor; the Road to World Prosperity* (Harper, New York, 1957).

21. Nurkse, R., *Equilibrium and Growth in the World Economy* (Harvard Univ. Press, Cambridge, Mass., 1961).

22. The President's Water Resources Policy Commission, *A Water Policy for the American People* (U.S. Govt. Printing Office, Washington, D.C., 1950).

23. Renshaw, E. F., *Towards Responsible Government: an Economic Appraisal of Federal Investment in Water Resources Programs* (Idyia Press, Chicago, 1957).

24. Rosenstein-Rodan, P. N., "Problems of industrialization of eastern and southeastern Europe," *Economic J.* **53**, 202-211 (1943).

25. Rostow, W. W., *The Process of Economic Growth* (Norton, New York, 1952).

26. Schultz, T. W., "Investment in human capital," *Am. Econ. Rev.* **51**, 1-17 (1961).
27. Scitowsky, T., "Two concepts of external economies," *J. Political Economy* **62**, 143-151 (1954).
28. Viner, J., *International Trade and Economic Development* (Free Press, Glencoe, Ill., 1952).
29. ———, *Studies in the Theory of International Trade* (Harper, New York, 1937).

# Legal Aspects of a National Water Program

Morris K. Udall

*Congress of the United States, House of Representatives, Washington, D.C.*

Every year natural events dramatize the need for better control over, and better use of, water resources. The year 1961 was no exception. Severe drought ravaged a large section of the Great Plains, causing loss of crops and hardship conditions for ranchers and farmers over a broad area. Then, even while measures to alleviate the effects of drought were still being taken, hurricane Carla struck the Texas Gulf Coast with savage fury and followed a course northward across the eastern part of the Great Plains. The severe rainstorms that accompanied the hurricane caused record-breaking floods in many smaller tributaries of the lower Missouri and Arkansas rivers, and extensive flood damage was experienced in many localities. There will be other such occurrences in the years to come. One locality will suffer drought while another is flooded. Along with these catastrophic natural occurrences, our ever-increasing use of water emphasizes the importance to all Americans of achieving the best possible use and control of the nation's water resources.

It is in the light of problems such as these—lack of precipitation and drought in some places; excessive precipitation and flood in others, perhaps even in the same river basin; growing demands for water for conflicting and irreconcilable uses—that a long-range national water program should be considered. Today we have no national water policy, or a national water "code," in the sense of a systematic body of law. Actually, a series of federal codes deal with water resources. When taken over-all, these are patchwork and anything but systematic. There are conflicts and inconsistencies. These individual acts and laws have been developed piecemeal by the evolutionary process of the passing of legislation when the need for particular action became obvious enough to develop the public support necessary for any successful legislative effort. The evolutionary process is continuing and will continue. It is to be hoped that public support will demand the elimination of the conflicts and inconsistencies that impede our progress toward achievement of national goals in water-resources development.

Before discussing the most pressing needs for legislative action to amend and modernize our federal water laws, we should take stock, briefly, of where we are, and how we got there.

## HISTORICAL BACKGROUND

All federal legislation in the field of water resources is enacted by the Congress in implementation of powers set forth or implied in the Constitution of the United States. Specific portions of the Constitution that are generally regarded as giving rise to authority for federal legislation in the field of water and related resources are the commerce, property, war-powers, and general welfare clauses, as well as the treaty-making and consent-to-interstate-compact clauses.

The first and oldest legislative developments in water resources were undertaken under the commerce clause. Improvements to navigable waters were made as early as 1824 under the power granted to regulate commerce among the several states. For almost a century and a half since the first use of this constitutional power, a whole body of federal statutes has grown up to govern activities in the field of navigation and in flood control. These range from the laws that authorized the first, and minor, improvements of navigable rivers and harbors on a project-by-project basis by the annual appropriation of funds to those that authorize the gigantic flood-control project along the lower Mississippi River, which will cost more than a billion and a half dollars if and when it is ever completed, and the great multiple-purpose river-basin development on the Columbia and Missouri rivers, where the generation of hydroelectric power is one of the important purposes. In between, projects of all types and sizes have come in all parts of the country.

A second great body of federal law has developed under the

property clause of the Constitution. Beginning with the Swamp Land Acts of 1850 and 1860 (*1*), which authorized the granting of swamp and overflowed lands to certain states on the condition that proceeds from the sale of the lands would be used for drainage and flood protection, the Congress has passed a growing body of legislation dealing with water resources in connection with the management and disposal of the public lands. Some of the first important legislation to deal with the use of water emanating from public lands was enacted in the form of the Mining Act of 1866 (*2*), which upheld vested water rights, and the Desert Land Act of 1877 (*3*), in which the federal government provided for nonnavigable waters rising from federal public lands to be open to public appropriation and use.

From these passive delegations of federal powers, the passage of time brought about substantial changes. In 1902, the federal Reclamation Act (*4*) was passed and set up a program for active federal development of the water resources of the West. At first this involved irrigation only but was later expanded to cover municipal water supply and hydroelectric-power development as a part of irrigation projects. As the program grew, it was expanded further by the enactment of legislation to cover these purposes generally, as well as navigation and flood control in their own right. Most recently, the preservation and propagation of fish and wildlife, when they were affected by reclamation projects, and the provision of recreational opportunities for the people of the United States were included in the program.

Probably the first multiple-purpose water development undertaken under the war-powers clause of the Constitution was the Wilson Dam and power plant at Muscle Shoals (*5*), which was authorized for the purpose of generating electricity to manufacture nitrates as a source of explosives during World War I. The controversy that arose over this project and the subsequent efforts to bring it to public use, which culminated in the establishment of the great Tennessee Valley Authority, have been discussed fully elsewhere and will be only briefly mentioned here. In court decisions upholding the constitutionality of the TVA Act, reliance has been placed also on the commerce clause (*6*). Laws related to the development of water supplies at military bases and of harbors for naval ships have led to a great many developments. From these, a whole body of legislation and subsequent court decisions have evolved, which appear to indicate that the federal government has extremely broad powers to deal with water resources under the war-powers clause.

The general welfare clause has come more recently into the picture as a basis for federal legislation that deals with water resources. This clause was first cited in court cases upholding the constitutionality of federal water-resources developments. It appears now to be generally conceded that the authority of the federal government under the general welfare clause can be extended to almost whatever length the Congress chooses in enacting water-resources legislation to promote the general welfare of the people.

Under the treaty-making powers assigned by the Constitution to the President, agreements have been reached with neighboring countries, and these have formed the basis for immense water-resources developments. The treaty with Mexico (7) involved an exchange of water in the Rio Grande for water in the Colorado River and led to a major series of water-conservation projects along the Rio Grande in Texas, as well as levees and other works on the lower Colorado River in Arizona. Legislative implementation of the agreement with Canada (8), covering the development of the St. Lawrence River for navigation and hydroelectric power, divided the project responsibilities. The state and provincial governments handled the hydroelectric-power features; federal governmental corporations handled the navigation features.

Over a long period of years the use of the interstate compact has been expanded from a device to divide the beneficial use of waters between adjacent states into one to facilitate the establishment of organizations for planning and taking positive action in the field of water resources. In the 87th Congress, first session, consent was given to a compact between the four states of the Delaware River Basin and the United States that set up a development agency for the Delaware River Basin (9). This appears to open a whole new chapter in the national water code.

Thus it can be seen that the approaches taken to water resources by the federal statutes are of almost infinite variety. Thousands of pages of statutes govern the activities of a score or more of federal agencies in all aspects of the conservation, development, and use of water resources. It was almost inevitable that these laws form the basis for many inconsistencies among policies of federal agencies. The Department of Agriculture pays farmers to clear, drain, and cultivate swamps and low-lying pothole areas, while the Department of the Interior spends money to acquire wetlands for conversion to wildlife habitat. The Army Corps of Engineers wants to release water for navigation, while the Bureau of Reclamation would hold it back for irrigation and hydroelectric-power generation at another season of the year. In some instances, both agencies are investigating the same projects at the same time, and occasionally both agencies seek appropriations to build the same project.

All of the agencies engaged in water-resources activities appear to have staunch supporters; therefore, many attempts to bring consistency and uniformity into agency programs by consolidating the agencies have been defeated. Some recent enactments, however, have consolidated the policies under which some of the programs of the several agencies are carried out. For example, the Water Supply Act of 1958 (*10*) provides uniform policies to govern the Army Corps of Engineers and the Bureau of Reclamation in this field; the Water Pollution Control Act amendments of 1961 (*11*) give to both agencies uniform instructions on streamflow regulation. Other examples could be cited. A very good possibility exists, therefore, that some progress can be made toward a systematized federal water code without major reorganization of federal agencies.

## RECENT EVALUATION OF THE WATER-RESOURCES SITUATION

Is the federal government doing enough to carry out the national interest in water-resources development? Should the laws that permit the occurrence of conflicts, such as those mentioned, be modified? These questions are asked with more frequency now because the population of the United States has slightly more than doubled in the period since the turn of the century, and the use of water for all purposes has increased almost 8 times. As the use of water presses on inexorably toward the limits of the available supply, our perceptiveness and knowledge of the interrelationships involved in the use of water for all purposes has increased. Simultaneously, the magnitude of the efforts required to deal with the contingent problems, which frequently transcend state lines, has become greater. Thus it follows that there has been a tendency toward increased reliance on the federal government to take action in the water-resources field, where many aspects are already reserved for federal action. This has led to frequent reviews of the over-all water picture.

A recent broad perspective on this whole situation is provided by the studies *(12)* and report *(13)* of the Select Committee on National Water Resources of the United States Senate. The committee found that gross water use in 1954, the base year of its studies, was at a rate of roughly 300 billion gallons per day and that this was expected to increase to about 560 billion gallons a day by 1980 and to about 890 billion gallons in the year 2000 *(13,* p. 6) . When this total is compared with the over-all runoff of all the streams of the United States, which is about 1100 billion gallons per day, it can be seen that there is cause for concern. This is particularly so because of the extreme variability of runoff, both geographically and in time of occurrence. One of the committee's studies includes a chart showing that the ratio of available runoff to projected water demand in 1980 ranges from 10 times in the lower Missouri River Basin to 3/100 in the southern Pacific basin *(14)* . Five of the river basins selected for the committee's studies would have a deficiency in water supply by 1980, and eight would be water deficient by the year 2000, under the committee's assumptions regarding economic growth and conditions of water use. The committee, however, made it plain that the promise of new technical developments will increase the possibilities for more efficient use and reuse of water, so that the necessary water supply can be made available in most areas of the nation without economic growth being unduly restricted by lack of water.

More important than the facts and figures that underlie the report of the Senate Select Committee are the broad programs of action recommended by the committee as the first steps toward seeing that solutions to the nation's water problems can be obtained. Basically they center on two major ideas. These are (i) the establishment of better methods of cooperative, comprehensive water-resources development planning, participated in by all agencies of the federal, state, and local governments concerned; and (ii) an improved research program to develop the scientific knowledge that will be the basis for increased efficiency of water use. Such increased efficiency will be essential if the nation's water needs are to be met.

## SCIENTIFIC RESEARCH PROGRAMS

The Senate Select Committee placed considerable emphasis on the need for scientific research to provide solutions for many of the water-resources problems that must be solved if our nation is to have water in the quantities and of the quality needed for continued economic growth. The fields singled out for particular attention are weather modification, desalting of saline and brackish waters, pollution abatement, evaporation and evapotranspiration reduction, and more efficient use of water for irrigation and industrial purposes. In addition, the committee called attention to the promise of the development of new technology in hydrometeorological forecasting and basic research and the application of nuclear energy in water-resources fields.

The Congress has been quick to take action authorizing and financing research where it is needed and where agreement could be reached among scientists about undertaking the necessary research effort. In 1961 legislation was enacted to expand the saline-water-conversion research program (15) and the pollution-abatement research program (16). Further action in the field of weather modification has been continued under the 1958 act (17), which authorizes the National Science Foundation to support a research program in this field. Substantial sums have been made available to federal agencies to carry on research and experimentation. Research programs of the federal agencies generally have been increasing as fast as the availability of research personnel will permit.

Over-all action toward coordinating and strengthening federal research programs will await the studies called for by the President to implement the recommendations of the Senate Select Committee. These involve an evaluation of the entire scientific research effort in the field of natural resources by the National Academy of Sciences, and a review of active federal research programs by the Federal Council for Science and Technology.

## COMPREHENSIVE RIVER-BASIN PLANNING

In the direction of improving comprehensive river-basin planning, the 87th Congress began study of a proposal that was sent up by the President to implement the Senate Select Committee's recommendations (*18*). This was in three parts.

The first title called for the establishment of a Cabinet-level water-resources council to coordinate the programs of the federal agencies that are concerned in water-resources development and to develop principles, standards, and procedures for the preparation of comprehensive water-resources plans and for the formulation and evaluation of federal water-resources projects. The council would be composed of the Secretaries of the Interior, Agriculture, Army, and Health, Education, and Welfare. The heads of other agencies would be invited to participate when matters affecting their responsibilities were to be considered by the council.

The second title of the bill would provide authority for the President to establish river-basin study commissions in the major river basins or groups of river basins in the United States. Under this authority comprehensive planning for water-resources development would be carried out cooperatively by the federal agencies concerned and the states. These commissions would be patterned somewhat along the lines of the Southeast Basins Study Commission (*19*) and the Texas Basins Study Commission (*20*), which are now engaged in developing comprehensive water-resources plans in their respective areas. The commissions would submit their reports to the council for transmittal to the President and the Congress.

The third title of the bill would provide for increasing the participation of the states in river-basin planning by setting up a program of federal grants-in-aid, to be matched by the states, with the funds used by the states to develop comprehensive planning programs. This would enable them to participate fully with the federal agencies in formulating the water-resources development plans authorized under the second part of the bill.

Joint hearings on this bill, cited as the "Water Resources Planning Act of 1961," were held by the Senate Committees on Interior and Insular Affairs and Public Works on 26 July and 16 August 1961, but no other action was taken during the 87th Congress.

An area of great confusion in the water-resources field has resulted from a lack of definite understanding of what should be the responsibilities of the federal, state, and local governments, as well as of how private development of water resources should be coordinated into the national over-all picture. The aforementioned legislation on planning would appear to establish a mechanism that would enable this perplexing problem to be worked out, by insuring that long-range comprehensive plans are developed with the full participation of all concerned. Eventual enactment of such legislation could provide the Congress with a basis for taking whatever action is needed, region by region, so that the contributions of all segments of government and private interests could be productively integrated.

## REGIONAL DIFFERENCES

Regional differences in climatic and water-supply conditions among the humid areas of the East, and the arid and semiarid areas of the West have had, and will continue to have, a very important bearing on the evolution of legislation that makes up the national water code. This is undoubtedly the principal difficulty preventing the establishment of any systematic water code that would deal uniformly with problems in all parts of the country. Although it is often said that the East will soon experience many of the shortages already felt by the West, there is a major difference. In the East, water is physically available to meet foreseeable needs if the necessary works are provided to regulate its quantity and to maintain its quality through frequent reuse. Thus, water shortages in the East are caused by a lack of sufficient works to make use of available water. In the West because consumptive uses are much greater, and the possibility of frequent reuse of water is thus decreased, the natural supply of water is insufficient to meet all needs at the exact place and time that they occur. This necessitates a different approach to water problems.

Tremendous works have been constructed in the West to get water to the places where it is needed. For example, the city of Los Angeles long since would have run out of water to meet its concentrated demands if it had not, in 1907, developed a vast system of conduits and aqueducts, and brought water from Owens Valley beyond the Sierras. Later the city tapped the Colorado River with the assistance of the federal government in the construction of the great Hoover Dam and other regulatory works on the lower Colorado River. Now, continuing to prepare for its above-average growth and attendant demands for water, Los Angeles, through the state agencies concerned, is taking steps to see that its water supply will be augmented in the future from the abundant water resources of northern California.

Similar action has taken place in my own state of Arizona, although on a smaller scale. First, the readily available surface waters were developed through the Salt River project and other works that completely utilized the waters of the Gila River and its tributaries. Subsequently, wells and pumping systems were installed and expanded to make use of the ground water that underlies the state. Ground-water levels are being drastically reduced, because we are pumping more than the recharge. Now plans are underway to bring water to the settled part of Arizona from the Colorado River through the central Arizona project.

In the state of Colorado, the efforts of the Bureau of Reclamation to move water from points of abundance to points of use are evident in the already completed Colorado-Big Thompson project and in the Frying Pan-Arkansas diversion, which is now before the Congress for consideration. Denver also has done a magnificent job in tapping the western slope areas of high runoff to provide for needs generated by the urbanization that is taking place.

Many other examples could be given of efforts in other western states to meet the magnified water needs caused by the increase in population and industrial activities. Yet with all of these efforts, in dry years there still may not be enough water to go around because of the continued growth of the West. From 1940 to 1960, the population of the United States grew by 27 percent, while the population of the 11 western states increased 50 percent, almost twice as much. The works to supply water for all these people and their economic activities will be costly. This is not a matter of water-resources development to stimulate economic activity; rather, it is a matter of providing water for the people and industries who have come to the West to locate because of their desire to live in favorable climatic areas. Billions have been spent; projects totaling tens of billions of dollars are already on the drawing boards; and hundreds of billions of dollars' worth of projects will be required within the next 40 years to provide our people with water in the amounts and of the quality that they need.

## LEGISLATION NEEDED

What kind of efforts will be required to make it possible to do this immense job? The first answers to this question are those discussed earlier: a coordinated attempt to plan for multiple-purpose development, and a coordinated research program to provide a basis for the most economical water development in the future. Then, going beyond the more exotic solutions, such as increased precipitation through weather modification and desalting of ocean and brackish waters, which do not as yet give definite promise of supplying additional water in the vast quantities needed, there must be legislation that faces up to the problems caused by the ever-increasing use of water. As the most important items of legislation, I would suggest (i) further recognition of the recreational and esthetic values of water, in order that these values may not be irretrievably lost as the country grows; (ii) provisions for allocation of water supplies that can ease eventual transitions from the use of water for lower purposes to productive economic purposes and to meet municipal and domestic demands; (iii) promotion of increased efficiency in the use of water; and (iv) formulation of new methods of sharing costs between the direct beneficiaries and the general public that can facilitate projects of the tremendous magnitudes that will be required in the future.

Some of these responsibilities should be assumed by the state legislatures. But if the states do not take the necessary action to assure that needs can be met, the likelihood exists that action will be taken by the federal government, possibly in some areas heretofore considered the sole provinces of the states.

Advances in technology will permit water demands to be satisfied without inhibiting economic growth. A national water policy is necessary so that no arbitrary legal handicaps will hinder this development.

## REFERENCES

1.  Act of 28 Sept. 1850, 9 Stat. 520; act of 12 Mar. 1860, 12 Stat. 3.
2.  Act of 26 July 1866, 14 Stat. 253.
3.  Act of 3 Mar. 1877, 19 Stat. 377.
4.  Act of 17 June 1902, 32 Stat. 388.
5.  National Defense Act of 1916, act of 3 June 1916, 39 Stat. 166.
6.  297 U.S. 288-372 (Ashwander case).
7.  59 Stat. 1219-1267; T.S. 944. Signed 3 Feb. 1944.
8.  5 U.S.T. 1784, entered into force 30 June 1952 and 17 Aug. 1954.
9.  Public Law 87-328, approved 27 Sept. 1961, 75 Stat. 688.
10.  Public Law 85-500, Title III, approved 3 July 1958, 72 Stat. 297,319.
11.  Public Law 87-88, approved 20 July 1961, 75 Stat. 204.
12.  U.S. Congress, Senate Select Committee on National Water Resources, *Water Resources Activities in the United States*, Comm. Prints 1 through 32 (U.S. Govt. Printing Office, Washington, D.C., 1959 and 1960).
13.  ———, S. Rept. 29, 87th Congr., 1st sess., 30 Jan. 1961.
14.  ———, *Water Supply and Demand*, Comm. Print 32 (U.S. Govt. Printing Office, Washington, D.C., 1960), p. 127.
15.  Public Law 87-295, approved 22 Sept. 1961, 75 Stat. 628.
16.  Public Law 87-88, approved 20 July 1961, 75 Stat. 204.
17.  Public Law 85-510, approved 11 July 1958, 72 Stat. 353.
18.  S. 2246, etc., . . . H.R. 8155, 87th Congr., 1st sess., 1961.
19.  Public Law 85-850, approved 28 Aug. 1958, 72 Stat. 1090.
20.  Public Law 85-843, approved 28 Aug. 1958, 72 Stat. 1058.

# Government Responsibility for Land and Water: Guardian or Developer?

Luna B. Leopold and Raymond L. Nace

*U.S. Geological Survey, Washington, D.C.*

Ideas and concepts become obsolete just as do specific techniques. Obsolescence is the inevitable companion of progress; in fact, it is a sign of progress, provided that the obsolescence is recognized.

## CHANGING ROLE OF GOVERNMENT

With the opening of the West, the federal government accepted a stewardship of vast land and water resources. This stewardship was conceived as involving the dual role of guardian and developer. The techniques and implications of this role were long in emerging. By the time the role was formalized—and before its implications were widely appreciated—events had moved around and beyond the original concept of stewardship. It became obsolete before it was fully operative. The inability of the government to adjust quickly to such altered circumstances is the main reason why natural resources problems have been multiplying since World War II faster than government has been able to cope with them.

The word *guardian* implies protection from exploitation. In an earlier day, even very simple exploitations of land and water produced attractive returns, and large-scale exploitation created many personal fortunes. The exploitation of resources during the nineteenth century has been said to have been essential to create the capital needed for development. To a degree at least, this was true, but regardless of the necessity, nearly everyone now seems to agree that it was equally necessary, and certainly proper, for government to step in as guardian of the long-term public interest.

Hydraulic mining of gold was lucrative to the entrepreneur but ruinous to the land; concomitant downstream sedimentation damaged many miles of stream valley whose welfare was ignored by the exploiters. Protection of the land from such exploitation was an overriding necessity, and hence guardianship became a clear responsibility of government.

The government's role of developer was also a logical outcome of the country's progress, but the actual extent to which that role was fulfilled has been greatly exaggerated. In irrigation agriculture, for example, the larger amount of development in the West has been by private enterprise, not by government project.

Irrigation transformed many parts of the West, spurred the establishment of retail businesses and supporting services, and provided new markets as well as products. Expansion of American enterprise in the West was encouraged by the government, in part, as a direct developer and, in part, by its permitting large returns to individuals and small groups from the development of water for irrigation, homesteading of public land, mineral development, forest harvesting, and similar activities.

The government's role as developer of land and water resources was appropriate when expansion and development were, indeed, keys to economic growth—the "staff of national life," if you will. A classic example in the eastern United States is the Erie Canal. In one decade this canal transformed New York City from a small town to the leading metropolis of the eastern seaboard. Important returns to society from developments like this were the enrichment and expansion of community life.

At the present time, pressure is mounting from many directions for government to increase the scope of its development activities. But now and in the foreseeable future the main need is neither for guardianship nor for development in the traditional sense.

## EMERGENCE OF INCOMPATIBILITIES

Both protection and development were needed in past years, but the need for each occurred in different spheres and for different purposes. As the economy expanded, the two functions collided. Purposes that were quite valid for separate functions became contradictory when they were used to support projects or plans dealing with the same resource or the same area.

### Protection versus development

Protection of the land by rigid restriction of hydraulic mining was unrelated to, and did not conflict with, encouragement of simultaneous developments elsewhere, such as development of water for irrigation in a nearby area. Similarly, protection of the national interest by strict control of lumbering practices in national forests did not conflict with provisions for the patenting and use of other land resources under the Homestead Act.

In these circumstances the federal government promoted the public interest by controlling exploitation of one resource while simultaneously promoting development of other resources. In each case the national interest seemed clear, and the protective and developmental actions were mutually exclusive and discrete.

As the national community grew, however, such separations became less distinct. Differing actions more and more often affected geographic areas and resources that overlapped or were identical. The national interest became progressively more difficult to define, because specific interest in one aspect of development became contrary to specific interest in another aspect. Protection and development were no longer either exclusive or discrete, and within each function versatility begat incompatibility.

In the development of the Missouri River Basin, for instance, several types of governmental activity were authorized. One obvious need was for flood control. For maximum effectiveness, a flood-control reservoir must be kept at low stage or even empty at critical times in readiness to receive floodwaters. But irrigation projects impose special requirements for water storage and distribution, and these requirements are quite different from those for flood control. In addition, navigation on the Missouri River had fallen to a low ebb. Ease of navigation was improved by channel dredging, but it still imposed certain storage requirements. Controlled releases of water to maintain navigational stages were necessary. Wildfowl habitats were involved also. Certain watershed lands were undergoing serious erosion, and control of this required range rehabilitation, regulation of grazing, and installation of small structures. Floods in tributaries called for dams on many small streams. Pollution control necessitated maintenance of certain minimum flows. Finally, power-generation needs imposed certain operational requirements for storage and release of water.

These same factors, with variations, require consideration in the basins of the Colorado, the upper Mississippi, the Arkansas-White-Red, and many other rivers.

Which of these activities dealing with land and water resources are developmental, and which are protective? Flood control protects certain public interests, but land enhancement and development are important corollaries. Is flood control primarily protective or developmental? Wildlife resources usually suffer a net injury from programs of land and water development, even though plans may provide for some local wildlife development benefits. Thus, wildlife resources usually need protection but often are subject to just the opposite.

### Unwanted side effects

Upstream land management and the operation of small reservoirs for flood control are known to decrease the downstream water yield of a river system. In any specific situation, the extent of the decrease is difficult to assess quantitatively, although the nature of the effect can hardly be gainsaid. Similarly, construction of a large reservoir on a main stream sets off a chain of downstream changes that involve river regimen, erosion, and sediment transport and deposition, often with extensive damage, which is costly to counteract. Thus, protection or development at one place may instigate damage elsewhere.

### Wilderness—antithesis of development

Still another example of confusion of interests and roles is wilderness, which is generally considered to be a valuable resource. If wilderness has great value to some of the people of the nation, then it has a national value by the same reasoning that justifies government expenditures for local flood control. Wilderness, by its very nature, is the reciprocal of development: its extent is inverse to the geographic extent of economic development. Wilderness is a resource that cannot be created, so it must be protected. It is not subject to development in any accepted sense of the word. In this case, "protection" requires not merely protection from exploitation but prevention of any development at all.

The foregoing examples could be elaborated and others cited. It seems clear, however, that resource protection or development at one point in space or time can, and often does, adversely affect resources at another place or time.

## RECAPITULATION

During the early history of the nation, governmental activity became necessary to protect the interests of society at certain times and places; at others there was a concomitant need to develop land and water resources, as an aid to economic progress. With progress came overlap and conflict between these roles of government. Thus, the concept of government with discrete responsibilities as protector and developer became obsolete.

Despite the obvious conflict, the thinking in terms of two distinct roles has continued to dominate the approach of government to land and water problems. Each activity still has its supporters and apologists. The pillboxes of protection and development continue to hum, although they have been outflanked by the panzers of progress. The conflict is hidden behind the fashionable cloaks of "conservation" and "multiple-purpose development." The shibboleth of conservation connotes in the public mind a Good Thing; everyone is for it because it is all things to all men. So all land- and water-resources activities are called "conservation"—flood control, erosion prevention, pollution abatement, fish and wildlife preservation, drainage of wetlands—in fact, any and all activities, no matter how antithetical they are.

Multiple-purpose development is a hybrid species of the same genus as conservation. It offers something to everybody, although some of the purposes are diluted to the point of extinction. To show that fish and wildlife benefits are derived from the construction of regulatory reservoirs and the dredging of channels in multiple-purpose river-basin development requires high-class legerdemain, but it is attempted.

What is the basic trouble? If guardianship and development in the old sense are no longer appropriate, what new concept is necessary?

## BASIC FLAWS OF CONCEPT AND ACTION

The basic trouble is that traditional concepts of protection and development are naive in relation to the complex nature of land and water problems in a mature society. The approach to these problems has been, and continues to be, a strictly engineering approach. Projects are designed by formula and template. However useful and effective this may have been in an earlier day, it is not sufficiently sophisticated for current problems. Its inadequacies will, in fact, be dangerous in the future, because the unforeseen or ignored "side effects" of engineering manipulations often set off chains of unwanted consequences, which tend more and more to vitiate the whole purpose of development and protection.

## PREVISION, NOT HINDSIGHT, IS NEEDED

Prevision—vision into the future—is an unescapable requisite to better planning. This need goes far beyond mere qualitative prediction of specific consequences of management, such as increased mineralization of water or salinization of soils in irrigated areas. Rather, there is urgent need for prevision of all the significant effects and their ramifying interplay—not only of a single possible management action, but of a variety of alternative actions among which a choice may be made. Further, this analysis must be applied to effects that are regional as well as local, upstream as well as downstream, direct and indirect, desirable and undesirable, physical and chemical, hydrologic and biologic, economic and sociologic. Only when there is prevision of the potential consequences of alternative actions can we exert any real choice or control over our own destiny. This is a far cry from the present situation, in which the legislator or executive is confronted with a single "multiple-purpose" proposal and must, in effect, take it or leave it.

## FAILURE OF THE YARDSTICK

Economic need often is cited as justifying governmental assistance in development projects. In our opinion, "economic need" often is less a need than a desire. A local group, for example, desires development by government in order to increase the flow of economic goods through the local economy. This desire may stem from a very real local need; but such a need should be weighed from the national standpoint, and in relation to alternatives. Weighing implies estimation of effects.

In order to develop more sophisticated concepts, we must reappraise the nature of government responsibility and squarely face the question: What should be the real purpose and philosophy behind government activity in land and water?

It seems to us that a first step toward answering this question would be to reevaluate the criteria for determining what is in the public interest—what is, in fact, the public good. Monetary value is not the total substance of public worth, nor is financial gain the whole measure of the social good. The fiscal yardstick could lead us into a cultural desert where all the signposts are dollar signs.

We still have no uniformly accepted guides for assessing esthetic or spiritual values. These values do exist, and they are the most subtle, the most sensitive, and certainly the most easily lost of all values. The value of a park, whether it be a Yosemite, the patch of grass and trees comprising a New England common, or the plaza of a western village, cannot be measured solely by its assessment as real estate. Or, if a park is evaluated in terms of goods sold and services rendered—hotdogs, soft drinks, plastic water toys, fishing tackle, gasoline—then its true value is overlooked entirely. The true value can be expressed only in terms of the national life and national spirit, and therefore it can be maintained and protected only at governmental levels.

## STEPS TOWARD NEW HORIZONS

The dual government role of developer and guardian is well established, if not thoroughly entrenched. But there is an overwhelming need to revise the whole philosophy that governs these roles. Governmental actions in the past were aimed at maintaining monetary value for the public good as against the pecuniary gain of private interests. Government, however, has now entered a situation in which it must guard the public interest against its own activities—especially by maintaining nonmonetary values for the public good against inroads of government activity in the name of development for quasi-public monetary gain.

Two things are needed to establish this new role. First, increased research is necessary to link a sophisticated level of economic theory with the hard facts of physical and biological science. The science of resources management has yet to be defined, let alone practiced. Second, more and better knowledge is needed about the environment itself—its interactions, its internal workings, and its varied responses to the multitudinous activities of man. Present knowledge of the environment is insufficient to enable us to forecast and estimate the long-term effects of alternative actions. The overriding responsibility of government is to assure that society will obtain maximum cultural and material benefits from resources over the long-term future.

As techniques in economics and in environmental sciences are being developed, it is imperative that we make up our national mind about the kind of world in which we choose to live. If esthetic, ethical, and nonmonetary values are worthless to us, then the task is easy. In all probability, however, Americans will not be satisfied with a financially lucrative economy in an environmental desert. Therefore, let us raise our eyes from the ground at our feet to the horizon of the nation. Let us look up from the intensive cultivation of flowerbeds in our suburban house lots and turn some energy to cultivation of our national backyard.

As a people, let us assert that the role of government is to protect those resources that otherwise will fall before the bulldozer of governmental development. Development will pay its own way in dollars; the flowerbeds of the national homestead will pay their way in values that no amount of dollars can buy.

## SUMMARY

The historic role of government as both developer and guardian of land and water resources has been changed by events and by the reaction of the environment to man's activities.

There are at present two salient needs. (i) Government must guard the general public interest against the activities of government itself. Particular attention must be devoted to the maintenance of nonmonetary values, which presently are being sacrificed in the name of development for quasi-public monetary gain. (ii) There is a need for facts and knowledge sufficient to permit us to foresee the short, and long-term environmental effects of alternative developmental programs or projects.

# Index